D1259563

Edited by

ARTHUR G. STEINBERG, Ph.D.

Francis Hobart Herrick Professor of Biology,
Department of Biology, and
Professor of Human Genetics,
Case Western Reserve University,
Cleveland, Ohio

ALEXANDER G. BEARN, M.D.

Senior Vice President,
Medical and Scientific Affairs,
Merck Sharp & Dohme International,
Rahway, New Jersey

ARNO G. MOTULSKY, M.D.

Professor of Medicine and Genetics,
Director, Center for Inherited Diseases,
University of Washington,
Seattle, Washington

BARTON CHILDS, M.D.

Professor of Pediatrics,
The Johns Hopkins University,
Baltimore, Maryland

Progress in

MEDICAL
GENETICS

NEW SERIES

Volume III

1979
W. B. SAUNDERS COMPANY
Philadelphia, London, Toronto

W. B. Saunders Company: West Washington Square
Philadelphia, PA   19105

1 St. Anne's Road
Eastbourne, East Sussex BN21 3UN, England

1 Goldthorne Avenue
Toronto, Ontario M8Z 5T9, Canada

Progress in Medical Genetics — New Series, Volume III

ISSN   0079-6441
ISBN   0-7126-8599-4

Last digit is the print number: 9   8   7   6   5   4   3   2   1

FOREWORD

Increasingly during the past decade, it has become apparent that medical genetics is an important subspecialty of clinical medicine. Unlike many subspecialties, however, genetics has relevance to all branches of medicine. In addition to the identification of genetic syndromes determined by single genes, it is evident that genetic factors play an important role in the determination of susceptibility to a wide spectrum of human disease.

In this volume of *Progress in Medical Genetics*, a number of medical topics have been reviewed critically by leaders in the field. Three of the subjects have been selected from the field of endocrinology, a subspecialty of medicine increasingly influenced by advances in genetic knowledge.

A discussion of the various genetically determined forms of hypogonadism is informatively undertaken by Robert L. Summit (Chapter 1). Included in the discussion are those important abnormalities of sexual differentiation that are caused by a cellular unresponsiveness to testicular androgens. Even since Francis Galton wrote his classic treatise on "The History of Twins as a Criteria of the Relative Powers of Nature and Nurture" more than 100 years ago, twins have been used, and, quite as often, misused as subjects for biomedical research.

Walter E. Nance (Chapter 2) examines the effectiveness of studies on twins in the analysis of quantitative traits in genetics. Well aware of the limitations and pitfalls inherent in classic twin studies, Nance focuses on the usefulness of studies on monozygotic twins and their normal offspring to help dissect genetic-environmental interactions.

Sexual development forms the subject of a fine review by Stephen S. Wachtel and Susumo Ohno (Chapter 3). Drawing on their own extensive experience, as well as reviewing the literature, these authors

v

advance the hypothesis that the serologically detectable H-Y antigen is the primary determinant of vertebrate sex. Their article entitled "The Immunogenetics of Sexual Development Diseases" forms a timely review of an important subject.

The development of radioimmunoassay has enabled the measurement of very small quantities of hormones in biologic fluids. The discovery of increased quantities of hormones in a variety of tumors, particularly those affecting the thyroid and pancreas, has led to the delineation of a number of hereditary syndromes affecting multiple endocrine glands. These syndromes, which may be associated with hyperfunction or hypofunction, are well reviewed by R. Neil Schimke (Chapter 4).

Inherited immunodeficiency diseases have fascinated pediatricians, immunologists, and geneticists since Bruton first described X-linked agammaglobulinenia in 1951. In a chapter entitled "Inherited Immunodeficiency Diseases: Relationship to Lymphocytic Metabolic Function," Eloise R. Giblett and Stephen H. Polmar (Chapter 5) review adenosine deaminase deficiency and nucleoside phosphylase deficiency and discuss their relevance to susceptibility to microbial infections.

Dr. Marcello Siniscalco in an authorative and extensive article entitled "Approaches to Human Linkage" brings this volume to a close with an extensive and critical evaluation of linkage in man (Chapter 6). Recent developments in somatic cell genetics have enabled the human chromosome map to be filled at an astonishing speed, and these advances are discussed with both rigor and clarity.

The editors again wish to express their gratitude to the authors for the care with which they have prepared their manuscripts. Thanks to them, this volume of Progress in Medical Genetics upholds the high standards set by *their* predecessors.

CONTENTS

5

6

Genetic Forms of Hypogonadism in the Male*

ROBERT L. SUMMITT

Departments of Pediatrics, Anatomy, and the Child Development Center, University of Tennessee Center for the Health Sciences, and LeBonheur Children's Hospital Memphis, Tennessee

*This work was supported in part by Special Project No. 900, Division of Health Services, MCHS, DHEW, and by a grant from the National Foundation — March of Dimes.

INTRODUCTION

Male sex determination occurs when an X chromosome–bearing ovum is fertilized by a Y chromosome–bearing sperm. Under normal circumstances, a sequence of events is initiated in the presence of an XY sex chromosome complement, occurring under the influence of genetic factors, some of which are not well understood. This sequence begins with the development of a testis. Compounds elaborated by the testis (at least partially under the influence of gonadotropins elaborated by the placenta and the fetal pituitary gland) control the differentiation of the male internal ductal system, the suppression of the female internal ductal system, and the male differentiation of the bipotential embryonic external genitalia. Once genital differentiation is complete, and a male infant is born, the testes enter a relatively nonfunctional period. They become active again in the second decade of life, at which time, under the influence of pituitary gonadotropins that stimulate testicular maturation, they induce pubertal development and the production of mature spermatozoa.

Included in this discussion of genetic forms of male hypogonadism are those abnormalities of sex differentiation that result from a cellular unresponsiveness to testicular-derived androgens. Conversely, true hermaphroditism is not included.

THE NORMAL PROCESS

Formation of the Testicle. Prior to about 42 days of intrauterine life, the gonads of both XX and XY human embryos appear identical (Jirasek, 1977a, 1977b). Even earlier, however, primordial germ cells are identifiable in the entoderm of the allantois and in adjacent portions of the yolk sac. As a matter of fact, the presence of a primordial germ cell has been described by Hertig et al. (1956) among the eight cells of the inner cell mass of a 4½-day-old human blastocyst. Jirasek (1977a) has observed the migration (by ameboid movement) of primordial germ cells from their points of origin in the hindgut to the gonadal primordium in 35- to 40-day-old human embryos. The differentiation of the definitive testis from the gonadal primordium, which is derived from mesoblastic and interstitial cells of the midportion of the urogenital ridge, occurs in the 7- to 8-week-old embryo. Testicular cords form, accompanied in the ensuing 2 weeks by an increase in testicular connective tissue. According to Jirasek (1977a), Leydig cells are first identifiable in the

ninth week of embryonic life; they reach their maximum number by
the end of the third month and then decline to become undetectable in early infancy. The seminiferous tubules and rete testis develop lumina during the second half of intrauterine life, but neither
Sertoli cells nor spermatogonia mature in utero.

The genetic mechanisms governing the differentiation of the
primitive bipotential gonad into a testis are not well understood.
The inherent direction of gonadal differentiation is toward an ovary
(O and Short, 1977). In the human, this inherent direction is taken
in the absence of a Y chromosome. In the early 45,X fetus, the
ovary is not apparently different from that of the normal 46,XX
fetus. Even early stages of meiosis can be observed in the germ
cells of the 45,X fetus. The fact that germ cell attrition has become
prominent, and primary follicle formation is seen to be defective in
the late 45,X fetus, as well as in the fetus that has a structural abnormality of one X chromosome, involving loss of its short arm
(Singh and Carr, 1966; Carr et al., 1968), indicates that genes in the
short arm of the X chromosome are necessary for normal primary
follicle formation. When normal primary follicle formation does not
take place, the oocytes contained therein degenerate. The germ
cells of the 46,XX female contain two active X chromosomes, in
contrast to somatic cells in which one X chromosome is inactivated
in early embryonic life (Lyon, 1974). The presence of two active X
chromosomes in a primordial germ cell is thus necessary for maintenance of follicle differentiation, and in the 45,X fetus, the presence
of only one X chromosome in germ cells is the factor that results in
defective follicle formation and the in utero attrition in most 45,X
females of all germ cells.

The discovery of a histocompatibility antigen, the H-Y antigen
(Goldberg et al., 1971), which is apparently the product of a gene
located in the short arm and perhaps also in the proximal long arm
of the Y chromosome, had led Wachtel and associates (1976) and
Ohno (1976a) to propose that this antigen is the product of a Y-
borne gene that governs the differentiation of the primitive gonad
into a testis. The mechanism whereby the H-Y gene product initiates and maintains testicular differentiation has been the subject
of several investigations. The demonstration by Ohno (1978) that
H-Y–positive mouse gonadal cells in rotation culture autonomously
reorganize seminiferous tubule-like structures, whereas similar cells
stripped of H-Y antigen in the presence of an excess of H-Y antibody organize follicle-like structures, each of which has a primordial germ cell as its center, has shed important new light on the
problem (Fig. 1). Thus, testicular organization appears to be the re-

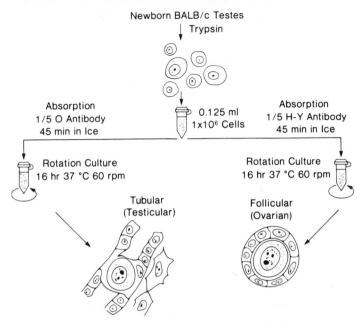

Figure 1. Reaggregation experiment performed on dissociated XY (H-Y positive) gonadal cells from a newborn mouse testis in rotation culture. Such cells, lysostripped of H-Y antigen by an excess of H-Y antibody, reorganize in vitro to form ovarian follicle-like aggregates (right), whereas the same cells retaining H-Y antigen reorganize to form seminiferous tubule-like structures (left). (From Ohno, S. 1978. The role of H-Y antigen in primary sex determination. JAMA 239:217–220. Copyright 1978, American Medical Association.)

sult of the action of a plasma membrane protein, the H-Y antigen. Wachtel (1977) has suggested that a plasma membrane receptor is also necessary for the action of H-Y antigen. The fact that patients who have an isochromosome for the long arm of Y [i(Yq)] are females with streak gonads (Jacobs and Ross, 1966; Robinson and Buckton, 1971; Böök et al., 1973) indicates that the H-Y gene is located in the short arm of the Y chromosome, near the centromere. The presence of testes in patients with ring Y chromosomes (necessarily lacking, in all likelihood, at least the telomeric portions of both long and short arms) suggests that the testis-determining locus is not in the distalmost portion of the short arm of Y (German et al., 1973).

    Differentiation of the Male Internal Ductal System. The internal ductal system of the male — including epididymis, vas deferens, seminal vesicle, and ejaculatory duct — is the product of the mesonephric, or wolffian, duct of the embryo, whereas the ductal

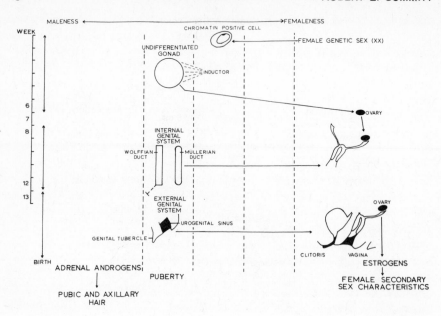

Figure 2. Normal female sex differentiation. (From Summitt, R. L. 1975. Sex Determination, Differentiation and Development. In Synopsis of Pediatrics, Hughes, J. G., (Ed.), pp. 572–613. St. Louis, C. V. Mosby Company.)

system of the female — including fallopian tubes, uterus, and cephalad portion of the vagina — results from differentiation of the paramesonephric, or müllerian, duct of the embryo. In the early embryo, both systems are present, and depending on the presence or absence of a testis, one ductal system will differentiate and the other regress. As with gonadal differentiation, the inherent property of the embryo is the differentiation of the müllerian duct system and the regression of the wolffian duct system (Ohno, 1978) (Fig. 2). However, in the presence of a testis, the wolffian duct differentiates to form the ductus epididymis, the vas deferens, the seminal vesicle, and the ejaculatory duct (Fig. 3). It has been shown that testosterone is the principal androgen produced by the Leydig cells of the fetal testis (Huhtaniemi et al., 1970; Reyes et al., 1973). Its synthesis is detectable at about 8 weeks' gestation and is maximal at 17 to 21 weeks (Siiteri and Wilson, 1974). The development of the fetal wolffian duct system depends on testosterone elaborated by the testis (Jost, 1953, 1970). It appears that, in wolffian duct differentiation, the androgen elaborated by a testis influences the ipsilateral but not the contralateral wolffian duct system. This was shown by the experiments of Jost (1953, 1970) and indicates that wolffian duct induction is a local tissue phenomenon and is not mediated by circulating androgens. Ohno et al. (1971) have suggested that testosterone is secreted by Leydig cells into the adjacent mesonephric duct, at which point it traverses the duct and is taken up by ductal cells, which it influences. In the absence of testicles, wolffian duct differentiation does not take place in the embryo; instead, uterus, vagina, and fallopian tubes develop (Jost, 1953, 1970).

Jost (1953) has shown that a fetal rabbit testis can be removed and replaced by a crystal of testosterone. When this is done, the wolffian duct system differentiates into definitive male ductal structures. In the same embryo, however, the ipsilateral müllerian duct system does not regress but differentiates into fallopian tubes, uterus, and vagina. This indicates that in addition to testosterone, the fetal testis must elaborate a second compound, which is concerned with müllerian duct regression. This has been given several names; we prefer the term *müllerian suppressive factor*. Its nature has been at least partially elucidated by Josso et al. (1977) as a high molecular weight polypeptide. Like testosterone, the müllerian suppressive factor elaborated by a testis acts only on the ipsilateral müllerian duct system. It has been suggested that müllerian sup-

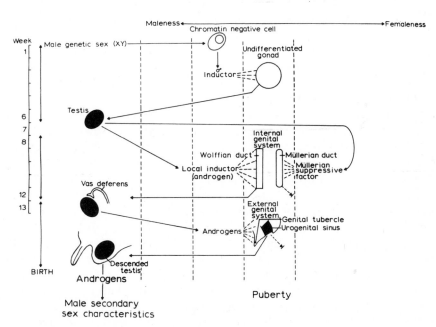

Figure 3. Normal male sex differentiation. (From Summitt, R. L. 1975. Sex Determination, Differentiation and Development. In Synopsis of Pediatrics, Hughes, J. G. (Ed.), pp. 572–613. St. Louis, C. V. Mosby Company.)

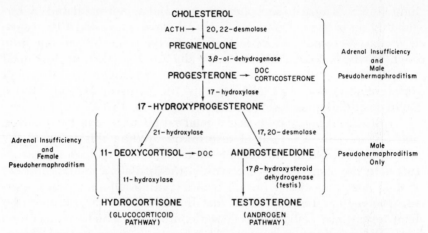

Figure 4. Biosynthesis of cortisol, testosterone, and dihydrotestosterone from cholesterol, showing enzyme systems involved. The first step showing $20\alpha,22R$-desmolase also involves 20α-hydroxylase and $22R$-hydroxylase. (Modified from Wilson, J. D., and J. L. Goldstein. 1975. Classification of Hereditary Disorders of Sexual Development. In Genetic Forms of Hypogonadism, Birth Defects. Original Article Series, Bergsma, D., (Ed.), pp. 1–16. White Plains, The National Foundation.)

pressive factor is produced by the Sertoli cells of the fetal testis (Josso et al., 1977).

The development of the male genital ductal system and the suppression of the female genital ductal system depends on the presence of a testis. The testis must contain functioning Leydig cells. These Leydig cells must be able to synthesize biologically active testosterone from a cholesterol precursor. The conversion of cholesterol to testosterone requires a series of biochemical reactions, each of which depends on a specific enzyme system (Fig. 4). The Sertoli cells of the testis must also elaborate müllerian suppressive factor. In addition, the cells influenced by these two hormones must be capable of responding to them. If any of the processes necessary for wolffian duct induction and müllerian duct suppression fail, male internal ductal differentiation will be defective.

The foregoing has implied that the elaboration of testosterone and müllerian suppressive factor by the fetal testis is under direct genetic control. In fact, little is known about what influences the secretion of müllerian suppressive factor. The pattern of maternal serum concentrations of chorionic gonadotropin (CG) (Clements et al., 1976; Winter et al., 1977) has a close temporal relationship to fetal testicular testosterone production and, as suggested by Winter and associates (1977), might be a major stimulus of fetal Leydig cell function. In contrast, fetal pituitary gonadotropins, luteinizing hormone (LH) and follicle-stimulating hormone (FSH), cannot be demonstrated until 11 weeks of fetal life, after initiation of wolffian duct differentiation, and even at peak periods do not reach levels of concentration near those of CG. Winter et al. (1977) have suggested that CG might be influential in initiating Leydig cell function, and pituitary gonadotropins might have a later influence on their function. The fact that normal male genital differentiation takes place in anencephalic fetuses further indicates that gonadotropins of placental origin (CG) rather than those of pituitary origin (LH and FSH) are the major influence on Leydig cell function.

Differentiation of the External Genitalia of the Male. Up to about 9 weeks' gestational age, the external genitalia of male and female human embryos are identical. The genitalia of both are characterized by the presence of a urogenital sinus delineated by an anteriorly located genital tubercle and laterally located genital folds and genital swellings (Fig. 5). In the female, the genital tubercle becomes the clitoris, the urogenital sinus becomes the urethra and caudad portion of the vagina, the genital swellings become the labia majora, and the genital folds become the labia minora. In the male, the genital tubercle becomes the glans penis, the genital folds become the shaft of the penis, and the genital swellings become the scrotum. The urogenital sinus is enclosed as the posterior urethra. In the male, the process of masculinization is complete by the fourteenth week of gestation.

This process in the male is under the influence of androgenic hormones. Evidence that dihydrotestosterone is the androgen that mediates masculinization of the bipotential external genitalia in the target cell is provided by clinical evidence (to be discussed later) and the demonstration that, prior to the stage of fetal development at which differentiation of the external genitalia takes place, the anlage of the external genitalia acquires the capacity to convert testosterone to dihydrotestosterone (DHT) (Siiteri and Wilson, 1974).

Available evidence indicates that the ability of any mammalian cell (except the male germ cell) to respond to androgen depends on the action of a nuclear cytosol-binding androgen-receptor protein specified by an X-linked gene (Ohno et al., 1971, 1977; Simpson, 1977). Thus, as with differentiation of the male internal genitalia, masculinization of the external genitalia is under the genetic control of multiple determinants: those governing the formation of a testis, those determining the differentiation of Leydig cells within the testis, those controlling the elaboration of the enzymes necessary for the biosynthesis of testosterone and its conversion in target cells to dihydrotestosterone, those mediating the synthesis of nuclear cytosol-binding androgen-receptor protein, and probably others.

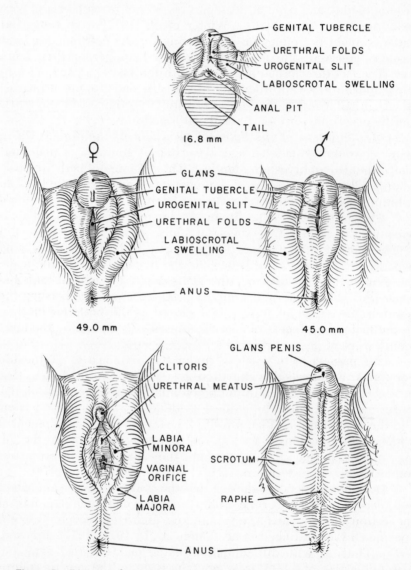

Figure 5. Bipotential primitive external genitalia (top), changes occurring in female differentiation (left), changes in male differentiation (right). (From Grumbach, M. M., and Van Wyk, J. J. 1974. In Textbook of Endocrinology, Williams, R. H. (Ed.), p. 442. Philadelphia, W. B. Saunders Company.)

Further Aspects of Gonadal Function in the Male. After the birth of a male infant, plasma testosterone levels rise to a peak at an average of 150 to 200 ng/dl by 1 to 2 months of age and then, by 6 months of age, decrease to very low levels that persist throughout childhood (Winter et al., 1976). From then until puberty, the male gonad is essentially nonfunctional.

The genetic mechanisms governing the onset of puberty and male gonadal function throughout adult life are poorly understood (Root, 1973). Several observations make it quite clear that genetic factors are involved. The physiologic changes that take place at puberty are under the control of the hypothalamic-pituitary-gonadal axis, with the additional requirement that androgen target cells have the ability to respond to androgen. Genetically determined conditions are known that involve defects at each level of this axis. Additionally, similarities exist relative to the ages of onset of puberty in close relatives, such as mothers and daughters and fathers and sons.

It is apparent that sexual maturation at puberty is not produced by a sudden "turn-on" of the hypothalamic-pituitary-gonadal axis but that it is the result of changes in the sensitivity of hypothalamic feedback-receptor sites to inhibition by gonadal hormones. Plasma concentrations of gonadotropins rise steadily in the several years preceding significant increases in testosterone concentrations, increase in testicular size, or clinical manifestations of sexual maturation (Winter and Faiman, 1972). In addition, sexual maturation occurs in conditions such as Klinefelter syndrome, indicating that endocrine function is possible in a testis in which seminiferous tubular function is severely compromised.

HYPOGONADISM

The term *hypogonadism* is defined (Dorland's Illustrated Medical Dictionary, 1974) as "a condition resulting from or characterized by abnormally decreased functional activity of the gonads, with retardation of growth and sexual development." From the foregoing, it should be apparent that decreased or absent gonadal functional activity can result from defects at the level of the hypothalamus, the pituitary gland, and the gonad itself. In addition, the definition, considered in its most liberal interpretation, can and in this discussion will be taken to include the defective ability of target cells to respond to gonadal hormones. Table 1 is a classification of conditions that encompass hypogonadism in the male. The two main cat-

Table 1.   Classification of Genetic Forms of Hypogonadism in the Male

I. Forms leading to abnormal sex differentiation
   A. XY gonadal dysgenesis
   B. XY gonadal agenesis
   C. Incompletely masculinized male (male pseudohermaphroditism)
     1. Type with female external genital phenotype
       a. Leydig cell aplasia (testicular unresponsiveness to LH and HCG)
       b. Complete or very severe biochemical defect in androgen biosynthesis
         (1) Defect in conversion of cholesterol to Δ^5 pregnenolone due to a defect in enzyme system that includes 20α-hydroxylase, 22R-hydroxylase, and 20,22R-desmolase
         (2) 17α-hydroxylase deficiency
         (3) 17,20-desmolase (lyase) deficiency
       c. Complete androgen insensitivity syndrome
         (1) Cytosol binding protein defect demonstrable
         (2) Cytosol binding protein defect not demonstrable
     2. Type with intersex genitalia
       a. Testicular dysgenesis (dysgenetic male pseudohermaphroditism)
       b. Defects in testosterone biosynthesis
         (1) Defect in conversion of cholesterol to Δ^5 pregnenolone due to defect in enzyme system that includes 20α-hydroxylase, 22R-hydroxylase, and 20,22-desmolase
         (2) 3β-hydroxysteroid dehydrogenase deficiency
         (3) 17α-hydroxylase deficiency
         (4) 17,20-desmolase (lyase) deficiency
         (5) 17-ketosteroid reductase (17β-hydroxysteroid oxidoreductase) deficiency
       c. Defect in conversion of testosterone to 5α-dihydrotestosterone due to deficient 5α-reductase activity in androgen-responsive target tissues
       d. Incomplete androgen insensitivity syndrome
         (1) Cytosol binding protein defect demonstrable
         (2) Cytosol binding protein defect not demonstrable
       e. Others—usually with associated nongenital anomalies
         (1) Brachio-skeleto-genital syndrome
         (2) G syndrome
         (3) Hypertelorism-hypospadias syndrome
         (4) Lenz microphthalmia syndrome
         (5) Meckel syndrome
         (6) Syndrome of pseudohermaphroditism, renal anomalies, and Wilms tumor
         (7) Smith-Lemli-Opitz syndrome
II. Forms with male phenotype
   A. Chromosome abnormalities
     1. Klinefelter syndrome and variants
     2. XYY male
     3. XX male
     4. 45,X/46,XY mosaicism
     5. Autosomal abnormalities
   B. Male with persistent müllerian structures
   C. Male with incomplete wolffian differentiation (cystic fibrosis of pancreas)
   D. Anorchia
   E. Hypogonadotropic hypogonadism (hypothalamic-pituitary axis in origin)
     1. Pituitary dwarfism (multitropic pituitary hormone deficiency)

(Continued)

Table 1. Classification of Genetic Forms of Hypogonadism
in the Male (*Continued*)

2. Isolated bihormonal gonadotropin deficiency (LH and FSH)
   a. Due to absence of gonadotropin releasing factor
   b. Due to pituitary defect
3. Isolated LH deficiency
4. Isolated FSH deficiency
F. Hypergonadotropic hypogonadism (gonadal in origin)
   1. Germinal cell aplasia
G. Forms with associated abnormalities
   1. Hypothalamic-pituitary axis in origin
      a. Kallmann syndrome
      b. Ataxia-hypogonadism syndrome
      c. Nevoid basal cell carcinoma syndrome
      d. Biemond syndrome
      e. Carpenter syndrome
      f. Crandall syndrome
      g. Ichthyosis-hypogonadism syndrome
      h. Kraus-Ruppert syndrome
      i. Laurence-Moon-Bardet-Biedl syndrome
   2. Gonadal in origin
      a. Alström syndrome
      b. Ataxia-telangiectasia syndrome
      c. Borjeson syndrome
      d. Fanconi syndrome
      e. Fraser syndrome
      f. Geominne syndrome
      g. Multiple lentigines syndrome
      h. Myotonic dystrophy
      i. Noonan syndrome
      j. Osteochondritis dissecans syndrome
      k. Prader-Willi syndrome
      l. Rothmund-Thomsen syndrome
      m. Russell-Silver syndrome
      n. Sohval-Soffer syndrome
      o. Van Bentham syndrome
      p. Weinstein syndrome
      q. Werner syndrome
      r. Xerodermic idiocy syndrome

egories within this classification are (1) those conditions that involve abnormalities in the process of differentiation of the genital apparatus and are necessarily expressed prenatally, leading to an infant whose genital phenotype is other than that of the normal male; and (2) those conditions in which the external genital phenotype is that of the normal male but in which later gonadal function is defective. Obviously, any defect operating prenatally will have postnatal effects. Those conditions that are expressed only postnatally have no efffect on the qualitative aspects of the genital phenotype; i.e., the genital phenotype is that of the normal male, but maturation and adult function are defective or absent.

Forms of Hypogonadism Leading to Abnormal Sex Differentiation

XY Gonadal Dysgenesis

The normal process of sex differentiation in the genetic male depends on the differentiation of a testis from the bipotential primitive gonad of the embryo. As discussed previously, current evidence indicates that a gene located in the short arm (and perhaps also in the long arm) of the Y chromosome determines a cell surface antigen, the H-Y antigen, which in some manner leads to the formation of a testis. Wachtel (1977) has suggested the necessity of a second gene for testis formation, perhaps located in the X chromosome, determining a receptor for the H-Y antigen. If the H-Y antigen is not produced or if it is produced but cannot function because of a defective plasma membrane receptor, a testis will not form. German et al. (1978) have proposed two possible mechanisms that would result in failure of testis formation in the presence of a functional H-Y determinant: (1) The presence of a structural gene for testis differentiation in the X chromosome may be induced by the product of the Y-linked H-Y determinant acting as a controlling element; or (2) the H-Y product may be the structural element, the controlling factor being produced by the X-borne gene. (Familial cases of XY gonadal dysgenesis could not possibly result from a mutant H-Y determinant because each affected person has a *different* Y chromosome, each of which was obviously functional in the father.) In any of these events, even though the genetic sex is male, sex differentiation will produce a female genital phenotype. At least 92 cases of XY gonadal dysgenesis have been described in the human (Simpson, 1977; Simpson et al., 1971), including 13 familial aggregates (Talerman, 1971; Simpson et al., 1971, 1976; Berger et al., 1972; Boczkowski et al., 1972; Anderson and Carlson, 1975; Fleishmann et al., 1976; Simpson, 1977; German et al., 1978). At birth, affected individuals generally have an unambiguously female phenotype, usually without associated nongenital anomalies. Clitoral enlargement has been noted in some cases. Patients are of normal stature or are even taller than the average female. In those individuals with short stature, the presence of an undetected 45,X cell line has been suggested (Simpson, 1977). Internal genitalia include normally differentiated vagina, uterus, and fallopian tubes, but ordinarily, the gonads are replaced by streaks of fibrous tissue similar to those in Turner syndrome. At the expected time of puberty, secondary sex characteristics do not appear, and the affected individual has primary amenorrhea.

German et al. (1978) have proposed that the failure of ovarian differentiation in both 45,X Turner syndrome and XY gonadal dysgenesis is due to a requirement that a locus in the X chromosome be *homozygous* if normal oogenesis is to occur. Although the gonadal streaks in XY gonadal dysgenesis are histologically similar to those in Turner syndrome (45,X or structural aberrations of the X chromosome), one property makes them quite different. Simpson (1977) has pointed out that a gonadoblastoma, or a dysgerminoma, occurs in 20 to 30 per cent of patients with XY gonadal dysgenesis.

Varying degrees of breast development have occurred in some patients with XY gonadal dysgenesis. The occurrence of breast development in some cases and, conversely, masculinization as manifest by clitoral enlargement in a number of affected patients, have both been attributed to endocrine activity emanating from hormone-secreting cells of a gonadoblastoma, which include granulosa, theca, and Leydig cells (Saunders et al., 1975; McDonough et al., 1976).

Although a gonadoblastoma is not a malignant tumor, Scully (1970) has pointed out that 8 per cent of such tumors occur in association with another germ cell tumor that is malignant. These tumors may be found even in childhood (Sternberg et al., 1968; Similä et al., 1974; Isurugi et al., 1977). Thus, the gonads of any patient with XY gonadal dysgenesis should be removed at an early age. Simpson and Photopulos (1976) have discussed possible reasons why the gonads in XY gonadal dysgenesis are predisposed to neoplastic transformation. The two primary possibilities appear to be (1) a particular susceptibility to neoplastic transformation in poorly differentiated gonadal tissue in the presence of an XY sex chromosome complement, regardless of the etiology of the gonadal hypoplasia, and (2) that the gene or genes determining XY gonadal dysgenesis also determine the susceptibility to neoplastic transformation. The mutant gene could serve as the first "hit" in the "two hit" hypothesis proposed by Knudson et al. (1973), the second hit being a second (somatic) mutation or an environmental agent.

The first case of XY gonadal dysgenesis was apparently reported by Swyer (1955). Swyer considered the condition to be a form of male pseudohermaphroditism. However, it does not conform to the definition of male pseudohermaphroditism to be used in this discussion. It is one form of what was once called *pure gonadal dysgenesis* in order to distinguish those individuals with gonadal dysgenesis without other features of Turner syndrome from patients with Turner syndrome. The term *XY gonadal dysgenesis* is preferred, to separate the condition from pure gonadal dysgenesis with an XX sex chromosome complement. Although the majority of reported cases have been isolated occurrences, the observation of a number of families with more than one affected member points to a male sex-limited autosomal dominant gene or, more likely, an X-linked mutant gene as the genetic basis for XY gonadal dysgenesis.

Although similarities exist between the phenotypes of 45,X/46,XY mosaicism and XY gonadal dysgenesis in some patients, as well as between the gonadal abnormalities of the two conditions, they appear to be nosologically distinct entities (Simpson, 1977). The individual with the former condition is not, in the strict sense, a genetic male. In addition, 45,X/46,XY mosaicism is cytogenetic in origin, whereas XY gonadal dysgenesis is the result of a single gene mutation.

XY Gonadal Agenesis

This condition is to be differentiated from XY gonadal dysgenesis. The term was proposed by Sarto and Opitz (1973) to describe phenotypic females with eunuchoid habitus, normal female external genitalia or enlarged clitoris, infantile or occasionally fused labia, absence of vagina and uterus, and rudimentary fallopian tubes. No gonadal structures are identifiable in this condition. In contrast to XY gonadal dysgenesis, some patients with XY gonadal agenesis may have associated nongenital anomalies. Sarto and Opitz (1973) suggested that early but temporary testicular differentiation suppressed müllerian duct differentiation but was not sufficient to sustain male sex differentiation. Alternate suggestions (Simpson, 1977) have included defective ductal anlage, defective connective tissue, or a teratogen. At least one patient with apparent XY gonadal agenesis had a vagina but lacked a uterus and fallopian tubes. Simpson (1977) terms this condition *agonadia*. Although most cases have been sporadic, the description of two affected sibs by Overzier and Linden (1956) suggests a genetic etiology. More information will be necessary to clarify the situation.

Incompletely Masculinized Male (Male Pseudohermaphroditism)

By definition, this condition exists in the individual who is a genetic male (sex chromosome complement XY) and whose only gonadal structure is a testis but whose external genital phenotype is other than that of the normal male. In most cases, the testis is well differentiated, but occasionally, testicular differentiation is not complete. As indicated previously, normal male sex differentiation is not automatic in the presence of a testis. It depends on the presence of Leydig cells, the intactness of the biochemical pathway that converts cholesterol to testosterone in the Leydig cells and thence to dihydrotestosterone in the target cells, and the ability of those target cells to respond to testosterone or dihydrotestosterone, or both. An abnormality at any of these stages can result in defective male sex differentiation.

Incomplete Masculinization of the Genetic Male, Producing a Female External Genital Phenotype. The most severe degree of male pseudohermaphroditism is that in which no male differentiation of the internal ductal structures and the external genitalia occurs — that in which the external genital phenotype is unambiguously female. This type of male pseudohermaphroditism has been reported as the result of aplasia of Leydig cells, of a severe defect in testosterone biosynthesis, and of target cell insensitivity to androgen.

LEYDIG CELL APLASIA. A 35-year-old phenotypic female with testes but without histologically identifiable Leydig cells was reported by Berthezène et al. (1976). The patient failed to feminize at the expected time of puberty. The vagina ended blindly at a depth of 4 cm. Laparotomy revealed no uterus or fallopian tubes. Normal-appearing vasa deferentia and epididymides were identified. The authors postulated Leydig cell agenesis as the cause of the absence of testosterone, thus the failure of male sex differentiation. The suppression of müllerian structures is to be expected, since Sertoli cells were present in the patient's testes. A similar case was reported recently by Brown et al. (1978). Berthezène et al. (1976) did not believe that the vasa deferentia and epididymides had differentiated as the result of interstitial cells that had temporarily been able to secrete androgens but had then for some reason disappeared. They suggested, instead, that enough androgen had been elaborated by Sertoli cells to produce a vas deferens and an epididymis. This idea is difficult to envision, and its validation must await further evidence.

Although the occurrence of only two cases in no way proves that this condition is genetic in nature, Ohno (1976b) suggested that it might be the result of a genetically determined unresponsiveness to LH, i.e., an LH-receptor defect. Also, although the two reported patients have female external genital phenotypes, precedent exists for the suggestion that a less severe defect might produce intersex genitalia.

COMPLETE OR VERY SEVERE BIOCHEMICAL DEFECT IN ANDROGEN BIOSYNTHESIS. Defects involving three biochemical reactions necessary for testosterone biosynthesis have been reported in male pseudohermaphrodites with female external genital phenotypes. Two of the three reactions involve enzymes that are also necessary for the synthesis of cortisol (see Figure 4); thus, when either of the two enzyme systems is deficient, the victim has not only male pseudohermaphroditism but also severe adrenal failure.

Defect in Conversion of Cholesterol to Pregnenolone. At least three enzymes are necessary for the conversion of cholesterol to pregnenolone — 20α-hydroxylase, 22R-hydroxylase, and 20α,22R-desmolase (Imperato-McGinley and Peterson, 1976). Prader and Siebenmann (1957) reported a genetic male with male internal ductal differentiation but female external genitalia. The infant died at 6 days of age of adrenal failure. At autopsy, massive accumulation of lipid was noted in the adrenal cortical cells. Several more cases of this "lipoid hyperplasia of the adrenal gland" have been reported, and in 1962 Prader and Anders postulated a genetically determined defect in 20α,22R-desmolase as its cause. This was followed in 1968 by the report of Camacho et al., which identified a defect in the conversion of cholesterol to Δ^5 pregnenolone in lipoid adrenal hyperplasia. Then in 1972, Degenhart and associates provided evidence for a deficiency of 20α-hydroxylase as the cause. Either of these defects, or a defect in 22R-hydroxylase, could result in the same histologic picture in the adrenal gland and the same phenotypic abnormalities. One 8-year-old affected patient with a female genital phenotype, testes, and severe adrenal insufficiency was reported by Kirkland et al. (1973).

17α-Hydroxylase Deficiency. In 1970, New and Suvannakul described the first case of male pseudohermaphroditism due to 17α-hydroxylase deficiency in a genetic male with ambiguous genitalia. However, several genetic males with this condition have been reported subsequently with an unambiguously female external genital phenotype (Mantero et al., 1971; Alvarez et al., 1973; Heremans et al., 1976; Kershnar et al., 1976). The patients also had sexual infantilism, hypertension, and hypokalemia. The hypertension and hypokalemia have been attributed to an excess of deoxycorticosterone. At least two of the seven patients reported had some differentiation of the epididymis, but in one (Heremans et al., 1976), the epididymal tubules were only rudimentary. The patient of Heremans et al. (1976) had originally been diagnosed as having the testicular feminization syndrome, but the development of adrenal failure led to the correct diagnosis. Although most reported patients have represented isolated cases, Alvarez et al. (1973) and Mallin (1969) reported 17α-hydroxylase deficiency in siblings, and the parents of the patient of Goldsmith et al. (1967) were first cousins.

17,20-Desmolase Deficiency. In 1972, Zachmann et al. reported two maternal first cousins and a maternal aunt who were all genetic males with ambiguous external genitalia and testes. Investigation revealed an inability of testicular tissue to synthesize testosterone from progesterone, pregnenolone, 17α-hydroxyprogesterone, or 17α-hydroxypregnenolone, indicating a defect in 17,20-desmolase. In 1976, Goebelsmann reported a phenotypic female with a 46,XY sex chromosome complement who, at 16 years of age, was sexually infantile, with no müllerian duct derivatives. The patient had low plasma dehydroepiandrosterone sulfate (DHA-S) and androstenedione values, low urinary 17-ketosteroids and dehydroepiandrosterone (DHA) values, and a minimal rise in plasma DHA-S and androstenedione and urinary DHA values in response to adrenocorticotropic hormone (ACTH), all of which are indications of a deficiency of 17,20-desmolase.

The first two of these three defects in testosterone biosynthesis are inherited in an autosomal recessive manner, a point, among others, that differentiates them from the complete androgen insensitivity syndrome to be discussed next. However, the 17,20-desmolase defect appears to be an X-linked condition, and its differentiation from the complete androgen insensitivity syndrome in childhood must be made on biochemical grounds. Failure of feminization at puberty will differentiate the two conditions at that time. Each defect is quite rare; e.g., only one case of a definite female phenotype in 17,20-desmolase deficiency (Goebelsmann, 1976) has been described.

COMPLETE ANDROGEN INSENSITIVITY SYNDROME. Although the phenotype of this condition was recorded by several authors in the nineteenth century, it was not until 1953 that the condition was described in the modern literature. At that time, Morris (1953) reported a summary of 98 cases and first used the term *testicular feminization syndrome*. Morris classified the condition as a form of male pseudohermaphroditism, but the etiology and genetic mode were not recognized until much later. Because of the nature of the condition, to be discussed, we suggest that the term *complete androgen insensitivity syndrome* is preferable to *complete testicular feminization syndrome*.

A newborn infant with the complete androgen insensitivity syndrome presents no problem in sex assignment. The external genital phenotype is unequivocally female. The patient may require medical attention in childhood because of the presence of inguinal hernias, and when surgical repair of the hernia is undertaken, it is found to contain a testis. Unless an inguinal hernia supervenes, the patient may not come to the attention of a physician until adolescence, when primary amenorrhea occurs. Breasts develop normally, although body hair is deficient. Height and body proportions are usually normal, although, according to Simpson (1977), arms and legs may be disproportionately long and hands and feet disproportionately large. Psychosexual orientation is totally female.

The vagina ends blindly and is usually only a few centimeters deep. The uterus and fallopian tubes are absent, as are wolffian duct derivatives. The testes are normal in size, and whereas in most cases they are located in hernial sacs in the inguinal regions, they may descend into the labia or remain in the abdominal cavity.

Prior to puberty, the testes are histologically similar to undescended testes in the otherwise normal male, but in the affected adult the seminiferous tubules are small and contain mostly Sertoli cells with few if any spermatogonia, and the Leydig cells are hyperplastic and are often present in clusters. The breasts of the affected adult contain normal ductal and glandular tissue.

A dysgerminoma was found in one of the two patients described in detail by Morris (1953). In 1963, Morris and Mahesh extended Morris' earlier observations to include 187 cases, and among those cases, 11 patients had malignant testicular tumors, most often seminomas. The occurrence of gonadal neoplasia in the complete androgen insensitivity syndrome has been reported in a number of instances subsequently. The risk of testicular neoplasia in a patient with the complete androgen insensitivity syndrome appears to be slight prior to the age of 25 to 30 years. It would appear that the risk of testicular neoplasia at some time in the life of a patient with the complete androgen insensitivity syndrome is in the range of 2 to 5 per cent (Simpson, 1977). Simpson (1977) indicates that this risk is not significantly different from that in an otherwise normal male with a cryptorchid testis and may simply be a reflection of the location of the testis.

Plasma testosterone concentrations in the complete androgen insensitivity syndrome fall within the normal adult male range (French et al., 1965, 1966; Pion et al., 1965; Kase and Morris, 1965). The fact that concentrations of testosterone are much higher in the testicular venous plasma than in the peripheral venous plasma indicates that testosterone is testicular in origin. Estrogen secretion appears to be no different from that in most men and may be as much as in some women (Naftolin and Judd, 1973). In addition, the estrogen is also primarily testicular in origin, since testicular vein concentrations are much higher than those in peripheral veins (French et al., 1965). Plasma FSH levels are normal, but LH levels are elevated. When testosterone is administered to a patient with the complete androgen insensitivity syndrome, virilization and nihas dealt only with those forms producing a female external genital phenotype. Discussion will now turn to those forms in which the external genital phenotype is ambiguous, creating, for example, a problem in sex assignment in the newborn. Forms of male pseudo-hermaphroditism in which the external genital phenotype is female may be viewed as more severe than those with intersex geni-talia. Since single gene mutations are responsible for the forms of male pseudohermaphroditism with female external genitalia, it might be postulated that the forms with intersex genitalia are also due to single gene mutations, resulting in less severe en-zyme deficiencies in testosterone biosynthesis or a less severe defi-ciency in the androgen cytosol-binding protein. Whether the less severe deficiency is the result of a mutant gene that is allelic to the gene producing the more severe phenotype with the same deficien-cy is unknown at this time, but the notion is attractive.

TESTICULAR DYSGENESIS (DYSGENETIC MALE PSEUDOHER-MAPHRODITISM). Although the term *dysgenetic male pseudoher-maphroditism* has been used by others to describe various phenotypes and varying types of gonadal dysfunction (Federman, 1967), the desig-nation *testicular dysgenesis* will be used here to describe those 46,XY patients with intersex genitalia whose gonads have definite testicular elements but yet are not normally differentiated. Case 1 of Chemke et al. (1970) would appear to fulfill the criteria for this designation. We have had the opportunity to see a patient with ambiguous external genitalia, a vagina that opened into the posterior urethra, a uterus, fallopian tubes, and other ductal structures resembling vasa deferentia on histologic examination. Only one gonad was found, adjacent to one of the vasa deferentia, on the left. It included abundant connective tissue with occasional seminiferous tubules showing focal calcifica-tion, no lumina, occasional Sertoli cells, and a single layer of apparent spermatogonia (Fig. 7). The boy had several associated nongenital anomalies but was normal mentally. Chromosome analysis revealed an XY sex chromosome complement but also an apparently balanced autosomal translocation. The relationship among the translocation, the nongenital anomalies, and the ambiguous genitalia is unclear, but the gonadal structure, though not a normal testis, contained testicular elements. We suggest that the testicular dysgenesis was causally relat-ed to the abnormal internal and external genitalia. Apparently, in addition to the deficiency of androgen, the presence of a uterus and fallopian tubes indicated a deficiency of müllerian suppressive factor as well.

The occurrence of XY gonadal dysgenesis in the two sisters of Chemke's patient (1970) suggests a relationship between XY gonadal

trogen retention do not occur (Wilkins, 1957; French et al., 1966; Strickland and French, 1969; Castaneda et al., 1971; Rosenfield et al., 1971). It has been suggested that the defect is a failure of the conversion of testosterone to dihydrotestosterone, but normal plas-ma levels of DHT (Imperato-McGinley and Peterson, 1976) and the formation of normal 5α-reduced steroids by the testis (Richards and Neville, 1974) have refuted that suggestion. In addition, the failure of response to administered DHT (French et al., 1966; Strickland and French, 1969; Castaneda et al., 1971; Rosenfield et al., 1971) further indicates that 5α-reductase deficiency is not the cause of the condition called the testicular feminization syndrome.

The foregoing evidence points to a defect that occurs beyond the stage of the conversion of testosterone to DHT as a cause of the complete androgen insensitivity syndrome. Bullock at al. (1971) pro-posed that the androgen insensitivity in the genetic male mouse with the testicular feminization syndrome (tfm/Y) is due to a failure of the concentration of androgens at active sites in the nucleus. These findings were extended by others, and defective binding of DHT in cultured genital skin fibroblasts has been demonstrated in humans with the "complete testicular feminization syndrome" (Keenan et al., 1974; Griffin et al., 1976; Kaufman et al., 1976a). These data point to an inability of testosterone and DHT to bind to a cytosol receptor protein in the androgen target cell. Ohno et al. (1971) have proposed, and Pinsky (1977) has elaborated the con-cept, that the cytosol-receptor protein normally binds to testos-terone and DHT in the cytoplasm and that this complex then enters the nucleus, where it binds to the genome, thereby activating the genes necessary for male sex differentiation. Therefore, the defect in the complete androgen insensitivity syndrome has been shown to be a deficiency of the cytosol-receptor protein or a functional abnor-mality in the molecule (Fig. 6). The facts that the plasma LH level is elevated in the androgen insensitivity syndrome and that LH can be suppressed in affected patients by administered estrogen but not by administered androgen (Imperato-McGinley and Peterson, 1976) are evidence that cytosol binding of androgens is also defective in the hypothalamus, thus interrupting the normal hypothalamic-pituitary-gonadal axis. Recent findings by Kaufman et al. (1976b) and by Amrhein et al. (1976) suggest heterogeneity in the complete androgen insensitivity syndrome in that cultured fibroblasts from some patients bind DHT at normal or near normal levels. Pinsky (1977) indicates that this heterogeneity may reflect a partial defi-ciency of cytosol-receptor protein in the instances in which binding appears to be near normal or that the abnormality in those cases is

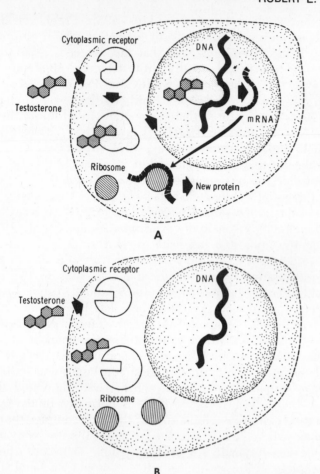

Figure 6. Diagrammatic representation of mechanism of androgen action at cellular site, involving binding by cytosol receptor protein and transfer to the nucleus, where androgen-receptor complex binds to genome. A. Normal binding. B. Situation in androgen insensitivity syndrome. Cytosol receptor protein mutation has altered structure of molecule, preventing its binding to androgen. (From Imperato-McGinley, J., and R. E. Peterson. 1976. Male pseudohermaphroditism: The complexities of male phenotypic development. Am. J. Med. 61:251–272.)

qualitative in addition to the degree of quantitative deficiency. Amrhein et al. (1976) suggested that the defect in those patients with normal androgen binding might be the result of a mutation that is allelic to that in which the cytosol-binding protein is deficient. That mutation would determine a structural alteration in the receptor molecule, inhibiting its interaction with nuclear chromatin. An alternative suggestion was that the problem might be a mutation in a gene determining another protein necessary for androgen action.

The occurrence of breast development in the complete gen insensitivity syndrome is interesting. Neumann and (1966) have presented evidence that artificially induced inhibi androgen in the fetal rat permits female organogenesis of the mary glands. This suggests that some form of "imprinting" of mary anlagen may be a function of androgen in the fetus, th hibiting the later development of mammary glands. If this c can be applied to man, it could be postulated that androgen in tivity in cells of the mammary anlagen might prevent such im ing. Further, it is not unreasonable to assume that the absen breast development in a normal male is a function of a physic balance between androgen and estrogen (Imperato-McGinley Peterson, 1976). When that balance is interrupted by insensitivi androgen, estrogen can and does act unopposed, with resu breast development not unlike that in the normal female.

Although target cell unresponsiveness to androgen account the lack of wolffian duct structures in the complete androgen in sitivity syndrome, it cannot explain the absence of uterus and f pian tubes. It must be recalled that in addition to testosterone, fetal testis elaborates a second compound, a high molecular we peptide called *müllerian suppressive factor*. Müllerian suppres factor is apparently produced normally in the complete andro insensitivity syndrome, and its action is not prevented by the m tion determining the defective androgen cytosol-binding prot Thus, although wolffian duct differentiation cannot be induc müllerian suppression does occur. The result is the absence of internal genital ductal structures.

In all likelihood, the complete androgen insensitivity syndro is inherited in an X-linked manner. Since affected males cannot produce, X-linked inheritance cannot be differentiated from au somal dominant inheritance with genetic male sex limitation on t basis of pedigree analysis alone. Linkage studies have not been i formative in the human. Phenotypes similar to complete androge insensitivity in the human have been described in several oth mammals. X-linked inheritance has been documented in the rat an the mouse (Simpson, 1977; Lyon and Hawkes, 1970). In additio and of considerable importance, the locus responsible for androge cytosol-receptor protein has been shown to be X-linked (Meyer e al., 1975). If, then, the defect in the cytosol-binding protein is th ultimate defect in the complete androgen insensitivity syndrome the localization of the gene for the cytosol-binding protein to the X chromosome means that the syndrome is X-linked.

Incomplete Masculinization of the Genetic Male with Intersex Genitalia. So far, the discussion of male pseudohermaphroditism

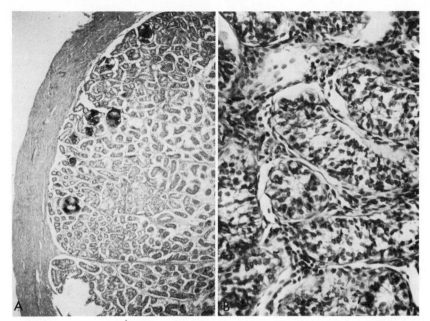

Figure 7. Photomicrograph of dysgenetic testis from patient with testicular dysgenesis. A. Multifocal calcification and very thick tunica albuginea (magnification 12.5×). B. Immature seminiferous tubules (magnification 125×). (Courtesy W. M. Gooch, III, M.D.)

dysgenesis and testicular dysgenesis. Testicular dysgenesis is most likely a heterogeneous category of male pseudohermaphroditism, and its exact nature in at least some cases is yet to be elucidated. Although the gonadal histologic appearance is not different from that seen in some patients with 45,X/46,XY mosaicism, the familial nature of Chemke's cases and the absence of a 45,X cell line in our patient and in others indicates that testicular dysgenesis can occur in the absence of 45,X/46,XY mosaicism.

DEFECTS IN TESTOSTERONE BIOSYNTHESIS. Defects in which a female external genital phenotype has been reported have already been discussed. Each of those three defects, plus the defects at the other two steps in testosterone biosynthesis, also produce male pseudohermaphroditism with *intersex* genitalia. As noted previously and as shown in Figure 4, three biochemical steps in the conversion of cholesterol to testosterone are shared by the biosynthetic pathway producing cortisol. Thus, in defects involving those three steps, male pseudohermaphroditism may be accompanied by adrenal insufficiency. In the other two defects, involving 17,20-desmolase and 17-ketosteroid reductase, adrenal insufficiency does not occur.

Defect in Conversion of Cholesterol to Pregnenolone. As pointed out previously, the enzymes 20α-hydroxylase, 22R-hydroxylase, and 20α,22R-desmolase are active in the conversion of cholesterol to Δ^5 pregnenolone. Prader and Siebenmann (1957) first reported "lipoid hyperplasia of the adrenal gland," in male pseudohermaphrodites with female genital phenotypes. Camacho and associates (1968) described a defect in the conversion of cholesterol to pregnenolone in an infant with lipoid hyperplasia of the adrenal gland who was a genetic male with intersex genitalia. Their patient died late in the first year of life, and they suggested that he had a milder form of the same condition described earlier by Prader. Prader and Anders (1962) pointed out parental consanguinity in some of the cases from Switzerland, and it is apparent that in all instances of a defect in the conversion of cholesterol to pregnenolone, the mode of inheritance is autosomal recessive.

3β-Hydroxysteroid Dehydrogenase Deficiency. This enzyme is required for the conversion of pregnenolone to progesterone and of dehydroepiandrosterone to androstenedione (See Figure 4). Thus, it is necessary for the production of cortisol, aldosterone, estrogens, and androgens. In the genetic male, a deficiency of this enzyme would be expected to produce male pseudohermaphroditism and adrenal failure. The first cases of 3β-hydroxysteroid dehydrogenase deficiency were described in 1961 and 1962 (Bongiovanni, 1961, 1962; Bongiovanni and Eberlein, 1961). Affected males had intersex genitalia, and four of six patients died in early infancy of adrenal failure. Since Bongiovanni's report, a number of other cases have been described with survival at least to adolescence (Parks et al., 1971). Thus, there appears to be a spectrum of severity in the phenotype resulting from deficiency of 3β-hydroxysteroid dehydrogenase, much like that seen in 21α-hydroxylase deficiency and other known genetically determined conditions. Different degrees of severity even in the same family have been described; two brothers of the 13-year-old male reported by Parks et al. (1971) had died in infancy of adrenal failure.

Wolffian duct differentiation is normal in this condition, and it would appear that even when the defect is severe, some degree of masculinization of the external genitalia occurs, perhaps because dehydroepiandrosterone, although known to be a weak androgen, exerts some masculinizing influence. The external genital phenotype ordinarily includes a small phallus, severe second or third degree hypospadias, and partial fusion of the labioscrotal folds. The inheritance is autosomal recessive.

17α-Hydroxylase Deficiency. As mentioned previously, New and Suvannakul (1970) reported the first case of 17α-hydroxylase deficiency. Their patient had ambiguous external genitalia with normal wolf-

fian duct differentiation, in contrast to incomplete wolffian differentiation with female external genital phenotypes in patients described
later. 17α-Hydroxylase deficiency is rare, although Simpson (1977) has
indicated that it might be more common than generally appreciated
because the phenotype is similar to that in the incomplete androgen
insensitivity syndrome. Some genetic males with 17α-hydroxylase
deficiency develop gynecomastia. As a result, some male pseudohermaphrodites, who are thought to have the incomplete androgen insensitivity syndrome because they have breast development, actually may
have 17α-hydroxylase deficiency. Whereas the incomplete androgen
insensitivity syndrome is inherited in an X-linked recessive manner,
the mode of inheritance of 17α-hydroxylase deficiency is autosomal
recessive. Nevertheless, in any patient suspected of having the incomplete androgen insensitivity syndrome, 17α-hydroxylase deficiency
should be excluded.

   17,20–Desmolase Deficiency. As discussed in the section on male
pseudohermaphroditism with a female genital phenotype, the first
three cases of 17,20-desmolase deficiency, reported by Zachmann et al.
(1972), had intersex genitalia. In that family, incubation of testicular
slices with radioactive-labeled androstenedione and dehydroepiandrosterone revealed no defect in testosterone biosynthesis. However,
testosterone could not be synthesized from other precursors, indicating
that conversion of 17-hydroxypregnenolone to dehydroepiandrosterone and of 17-hydroxyprogesterone to androstenedione was defective (see Figure 4). The pedigree of the family studied by Zachmann
strongly suggested an X-linked mode of inheritance in 17,20-
desmolase deficiency.

   17–Ketosteroid Reductase (17β-Hydroxysteroid Oxidoreductase)
Deficiency.   Saez et al. (1971) reported 2 siblings who were reared as
females until puberty. Saez' description does not indicate with certainty whether the external genitalia were obviously ambiguous prior
to puberty; however, at puberty, masculinization occurred with enlargement of the clitoris and the appearance of a male pattern of body
hair but with breast development also. At laparotomy, the uterus and
fallopian tubes were found to be absent; an apparent vas deferens was
found on each side. Further studies revealed decreased plasma concentrations of testosterone but definitely increased levels of androstenedione (Saez et al., 1972). Goebelsmann et al. reported one additional
case in 1973, and in 1974, Givens and associates described two siblings
(Figs. 8A and 8B) who were originally reported as having pseudovaginal perineoscrotal hypospadias (Opitz et al., 1971). The two siblings in
Givens' report had no gynecomastia. Their disorder may represent a
more severe enzyme deficiency than those previously reported. Wolf-

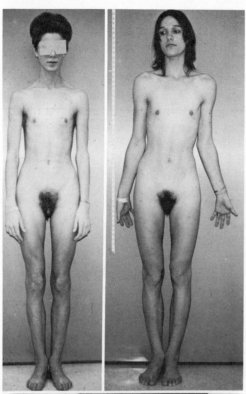

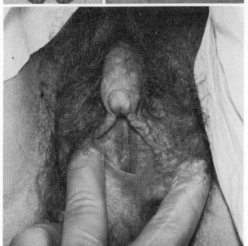

Figure 8. Sisters with male pseudohermaphroditism due to 17-ketosteroid reductase defect. *A.* Full view of sisters. *B.* External genitalia of older sister. (In part from Summitt, R. L. 1977. Disorders of Sex Differentiation. In Gynecologic Endocrinology, Givens, J. R. (Ed.), pp. 69–92. Chicago, Year Book Medical Publishers, Inc.)

fian duct structures are generally present in affected genetic males. Striking masculinization has occurred in reported cases, even in those with gynecomastia. Pedigrees involving more than one affected member indicate an autosomal recessive mode of inheritance, although 17-ketosteroid reductase deficiency in the rat is inherited in an X-linked manner (Goldman, 1970).

DEFECT IN CONVERSION OF TESTOSTERONE TO 5α-DIHYDRO-TESTOSTERONE DUE TO DEFICIENT 5α-REDUCTASE ACTIVITY. In 1974, Walsh et al. reported two 46,XY siblings with intersex genitalia and palpable labial gonads. Both had clitoral enlargement. Whereas one had a blind-ending vagina, the other had a single urogenital orifice. Both were reared as females, and at puberty, the older one experienced a growth spurt, phallic enlargement, lowering of the voice, development of a masculine habitus, and lack of breast development. The two sibs conformed to what Walsh and his colleagues in Dallas (1974) termed *incomplete male pseudohermaphroditism, type 2*, which is analogous to pseudovaginal perineoscrotal hypospadias. The siblings had normal wolffian duct structures, although the external genitalia were ambiguous, but the ejaculatory ducts emptied into a short, blind-ending vagina in the older sib. In the testes of the older sib, the seminiferous tubules contained well-developed Sertoli cells, many spermatogonia and primary spermatocytes, and some secondary spermatocytes and spermatids. No mature spermatozoa were seen. Leydig cells appeared normal. The rate of dihydrotestosterone formation was measured in skin slices and shown to be markedly decreased in comparison with that in normal skin and skin from patients with the complete and incomplete androgen insensitivity syndromes. The authors suggested that a defect in the conversion of testosterone to DHT was the cause of male pseudohermaphroditism in the two siblings reported. They pointed out that the differentiation of the wolffian duct system is testosterone dependent, since at the time of wolffian duct differentiation, the capacity to convert testosterone to DHT has not developed in the tissues involved. They indicated further that differentiation of the urogenital sinus and external genitalia requires DHT, not testosterone. The capacity to convert testosterone to DHT is present in the tissues of the urogenital sinus and external genitalia *prior* to the onset of male sex differentiation. Thus, in the genetically determined absence of a capacity to convert testosterone to DHT, one would expect normal wolffian duct differentiation but defective masculinization of the external genitalia (Fig. 9). In abstract form (1974a), even prior to the appearance of Walsh's report and later in extenso (1974b), Imperato-McGinley et al. reported similar findings in 24 male pseudohermaphrodites in 13 families of a large inbred population isolate in the

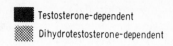

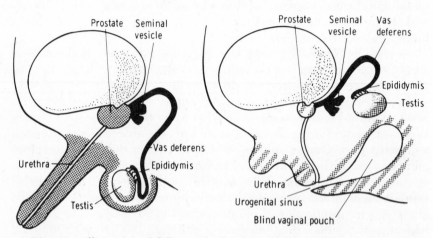

Figure 9. Illustration of differential role of testosterone and dihydrotestosterone in sex differentiation. (From Imperato-McGinley, J., L. Guerrero, T. Gautier, and R. E. Peterson. 1974. Steroid 5α-reductase deficiency in man. An inherited form of male pseudohermaphroditism. Science 186:1213–1215.)

Dominican Republic. They demonstrated a defect in the enzyme 5α-reductase as the primary deficiency in this form of male pseudohermaphroditism. Recent evidence presented by Leshin et al. (1978) indicates the possible biochemical and thus genetic heterogeneity in 5α-reductase deficiency.

Interestingly, in the community described by Imperato-McGinley and associates, the affected males had ambiguous genitalia at birth, with minimal masculinization of the external genitalia (Peterson et al., 1977). Before the nature of the disorder was recognized in the community in which the defect was found, affected children were reared as females. At puberty, however, their voices deepened, and they experienced marked masculinization, with phallic enlargement and increase in muscle mass. The phallic enlargement was so marked that the result was a functional penis. The scrotum became rugated, the testes descended, pubic hair appeared, and the patients had ejaculates. However, the prostate gland remained small, beard growth was scanty, acne did not occur, and the patients had no temporal hair recession. Testicular biopsies showed normal Leydig cells and normal seminiferous tubules with *complete* spermatogenesis.

The data of Peterson et al. (1977) indicated that not only was differentiation of the male external genitalia dependent on DHT, but prostate maturation, beard growth, and the appearance of acne were also DHT dependent, whereas increase in muscle mass, growth of the phallus and scrotum, and voice change were testosterone dependent. The administration of dihydrotestosterone propionate to two affected males resulted in a significant increase in body hair and enlargement of the prostate gland. No information is available on fertility, since, as Peterson et al. (1977) point out, natural insemination is impossible because of the severe hypospadias. Patients do have erections and ejaculations, and adult sexual orientation in almost all cases has been unequivocally male. The almost routine change of sexual orientation at puberty exhibited by the patients in an isolated social setting such as that described by Imperato-McGinley and Peterson is fascinating and would be very difficult in most other societies.

Studies by Peterson and associates (Imperato-McGinley et al., 1974b; Peterson et al., 1977) have traced the condition in the Dominican Republic back through seven generations to one woman. Extensive consanguinity in the pedigree is also a firm indication of a founder effect. In addition, investigation of phenotypically normal parents of affected patients reveals a biochemical defect that is intermediate between the normal and the known affected, and phenotypically normal female siblings of known affected males demonstrate the same biochemical defect as their affected male sibs. This evidence, plus the information gained from the family reported by Walsh, indicates an autosomal recessive mode of inheritance in 5α-reductase deficiency. The studies by Imperato-McGinley and Peterson, and by Walsh and his colleagues, allow an exciting insight into the genetic and biochemical control of sex differentiation and gonadal function in the male.

As mentioned previously, Walsh and associates (1974) considered their patients with 5α-reductase deficiency to represent examples of *incomplete male pseudohermaphroditism, type 2,* which they indicated was synonymous with *pseudovaginal perineoscrotal hypospadias (PPSH).* The PPSH phenotype — i.e., intersex genitalia with separate urethral and vaginal orifices or variable labial fusion and virilization at puberty with or without breast development — has also been shown to result from other defects, including 17-ketosteroid reductase deficiency (Givens et al., 1974). PPSH is a descriptive term that had some usefulness prior to the present era of sophisticated diagnostic techniques that allow more specific designation of defects producing defective masculinization. In our opinion, the term *pseudovaginal perineoscrotal hypospadias* is outdated and should be discarded in favor of terms that describe more exactly the defect that produces the abnormal genital phenotype.

INCOMPLETE ANDROGEN INSENSITIVITY SYNDROME. Previous discussion has dealt with the complete androgen insensitivity syndrome, and it mentioned that if one considers that condition to be the result of a severe or complete deficiency (or malfunction) of androgen cytosol-receptor protein, it is logical to assume that a less severe defect might allow partial masculinization of the internal and external genitalia of the genetic male, leading to an intersex phenotype. In their extensive review, Morris and Mahesh (1963) called attention to the occurrence of the testicular feminization syndrome with clitoral enlargement. They indicated that patients with clitoral enlargement might resemble the complete testicular feminization syndrome and "in such instances probably have a similar etiology," might be "essentially male," or might be "intermediate. . . ." More recent evidence has shown that a number of patients with similar conditions have the incomplete androgen insensitivity syndrome but that others have entirely different forms of male pseudohermaphroditism. Morris and Mahesh pointed out two additional and probably more important facts: (1) The incomplete and complete forms of the testicular feminization syndrome do not occur in the same family and thus are nosologically distinct, and (2) in families in which the incomplete forms occur, phenotypic variations are not uncommon. Failure to realize this last fact has led to nosologic confusion by some authors (Wilson et al., 1974;

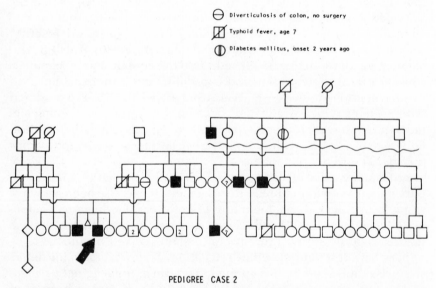

PEDIGREE CASE 2

Figure 10. Pedigree of patient with incomplete androgen insensitivity syndrome; androgen cytosol binding protein not demonstrable. (From Summitt, R. L. 1977. Disorders of Sex Differentiation. In Gynecologic Endocrinology, Givens, J. R. (Ed.), pp. 69–92. Chicago, Year Book Medical Publishers, Inc.)

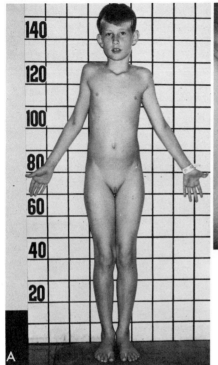

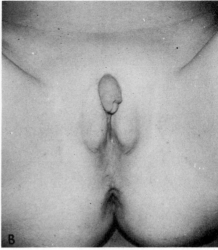

Figure 11. Patient whose pedigree appears in Figure 10. *A*. Full length view, pretreatment. *B*. External genitalia, pretreatment. (From Summitt, R. L. 1977. Disorders of Sex Differentiation. In Gynecologic Endocrinology, Givens, J. R. (Ed.), pp. 69–92. Chicago, Year Book Medical Publishers, Inc.)

Madden et al., 1975). In 1974, Wilson et al. described a large family in which patients with varying degrees of incomplete masculinization were evaluated. Androgen resistance was demonstrated, but the authors used the term *incomplete male pseudohermaphroditism, type 1.* In addition, the family had been previously reported as an example of Reifenstein syndrome (Bowen et al., 1965). A more recent study of two other families originally reported as having Reifenstein syndrome by Bowen et al. (1965) has revealed androgen insensitivity in both. In one patient, a deficiency of androgen cytosol-binding protein was demonstrated; in four others, normal binding activity was demonstrated, similar to the situation in the complete androgen insensitivity syndrome (Amrhein et al., 1976).

We have had the opportunity to examine a patient who is a member of a large family in which several individuals have had intersex genitalia and have feminized at puberty (Fig. 10). The patient presented at 12 years of age with a small, ventrally curved phallus, partially fused labia, and perineal hypospadias, along with gynecomastia (Fig. 11). He had been reared as a male, although a similarly affected sibling had

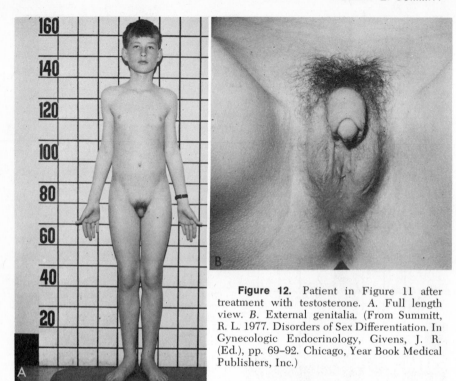

Figure 12. Patient in Figure 11 after treatment with testosterone. *A.* Full length view. *B.* External genitalia. (From Summitt, R. L. 1977. Disorders of Sex Differentiation. In Gynecologic Endocrinology, Givens, J. R. (Ed.), pp. 69–92. Chicago, Year Book Medical Publishers, Inc.)

been reared as a female. He responded to large doses of testosterone with phallic growth and the appearance of pubic hair (Fig. 12). Cultured genital skin fibroblasts from this patient studied in the laboratory of Dr. Leonard Pinsky have revealed deficiency of androgen cytosol-binding protein.

These findings are in keeping with the findings in Case 2 of Amrhein et al. (1977) and with those of Griffin et al. (1976), although in the majority of patients studied by Amrhein et al., androgen cytosol binding in cultured fibroblasts was normal in addition to 5α-reductase activity being normal. As in their patients with the complete androgen insensitivity syndrome with normal cytosol binding of androgen and normal nuclear uptake and retention of the DHT-receptor complex, Amrhein et al. (1977) suggested either a structural alteration in the receptor molecule, inhibiting its interaction with nuclear chromatin, or a mutation involving another protein necessary for androgen action as the primary defect in patients with incomplete androgen insensitivity but with no apparent defect in cytosol binding.

It would appear that a sizeable proportion of cases of male pseudohermaphroditism are the result of a defect distal to the step that converts testosterone to DHT. Nosologic heterogeneity is apparent among such patients, however, since a defect in androgen cytosol-binding protein is demonstrable in some but not in others. Even so, it would appear that in all families studied in which more than one case occurred, pedigree patterns point to an X-linked (or autosomal dominant with genetic male sex limitation) mode of inheritance.

A contemporary discussion of incomplete androgen insensitivity would not be complete without mention of Lubs syndrome (Lubs et al., 1959), the syndrome of Gilbert-Dreyfus (Gilbert-Dreyfus et al., 1957), the family described by Rosewater and associates (1965), and Reifenstein syndrome (Bowen et al., 1965). Each of these conditions was originally considered to be a distinct entity, based on the degree of defect in masculinization of the male fetus. Lubs syndrome was similar to the complete androgen insensitivity syndrome, and the syndrome of Gilbert-Dreyfus, Rosewater syndrome, and Reifenstein syndrome were progressively more masculinized. As previously noted, reinvestigation of one of the original families described as having Reifenstein syndrome (Wilson et al., 1974) revealed the presence of patients whose phenotypes actually conformed to each of these four eponymic syndromes. Thus, the nosologic distinctness of the Lubs, Gilbert-Dreyfus, Rosewater, and Reifenstein syndromes is invalid. In this era of more sophisticated means of evaluating androgen biosynthesis and responsiveness, terms such as these have outlived their usefulness and should be discarded in favor of more specific terms such as those in Table 1.

A diagnosis of the incomplete androgen insensitivity syndrome in the adult depends on the demonstration of the absence of a defect in testosterone biosynthesis or in the conversion of testosterone to 5α-dihydrotestosterone in a patient who is a genetic male (46,XY), has intersex genitalia, testes, and absent müllerian structures, and feminizes at puberty. In the prepubertal patient, the same requirements apply, with the obvious exception of pubertal feminization. Although a demonstration of defective androgen cytosol binding in cultured genital fibroblasts considerably strengthens the diagnosis, according to current nosology (see Table 1), such a defect cannot be demonstrated in all affected patients. It is important to emphasize that cytosol-binding activity should be tested on fibroblasts obtained from the genital area, not elsewhere, since androgen metabolism normally seems to be much more active in cells cultured from the genital area (Pinsky, 1977; Pinsky et al., 1972). In familial cases, an X-linked mode of inheritance further supports the diagnosis. Response to androgen administration probably should not be used as a discriminative test, since some patients who nosologically fit into the incomplete androgen

Table 2. Multiple Malformation Syndromes That Include Incomplete Masculinization of the External Genitalia

CONDITION	GENITAL ANOMALIES	OTHER ANOMALIES	MODE OF INHERITANCE
Brachio-skeleto-genital syndrome (Elsahy and Waters, 1971)	Perineoscrotal hypospadias	Maxillary hypoplasia, prognathism, fusion of cervical vertebrae, bifid uvula	Autosomal recessive
G syndrome (Esophogeal-facial-genital syndrome (Opitz et al., 1969)	Hypospadias, bifid scrotum, chordee	Parietal bossing, occipital prominence, failure to thrive, hoarse cry, slit-like palpebral fissures, hypertelorism, upward or downward slanting palpebral fissures, dysphagia	Autosomal dominant
Hypertelorism-hypospadias syndrome (Christian, 1973)	First degree to severe third degree hypospadias, cryptorchidism	Hypertelorism, cleft lip and palate, congenital cardiac defect, ear malformations, multiple lipomata, mental retardation, cranial asymmetry, strabismus	Autosomal dominant
Lenz microphthalmia syndrome (Herrmann and Opitz, 1969)	Hypospadias, cryptorchidism	Failure to thrive, mental retardation, microphthalmia or anophthalmia, microcephaly, micrognathia, dental anomalies, long cylindrical thorax, syndactyly, brachydactyly, pseudoclubbing of digits, camptodactyly, clinodactyly	X-linked recessive

Syndrome	Genital findings	Clinical features	Inheritance
Meckel syndrome (Meckel and Passarge, 1971; Opitz and Howe, 1969)	Intersex genitalia, persistent müllerian elements, cryptorchidism	Intrauterine growth retardation, posterior or dorsal encephalocele, microcephaly, sloping forehead, cerebral and cerebellar hypoplasia, microphthalmia, coloboma, cleft palate, micrognathia, slanted ears, short neck, short limbs, polydactyly, clubfeet, renal dysgenesis, lung hypoplasia, olfactory hypoplasia	Autosomal recessive
Pseudohermaphroditism, renal anomalies, Wilms tumor (Baraket et al., 1974; Monteleone et al., 1975)	Intersex genitalia, persistent müllerian elements, cryptorchidism	Congenital nephrosis, Wilms tumor	Unknown
Smith-Lemli-Opitz syndrome (Smith et al., 1964)	Intersex genitalia, cryptorchidism	Failure to thrive, mental retardation, microcephaly, epicanthal folds, ptosis of eyelids, strabismus, broad nasal tip with anteverted nostrils, pyloric stenosis, cardiac defect, inguinal hernia, renal anomaly	Autosomal recessive

insensitivity category respond to large doses of testosterone with masculinization and nitrogen retention.

OTHER TYPES OF MALE PSEUDOHERMAPHRODITISM WITH ASSOCIATED NON-GENITAL ANOMALIES. Several "multiple malformation syndromes" are known in which affected males have incomplete masculinization of the external genitalia. For the most part, the exact metabolic nature of the incomplete masculinization is not known. Those syndromes that include such findings are summarized in Table 2 (Simpson, 1977). A number of other syndromes are known that involve isolated hypospadias. They are not included in this category.

Forms of Hypogonadism in the Genetic Male with Male Phenotype

Chromosome Abnormalities

Several abnormalities of the sex chromosomes are known to be associated with a male genital phenotype but with evidence, in at least some cases, of gonadal dysfunction.

Klinefelter Syndrome. For purposes of this discussion, Klinefelter syndrome is defined as that spectrum of features occurring in individuals whose sex chromosome complements include at least two X chromosomes and one Y chromosome. Thus, any male whose phenotype resembles that of Klinefelter syndrome but who has no sex chromosome abnormality or whose sex chromosome complement does not conform to the above definition does not have Klinefelter syndrome.

Klinefelter syndrome derives its eponymic designation from the report of Klinefelter, Reifenstein, and Albright (1942), in which the authors described nine adult males with small testes, azoospermia, normal male external genitalia, gynecomastia, absence of secondary sex characteristics, and elevation of urinary gonadotropin excretion. The authors did not know the cause of the condition. It was suggested in 1956 that it was some variety of sex reversal (Bradbury et al., 1956; Plunkett and Barr, 1956; Witschi et al., 1956). It was not until 1959, when Jacobs and Strong reported a 47,XXY karyotype in an affected male, that it was determined that Klinefelter syndrome involved an extra sex chromosome. Since 1959, much has been learned about the phenotypic variability and the karyotypic spectrum in this syndrome, which has a frequency of approximately 1 in 1000 live male births, with no apparent racial or geographic predilection (Hook and Hamerton, 1977). Klinefelter syndrome is more frequent in mentally retarded populations than in consecutive newborns (Hamerton, 1971) and is probably more frequent among institutionalized psychotic or neurotic males (MacLean et al., 1968; Nielsen, 1969; Hambert, 1971) and among criminals (Casey et al., 1966; Jacobs et al., 1968; Hambert, 1971).

The phenotypic features of Klinefelter syndrome have recently been summarized by Simpson (1977). It is very seldom diagnosed prior to puberty. The condition is detected only in surveys of consecutive newborns or older children or when chromosome studies are done on male children with mental retardation. Laron and Hochman (1971) reported that testicular size in children with Klinefelter syndrome is smaller than in unaffected male children. Also, the eunuchoid body proportions of affected adults may be discernable in the child.

The phenotypic features in the adult are shown in Table 3, as collected by Simpson (1977). The most constant features (Simpson, 1977) are atrophy and hyalinization of the seminiferous tubules and a relative increase in the number of Leydig cells. Although the number of Leydig cells is relatively increased, the absolute volume is not. On histologic examination, the Leydig cells are abnormal, lacking crystalloids of Reinke, as well as being functionally abnormal with variably decreased androgen production and decreased functional reserve. The external genitalia are usually normal, except for small testes, but secondary sex development may be delayed or inadequate. Acne and temporal hair recession are unusual, and muscle development may be deficient. Only about 20 percent of affected males have obvious gynecomastia, although Simpson (1977) has indicated that 50 to 75 percent have increased parenchymal breast tissue. Affected males have a 20-fold increased risk of breast cancer as compared with normal males. Of 141 47,XXY males tabulated by Simpson (1977), six were mentally retarded. Furthermore, the fact that 1 percent of mentally retarded males have the 47,XXY Klinefelter syndrome emphasizes the intellectual effect of the extra X chromosome. Other personality variations occur, including poor motivation, poor adaptability, and reaction to stress with aggressive behavior. The average height of men with the 47,XXY Klinefelter syndrome is greater than that of 46,XY men, and eunuchoid or pseudo-eunuchoid body proportions are common. Somatic anomalies are few. Those encountered are usually minor and include scoliosis, kyphosis, pectus excavatum, clinodactyly of the fifth finger, dental anomalies, and altered dermatoglyphics. Dermatoglyphic features include a decreased mean digital ridge count, a proximally displaced axial triradius, and a decreased distance between the *a* and *b* digital triradii.

As pointed out by Simpson (1977), extra X chromosomes in males may be the result of primary meiotic nondisjunction in oogenesis or spermatogenesis, secondary nondisjunction involving 47,XXX oogonia

Table 3. Phenotypic Features of 47,XXY, 48,XXXY and 49,XXXXY
Klinefelter Syndrome (Simpson, 1977)

	KARYOTYPE		
CLINICAL FEATURE	47,XXY	48,XXXY	49,XXXXY
Mental retardation	6/141	29/29	28/28
Small testes	143/143	26/26	28/28
Hypoplastic penis	11/44	11/24	24/28
Gynecomastia	26/44	9/24	5/10
Wide-set eyes	0/143	2/25	20/23
Epicanthal folds	1/143	6/25	16/19
Upturned nose	0/143	0/25	5/23
Low-set ears	0/143	1/25	2/21
Malformed ears	0/143	1/25	11/21
Strabismus	0/143	2/25	11/21
Prognathism	0/143	2/25	8/16
Webbed neck	0/143	2/25	4/19
Short neck	0/143	0/25	14/19
Kyphosis	1/143	3/25	9/13
Scoliosis	0/143	2/25	4/9
Radioulnar synostosis	0/143	3/25	8/19
Abnormal ulna or radius	0/143	0/25	4/19
Clinodactyly of fifth finger (V)	2/143	7/25	23/26
Coxa valga	0/143	1/25	12/14
Genu valgum	0/143	0/25	6/24
Pes planus	0/143	1/25	10/24
Malformed toes	0/143	0/25	5/24
Pes cavus	2/143	0/25	0/24
Wide gap between the first and second toes	0/143	0/25	2/26
Talipes equinovarus	0/143	0/25	2/26

or 47,XYY spermatogonia, tertiary trisomy resulting from the segregation of a translocation, or mitotic nondisjunction in the zygote or
embryo. The increased mean age of mothers of males with Klinefelter
syndrome suggests meiotic nondisjunction in oogenesis as an important factor (Ferguson-Smith, 1958, 1963, 1966; Simpson, 1977). However, Edwards (1971) indicated that 39.1 percent of XXY males were
X^MX^PY. Klinefelter syndrome has been the result of segregation in a
balanced maternal translocation in only one reported case: that reported by Opitz et al. (1977) involving an X-14 translocation.

About 9 percent of patients with Klinefelter syndrome are mosaic; all but a few are 46,XY/47,XXY (Sanger et al., 1971). This is a
minimum estimate, as indicated by the investigation of Paulsen et al.
(1968), who found 46,XY/47,XXY mosaicism in the testes of six individuals. However, chromosome analysis on lymphocytes of the same six
patients revealed 47,XXY cells in only three. On an average, the
phenotypes of 46,XY/47,XXY patients are less abnormal than those of

nonmosaic 47,XXY individuals. Those patients with Klinefelter syndrome who have been reportedly fertile probably have 46,XY/47,XXY mosaicism.

46,XY/47,XXY mosaicism may result from nondisjunction or anaphase lag in a 47,XXY embryo or early zygote, or it could arise from nondisjunction in a 46,XY embryo with loss of the 45,X cell line.

According to the previous definition of Klinefelter syndrome, other possible karyotypes include 48,XXXY, 49,XXXXY, 48,XXYY, and 49,XXXYY. As indicated in Table 3, the phenotypes in 48,XXXY and 49,XXXXY patients are more severely altered than the phenotype in the 47,XXY patient. All 48,XXXY and 49,XXXXY patients are mentally retarded. Simpson (1977) was able to find reports of 40 cases of 48,XXXY Klinefelter syndrome and 70 cases of 49,XXXXY. The existence of more reported cases of 49,XXXXY may simply reflect a biased reporting of the more "unusual" cases. We have several unpublished 48,XXXY cases.

The mean maternal age (30.6 years) relative to cases of 48,XXXY Klinefelter syndrome is lower than that (32.3 years) relative to 47,XXY. Simpson (1977) has indicated that a 48,XXXY cell line may exist in a mosaic relationship more often than a 47,XXY cell line. These factors suggest that a mechanism other than meiotic nondisjunction in oogenesis might be responsible for the 48,XXXY karyotype. A maternal origin for all three X chromosomes was demonstrated in two patients by Xg blood group determinations (Zollinger, 1969; Greenstein et al., 1970), whereas the error in cell division was most likely localized to paternal meiosis I and II in a third patient (Pfeiffer and Sanger, 1973). Evidence in four families in which 49,XXXXY Klinefelter syndrome occurred indicates that all X chromosomes were maternal in origin (Sanger et al., 1971). Although a demonstration of maternal origin suggests a maternal meiotic error, postzygotic errors in cell division could be involved in 49,XXXXY as well as in 48,XXXY Klinefelter's syndrome, since in 49,XXXXY, mean maternal age is not increased, and mosaicism is often involved. Thus, the origins of both the 48,XXXY and 49,XXXXY karyotypes may involve multiple cytogenetic mechanisms.

Borgaonkar et al. (1970) reported findings in 53 patients with a 48,XXYY karotype, and several cases have been described subsequently. Phenotypically, affected patients are taller than average males and males with 47,XXY Klinefelter syndrome. The ratio of the upper to lower body segments is usually less than that in the normal male. Gynecomastia was noted in 62.1 percent of patients. They have small testes and aberrations in secondary sex characteristics similar to those in 47,XXY patients. Affected patients also manifest some features attributed to the presence of two Y chromosomes, namely mental deficiency and personality deviations. Skeletal anomalies have frequently been encountered. Varicose veins were seen in five patients reported by Borgaonkar.

The mean maternal age is lower than that in the 47,XXY Klinefelter syndrome. Extra X chromosomes have been maternal in origin in some cases (Sanger et al., 1971) and paternal in others (de la Chapelle et al., 1964; Pfeiffer et al., 1966). Multiple cytogenetic mechanisms are thus involved in the origin of the 48,XXYY karyotype.

Only two instances of 49,XXXYY Klinefelter syndrome have been reported (Bray and Josephine, 1963; Lecluse-van der Bilt et al., 1974). Bray's patient was moderately mentally retarded and tall and had gynecomastia along with evidence of hypogonadism. No seminiferous tubules were identified on testicular biopsy. The patient of Lecluse-van der Bilt et al. (1974) had "intersex genitalia," in which the penis was small but not hypospadic and was shrouded by labioscrotal folds. He also had clubfeet. Later observation revealed retarded motor and mental development.

XYY Male.   Hypogonadism has not been a feature in most males with a 47,XYY karyotype. However, of 24 cases summarized by Court Brown (1968) that had not been ascertained in surveys, 9 were ascertained, at least in part, because of abnormal sexual development, manifest as cryptorchidism in 3 patients, hypospadias in 1 patient, and oligospermia in 1 patient. In one patient (Balodimos et al., 1966), the hypogonadism and the XYY karyotype were coincidental, since the proband had a sister and a brother with hypogonadism and normal chromosomes.

XX Male.   Although not a genetic male, the XX male is considered here because the phenotype is unequivocally male and includes testes. In 1972, de la Chapelle reviewed 45 cases, and Vague and associates summarized 85 cases in 1977. At least seven other cases have been reported (Sperling et al., 1973; Tysyachnyuk, 1974; Miyashita et al., 1976, de la Chapelle et al., 1977). Several patients who do not have a normal male phenotype but instead have intersex genitalia have been reported as XX males. The relationship of these cases to the XX male classification is uncertain, but apparently most of them have testes. The phenotype of the XX male is characterized by small testes and signs of pubertal and adult hypogonadism, mental retardation that is probably no more frequent than in the general population, a mean height shorter than the average for normal males, and few if any somatic anomalies. Most have been ascertained because of similarities to Klinefelter syndrome. On histologic examination, the testes reveal decreased size and numbers of seminiferous tubules, absence of germ cells, peritubular and interstitial fibrosis, and hyperplastic Leydig cells. Approximately one third of affected males have gynecomastia, and male development at puberty may be defective.

The etiology of the XX male has been discussed extensively (de la Chapelle, 1972; Simpson, 1977; Vague et al., 1977) and has centered around four propositions: (1) undetected mosaicism involving a Y-bearing cell line or an eliminated Y chromosome, (2) X-Y interchange, (3) Y-autosome translocation, and (4) a single gene mutation. The first of these propositions requires that a cell line containing a Y chromosome existed to induce testicular differentiation but was subsequently lost or was retained in an undetectable cell population. The lack of a maternal age effect in the XX male has been said to support such a hypothesis. The distribution of Xg blood group phenotypes in XX males is not significantly different from that expected in XX females, XY males, or XXY males, although it is farthest from the expectation in XY males and closest to that for XXY males (de la Chapelle, 1972).

Translocation of a small portion of the Y chromosome to an X chromosome or recombination between the X and Y chromosomes would result in the presence of testicular determinants in the X chromosome and male sex differentiation in an XX individual. The localization of the gene for the H-Y antigen to the paracentromeric region of the short arm of the Y chromosome (Jacobs and Ross, 1966; Robinson and Buckton, 1971; Böök et al., 1973; German et al., 1973) indicates that more than just the telomeric portion of the Y chromosome must be translocated. Anomalous Xg blood group inheritance has been put forth as support for the X-Y interchange hypothesis — i.e., an XX male who is Xg(a−) and whose mother is also Xg(a−), whereas the father is Xg(a+). Although X-Y interchange might eliminate the father's Xg^a gene from his X chromosome, if the Xg locus is in the extreme distal portion of the short arm of the X chromosome (X-Y association in male meioses is short arm end-to-end) (Chen and Falek, 1969; Pearson and Bobrow, 1970), this observed Xg distribution could also be explained by nondisjunction in maternal meioses, leading to an XX ovum, which is then fertilized by a sperm lacking a sex chromosome. The absence of fluorescence from an X chromosome to which the male determining portion of the Y chromosome is translocated or exchanged is of no discriminative value, since the male determining portion of the Y chromosome is not fluorescent.

Although Y-autosome translocation can explain the lack of a maternal age effect in the XX male, it cannot explain recorded anomalous Xg blood group distribution. Dosik et al. (1975) reported a 46,XX,17p+ male and suggested that the elongated short arm of chromosome 17 contained Y-derived material. Wachtel et al. (1976) reported observations of the presence of H-Y antigen in cells of four XX males, but in one patient, Dosik et al. (1976) had discovered a minor XXY cell line. In another patient, the short arm of one chromosome 17 was elongated. The authors postulated that the additional segment was the result of a Y-17 translocation. Still, no direct evidence exists for Y-autosome translocation in most XX males.

Two observations cast some light on the etiology of the XX male. Kasdan and associates (1973) reported a patient with XX true hermaphroditism who had an XX sibling with testes but intersex genitalia and a paternal uncle who was an XX male. Such a family is not compatible with X-Y interchange but is compatible with the occurrence of a gene for sex reversal inherited in an autosomal dominant manner with obligatory XX genetic sex limitation. Informative animal models include the *Sxr* (sex reversed) mutation in the mouse (Cattanach, 1971) and the gene *polled* in the goat (Hamerton et al., 1969; Soller et al., 1969). De la Chapelle and associates (1977) have recently described second cousins who are XX males and concluded that in that family, the etiology was probably a mutant autosomal gene (autosomal dominant with XX genetic sex limitation?).

Thus, the only direct evidence for a specific genetic mode leading to the XX male points to a single gene mutation. The occurrence of relatives with XX true hermaphroditism in two families (Berger et al., 1970; Kasdan et al., 1973) suggests that the expressivity of the mutant gene may vary to the extent that complete sex reversal does not always occur. Conversely, genetic heterogeneity is certainly possible among XX males, and further observations are desirable.

45,X/46,XY Mosaicism. A person with 45,X/46,XY mosaicism is not, strictly speaking, a genetic male. This phenomenon was mentioned briefly in relation to XY gonadal dysgenesis, primarily because of phenotypic and gonadal similarities between the two. Simpson (1977) considers, as do some others, 45,X/46,XY mosaicism to be a form of male pseudohermaphroditism. However, it does not conform to the restrictive definition of male pseudohermaphroditism set forth in this discussion. Relative to genitalia, the phenotypic spectrum associated with 45,X/46,XY mosaicism may range from unambiguously female (often with somatic features of Turner syndrome) on one end, through the entire spectrum of ambiguous genitalia, to male external genitalia on the other end.

Gonadal structure in 45,X/46,XY mosaicism, termed *gonosomal intersexuality* by Opitz (1973) and *mixed gonadal dysgenesis* by Sohval (1963) and by Davidoff and Federman (1973), may consist only of streaks indistinguishable from those in Turner syndrome, may include a streak gonad on one side and a histologically normal or dysgenetic testis on the other side, or may consist of bilateral testes. In those patients with bilateral streak gonads, the genital phenotype is ordinarily female; in those patients with a streak on one side and a testis on the other, an intersex phenotype is most often encountered; and in those patients with bilateral testes, the external genital phenotype is that of the normal male or involves hypospadias. Approximately 15 to 20 percent of those 45,X/46,XY patients with unilateral or bilateral streak gonads or with a dysgenetic testis develop gonadoblastomas or dysgerminomas (Simpson, 1977). The risk of neoplasia in those patients with bilateral testes appears to be lower, but conclusive data are lacking.

45,X/46,XY mosaicism most likely arises from mitotic nondisjunction or anaphase lag in an XY embryo. Simpson (1977) has called attention to the frequent presence of a structurally altered Y chromosome in 45,X/46,XY mosaicism and has suggested that such a structurally altered Y chromosome might predispose to its own loss in successive cell divisions. Mosaicism may be difficult to discern, and multiple tissues may need to be studied before discounting it, especially in a patient with a streak gonad on one side and a testis on the other. We have observed one phenotypically female patient with short stature, sexual infantilism, somatic features of Turner syndrome, and slight clitoral enlargement who had a streak gonad on one side and on the other side a testis that enveloped a gonadoblastoma. The karyotype of cultured lymphocytes and skin fibroblasts was 46,XY. Only in cells from the streak gonad was a 45,X cell line demonstrated (Summitt, 1970).

Whether patients with 45,X/46,XY mosaicism and male external genitalia are fertile is not known. Those cases reported are ordinarily seen because of phenotypic abnormalities, and in all probability, 45,X/46,XY individuals who have normal male genitalia and are fertile would not come to attention. Hamerton et al. (1975) reported an infant who had normal genitalia and a 45,X/46,XY/47,XYY karyotype, whereas Friedrich and Nielsen (1973) reported a phenotypically normal 45,X/46,XY male. We have observed an infant with 45,X/46,XY mosaicism with bilateral histologically normal testes and third-degree hypospadias. A vagina opened into the posterior urethra. There was no uterus, and vasa deferentia were discontinuous and emptied into the vaginal vault.

Thus, if one considers the presence of testes as the only gonadal tissue along with gonadal hypofunction and abnormal genitalia to be a form of male hypogonadism, some patients with 45,X/46,XY mosaicism can be classified as hypogonadal males.

Table 4. Genital Abnormalities in Males with Autosomal Imbalance

AUTOSOMAL IMBALANCE	GENITAL ANOMALIES
Duplication 2p	Hypoplastic external genitalia, shawl scrotum, cryptorchidism
Duplication 3p	Micropenis, hypospadias
Duplication 3q	Cryptorchidism
Duplication 4p	Small penis, hypospadias, cryptorchidism
Duplication 4q	Cryptorchidism
Deletion 4p	Hypospadias, cryptorchidism
Trisomy 8	Hypospadias, hypoplastic genitalia, cryptorchidism
Duplication 9p	Micropenis
Trisomy 9	Micropenis, cryptorchidism, abnormalities of the testes on histologic examination
Duplication 10p	Micropenis, cryptorchidism
Duplication 10q	Cryptorchidism
Duplication 11p	Cryptorchidism
Duplication 11q	Micropenis
Deletion 13q	Hypospadias, bifid scrotum
Duplication 14q	Cryptorchidism
Deletion 18q	Hypospadias, hypoplastic scrotum
Trisomy 21	Small penis, small testes, sparse facial hair, meiotic arrest
Deletion 21q	Hypospadias, cryptorchidism
Trisomy 22	Micropenis, cryptorchidism
Triploidy	Ambiguous genitalia with hypospadias, bifid scrotum, cryptorchidism, Leydig cell hyperplasia

Autosomal Abnormalities Associated with Male Hypogonadism

We have previously mentioned a child with severe third-degree hypospadias and cryptorchidism in whom the testes were severely dysgenetic and whose karyotype included an apparently balanced 3–14 translocation. Whether the chromosome rearrangement is causally related to the testicular dysgenesis is unknown, but such an explanation could apply, perhaps based on position effect.

Autosomal abnormalities may be associated with hypogonadism in affected males. Rundle and Sylvester (1962) reported reduced testicular size in males with Down syndrome. In 21-trisomic males, beard growth is sparse, libido is diminished, and sperm counts are reduced (Stearns et al., 1960; Smith and Berg, 1976). Spermatogenic arrest has been described by several authors, as summarized by Smith and Berg (1976). No documented instance exists in which a male with Down syndrome has fathered a child. Cryptorchidism is common in Down syndrome and in other autosomal abnormality syndromes.

Table 4 summarizes the genital findings in various autosomal imbalances (Summitt, 1978). Systematic testing of testicular function has not been undertaken in most autosomal syndromes, and reports deal primarily with the description of anomalies of the external genitalia in affected males. Whether these anomalies are the result of anatomic or functional abnormalities of the testes or of more complex dysmorphogenetic factors not directly related to gonadal function is not clear. The ubiquity of anomalies of the external genitalia in the male with autosomal imbalance suggests that the latter may be the case. However, Francke et al. (1975) found sparse seminiferous tubules, absent Leydig cells, and absent germ cells in a therapeutically aborted fetus in which trisomy 9 had been diagnosed prenatally. Probably the most striking and most constant genital ambiguity occurs in triploidy. Niebuhr (1974) noted similarities in this condition to the genital findings in 45,X/46,XY and 46,XX/46,XY mosaicism. He suggested that the genital ambiguity in triploidy might not be the result of imbalance between sex chromosomes and autosomes, which would prevent a single Y chromosome from imposing full masculinity as proposed by Mittwoch (1973), so much as an abnormal interaction between the three haploid sets of chromosomes.

Male with Persistent Müllerian Structures

Normally, in a genetic male the secretion by the fetal testis of müllerian suppressive factor leads to regression of the müllerian duct structures. However, about 80 instances (Simpson, 1977) have been reported in which an otherwise phenotypic male has had an intra-abdominal uterus and fallopian tubes. The patient may present with an inguinal hernia in which a uterus and fallopian tubes are found at the time of surgical repair, thus the terms, *uterine hernia syndrome* and *hernia uteri inguinale.* Wolffian duct structures are present, but it is unclear whether any affected males have reproduced, although fertility has been claimed (Brook et al., 1974). Although it has been repeatedly stated that, except for the persistence of müllerian duct structures, the genitalia are normal, six of eight patients reported by Brook et al. (1974) had bilateral cryptorchidism and the other two had unilateral crypt-orchidism.

The regression of müllerian ducts in the male fetus is apparently mediated through the action of a high molecular weight peptide secret-ed by the Sertoli cells of the fetal testis — the müllerian suppressive factor. The failure of müllerian duct regression in the presence of testes could be the result of a deficiency or a biochemical alteration of müllerian suppressive factor or the result of a target cell that is unre-sponsive to quantitatively and qualitatively normal müllerian suppres-sive factor (Simpson, 1977). Available evidence (Brook et al., 1974; Simpson, 1977) indicates that persistent müllerian structures are in-herited in an autosomal recessive manner, although the condition could be inherited in an X-linked manner. Brook et al. (1974) have indicated the presence of a seminoma in about 5 percent of affected males.

Although Simpson (1977) and others consider this condition to be a form of male pseudohermaphroditism, it does not conform to the restrictive definition of male pseudohermaphroditism used in this discussion. Perhaps it is nosologically "cleaner" to separate it on grounds of phenotype and pathogenesis.

Male with Incomplete Wolffian Differentiation

In 1968, Kaplan et al. described the absence of vasa deferentia at autopsy in ten males and at surgical exploration in seven males with cystic fibrosis of the pancreas. They further reported the occurrence of only 1 offspring from 15 married adult males with cystic fibrosis. In addition, semen analysis revealed aspermia in all samples from 25 affected males. The authors also mentioned a personal communication that reported "deficient epididymides and absent vasa deferentia" in ten males in a study by Landing and associates. In the cases adequately studied by Kaplan et al. (1968), seminal vesicles were absent or hypoplastic and, in most, epididymides were rudimentary or absent. Other abnormalities included unilateral or bilateral small testes and reduced numbers of spermatozoa on testicular sections, along with maturation arrest. However, active mitosis was found in all sections examined. In 1969, Valman and France found absent or hypoplastic, nonpatent vasa deferentia in each of ten males with cystic fibrosis who were between 56 hours and 15 years of age.

Cystic fibrosis is inherited in an autosomal recessive manner, and although genetic heterogeneity has been suggested, it has never been documented. The fact that a serum factor in affected patients inhibits ciliary movement in cells of isolated animal tracheae and the observation that ciliary movement is associated with pinocytic activity led Ohno et al. (1971) to suggest that such a defect is responsible for aplasia or hypoplasia of the wolffian duct structures in males with cystic fibrosis. The differentiation of the wolffian duct into the epididymis, vas deferens, seminal vesicle, and ejaculatory duct is dependent on locally acting testosterone. Ohno suggested that testosterone elaborated by the embryonic testis is normally secreted directly into the lumen of the wolffian duct and is then taken up by cells lining the duct by pinocytosis. In cystic fibrosis, this pinocytosis is defective, resulting in aplasia or hypoplasia of those structures derived from the wolffian duct.

Although Ohno's hypothesis lacks proof, hypoplasia or aplasia of the vas deferens in males with cystic fibrosis is extremely common, producing sterility in affected males.

Anorchia

Simpson (1977) indicates that approximately 80 cases of anorchia have been reported. Affected males have normal male external genitalia but on examination appear to have undescended testes. At surgical exploration, no gonads whatever are found, but wolffian duct structures are normally formed. In some cases, the penis is small. A diagnosis of anorchia should not be made until thorough exploration of the pelvis and abdomen have revealed no evidence of a testis, and it preferably should also be shown that in the adult, gonadotropins are elevated and that in the child, stimulation with human chorionic gonadotropin (HCG) produces no elevation of plasma testosterone.

The presence of normal male sex differentiation in the absence of testicles strongly suggests that at a time critical for sex differentiation in intrauterine life, testes were present but later disappeared for some reason. Such a phenomenon could result from an unknown teratogenic insult, from prenatal testicular torsion, or from a mutant gene. Identical twin pairs, both concordant and discordant, have been reported, and in two families, one sib had bilateral anorchia, whereas the other sib had unilateral anorchia. The phenotype known as anorchia may well be etiologically heterogeneous.

Accompanying anomalies do not usually occur. Obviously, patients will remain sexually infantile unless testosterone substitution therapy is initiated at the expected time of puberty. When testosterone therapy is used, secondary sex characteristics appear, and the patient can then have normal sexual function.

A related phenomenon is the syndrome of rudimentary testes (Grumbach et al., 1974; Simpson, 1977) in which testes, although present, are extremely small, whereas the external genitalia are unambiguously male, and wolffian duct derivatives are normally differentiated. The relationship of this condition to anorchia is unclear. The two have never been described in the same sibship, although Najjar et al. (1974) have reported five affected sibs with rudimentary testes, the offspring of consanguineous parents. The administration of HCG to one of Najjar's patients produced an abnormally low response, as indicated by plasma testosterone levels. The suggestion has been made (Simpson, 1977) that the syndrome of rudimentary testes is a less severe expression of the same defect, whatever its basis, that produces anorchia.

Hypogonadotropic Hypogonadism (Hypothalamic-Pituitary-Gonadal Axis in Origin)

The conditions discussed so far have manifestations prior to puberty, although, for various reasons, some of them are not detected until puberty or thereafter. In the section to follow, discussion will deal with those conditions that occur in males whose external sex differentiation in utero was completely normal but whose abnormal gonadal function becomes manifest at puberty and thereafter.

As reviewed in a previous section, the changes that take place at puberty are under the control of the hypothalamic-pituitary-gonadal axis. Plasma concentrations of gonadotropic hormones rise steadily in the years preceding puberty (Winter and Faiman, 1972; Grumbach et al., 1974), and apparently puberty is triggered when gonadotropin levels reach a point at which the gonads are stimulated to produce androgens (and estrogens) in amounts adequate to initiate and maintain pubertal changes and adult sexual function. If, for any reason, the hypothalamus does not secrete necessary gonadotropin-releasing factor or if the pituitary gland is not capable of elaborating LH and FSH, gonadotropin concentrations will not rise, and puberty will not take place.

Pituitary Dwarfism (Multitropic Pituitary Hormone Deficiency).   This condition encompasses a deficiency of two or more pituitary tropic hormones, growth hormone deficiency being a constant feature. It appears that gonadotropic hormones are virtually always deficient, and in addition, TSH or ACTH or both may be deficient. Although gonadotropin deficiency results in sexual infantilism, the most obvious feature of multitropic pituitary hormone deficiency is growth failure due to growth hormone deficiency. Growth hormone deficiency results in proportionate dwarfism, increased subcutaneous tissue, a high-pitched voice, and wrinkled skin. Gonadotropin deficiency produces lack of facial hair, small testes, and a small penis.

In 1971, Rimoin reported knowledge of at least 20 families in which multiple members had multitropic pituitary hormone deficiency. Parental consanguinity was common, and this factor plus multiple affected sibs of both sexes (the offspring of unaffected parents) indicated an autosomal recessive mode of inheritance. However, Schimke et al. (1971) reported two affected half-brothers who had the same mother but different fathers, suggesting an X-linked recessive mode of inheritance in that family. It appears that intrafamilial variability is not uncommon; in a single sibship, one member may lack all four tropic hormones, whereas another may lack only growth hormone and gonadotropins. This information should not be interpreted to mean that all cases of multitropic pituitary hormone deficiency are inherited; in fact most cases are isolated, and in all likelihood, the etiology is heterogeneous.

Ferrier and Stone (1969) have reported the presence of familial pituitary dwarfism in sisters, each with an abnormal sella turcica. The affected girls were 10 and 11 years old at the time of the report and showed evidence of thyroid-stimulating hormone (TSH) and ACTH deficiency but were too young to manifest signs of gonadotropin deficiency. They were mentally retarded, perhaps due to episodes of hypoglycemia. The parents were not consanguineous; nevertheless, the authors suggested that the mode of inheritance was autosomal recessive.

Isolated Bihormonal Gonadotropin Deficiency. As pointed out by Rabin (1975), the study of gonadotropin deficiency has been considerably enhanced by advances in the knowledge of glycoprotein hormones, by the development of radioimmunoassay for human FSH and LH, and by the identification of hypothalamic polypeptides that induce pituitary elaboration of TSH, prolactin, FSH, and LH. The first of these advances showed that FSH and LH (and also TSH and HCG) consist of two dissimilar subunits (α and β), which are noncovalently linked. The α subunit is similar or identical in the four hormones, but the β subunits are different and thus are apparently what confer biologic specificity on each. However, the α subunit is a necessary component of the hormone, since the β subunit itself is not biologically potent.

In isolated gonadotropin deficiency, both FSH and LH are deficient. In the affected male, the clinical manifestations include failure of the appearance of secondary sex characteristics, with lack of facial hair, a small penis, scant body hair, a small prostrate, and small testes. Testicular biopsy reveals immaturity of seminiferous tubules and absence of Leydig cells and may show early but arrested spermatogenesis. Considerable variability in severity of clinical signs has been reported. Plasma gonadotropin levels are low or even undetectable, and plasma testosterone levels are also very low.

Whether an individual patient has hypogonadotropic hypogonadism because of a defect in hypothalamic LRF or a defect in the pituitary gland can now be tested by the administration of LRF. The response in patients with isolated gonadotropin deficiency is heterogeneous; i.e., some respond, indicating an LRF defect, whereas others do not, indicating a pituitary defect.

It may be that the majority of patients with isolated gonadotropin deficiency have the autosomal dominant Kallmann syndrome (Simpson, 1977) (to be discussed later). However, the occurrence of affected females as well as males in the same sibships indicates autosomal recessive inheritance as the genetic mode in some families. Current evidence (Grumbach et al., 1974) suggests pathogenetic as well as genetic heterogeneity in isolated gonadotropin deficiency without Kallmann syndrome and perhaps also in Kallmann syndrome, since some patients in each category respond to administered LRF, whereas others do not. Alternatively, all patients studied by Matte et al. (1974) showed response to LRF. This suggests that lack of response might be due to problems with the LRF used or prior chronic nonstimulation of the pituitary gland by LRF (Naftolin et al., 1971; Oettinger et al., 1976).

Isolated LH Deficiency. Isolated LH deficiency would probably be expected to involve normal stimulation of spermatogenesis but not Leydig cells. A number of males have been described whose testes contain normal numbers of germ cells but practically no Leydig cells. They failed to undergo secondary sex development and have high-pitched voices, poor muscle development, and scant facial hair (Simpson, 1977). Normal FSH and decreased LH levels have been reported in affected patients (Faiman et al., 1968; Christiansen, 1972), but even so, Rabin (1975) suggests that *isolated LH deficiency,* also called the *fertile eunuch syndrome* (Faiman et al., 1968; Christiansen, 1972, Simpson, 1977); may simply be one end of a widely varying spectrum of isolated bihormonal gonadotropin deficiency and not a distinct nosologic entity.

Although most cases of apparent isolated LH deficiency have been sporadic, McCullagh et al. (1951) have described the defect in siblings. Simpson (1977) calls attention to the patient of Kjessler who, after administration of HCG and testosterone, fathered a child.

Isolated FSH Deficiency. Rabin (1975) has reported a female with apparent isolated FSH deficiency and also a male with Klinefelter syndrome who had FSH deficiency. The FSH levels responded minimally to LRF administration, whereas LH levels responded normally. The patient had germinal aplasia and aspermia. The report of so few patients with isolated FSH deficiency does not allow a determination of the possible genetic nature of the defect. The probability that this condition is also only one end of the spectrum of bihormonal gonadotropin deficiency cannot be ignored.

In both isolated LH deficiency and isolated FSH deficiency, patients have failed to respond to LRF administration with increased plasma levels to the deficient hormone. These factors suggest that the defect in these two abnormalities is pituitary in origin. This would be logical if LRF is the releasing factor for both LH and FSH.

Hypergonadotropic Hypogonadism

Only one condition, the *germinal cell aplasia syndrome,* will be considered under this heading. Another important condition involving primary gonadal failure, Klinefelter syndrome has already been discussed, and other conditions with associated nongenital features will be discussed later.

Del Castillo et al. (1947) described several males who were normally masculinized with secondary sex development yet were sterile. Because the testes were small, the condition has been considered to be an X chromatin–negative form of Klinefelter syndrome. However, the restrictive definition of Klinefelter syndrome used in this discussion and by others excludes any hypogonadal male whose karyotype does not include more than one X chromosome. The *germinal cell aplasia syndrome* is not caused by a chromosome abnormality. Most cases have been sporadic, but several families have been reported with two or more affected brothers (Howard et al., 1950; Weyeneth, 1956; Edwards and Bannerman, 1971). In those instances, at least, the condition appears to be inherited in an autosomal recessive manner, in an X-linked recessive manner, or as an autosomal dominant with male sex limitation.

Testicular biopsies reveal small seminiferous tubules completely or virtually completely devoid of germ cells. However, Sertoli cells and Leydig cells are preserved; thus androgen production and action are normal. Unlike Klinefelter syndrome, hyalinization and sclerosis of seminiferous tubules do not occur, although the tunica propria may be thickened. Internal ductal structures are normal. The patient's only complaint, then, is infertility. Patients ordinarily do not have gynecomastia.

As might be expected, since androgens are produced normally, LH levels are normal and, because spermatogenesis is defective, FSH levels are elevated (Paulsen, 1974). This can aid in the diagnosis, but the final diagnosis depends on the demonstration of germinal aplasia on testicular biopsy.

Forms of Hypogonadism with Associated Abnormalities

A number of syndromes are known in which hypogonadism occurs in the presence of features not involving the reproductive system. In some of these conditions, the hypogonadism is the result of gonadotropin deficiency (hypogonadotropic hypogonadism), whereas in others, the hypogonadism is primary in nature, in which case gonadotropin levels are elevated (hypergonadotropic hypogonadism).

Hypothalamic-Pituitary Axis in Origin

KALLMANN SYNDROME.   In 1944, Kallmann et al. called attention to the concurrence of anosmia and gonadal failure and showed that the familial occurrence of the condition was compatible with X-linked inheritance or with autosomal dominant inheritance with male sex limitation. It was later shown that females as well as males may be affected, and this fact plus the report by Merriam et al. (1977) of male-to-male transmission of Kallmann syndrome favor an autosomal dominant mode of inheritance in a number if not all of the cases. Still, Wegenke et al. (1975) point out that a number of pedigrees conform to the X-linked (or autosomal dominant with male sex limitation) mode of inheritance and that, if the gene is X-linked, affected females may represent a heterozygous manifestation of the gene effect. They even suggest that cases of Kallmann syndrome with deafness and cleft lip and palate may not, in fact, be Kallmann syndrome.

The clinical phenotype in Kallmann syndrome is similar to that in isolated bihormonal gonadotropin deficiency, with small testes and infantile but usually normally differentiated external genitalia. De Morsier (1954) showed hypoplasia of the olfactory tract as the cause of anosmia. Many affected males are cryptorchid. Associated anomalies have been described, including cleft lip and palate (Santen and Paulsen, 1973), deafness (Santen and Paulsen, 1973), and unilateral renal aplasia (Wegenke et al., 1975). The degree of hyposmia has appeared to be less severe in affected females than in affected males.

The nature of the gonadotropin deficiency has been studied by several investigators (Naftolin et al., 1971; Bell et al., 1973; Roth et al., 1973; Zarate et al., 1973; Matte et al., 1974; Rabin, 1975; Oettinger et al., 1976; Merriam et al., 1977) and heterogeneous responses to LRF have been found. This may suggest genetic and pathogenetic heterogeneity in Kallmann syndrome, or it may simply reflect the relative unresponsiveness of the chronically unstimulated pituitary gland to administered LRF (Naftolin et al., 1971; Oettinger et al., 1976). If the latter is the case, the gonadotropin deficiency in Kallmann syndrome is hypothalamic in nature, not pituitary.

ATAXIA-HYPOGONADISM SYNDROME. A number of familial cases of cerebellar ataxia associated with hypogonadism have been reported. The subject was discussed by Neuhaüser and Opitz (1975), who reported a sibship in which two females and probably two males with cerebellar ataxia and hypogonadotropic hypogonadism occurred. The condition in their family was inherited in an autosomal recessive manner; the parents of the affected sibs were second cousins. Volpe et al. (1963) described two affected brothers and an affected uncle with cerebellar ataxia and hypogonadotropic hypogonadism and indicated an X-linked mode of inheritance. As discussed by Neuhaüser and Opitz (1975), hypogonadism has been seen in association with cerebellar dysfunction of various types, including Friedreich ataxia. In some families, evidence points to autosomal recessive inheritance, whereas in others, the pattern of inheritance indicates a mutant X-linked recessive gene or an autosomal dominant mutant gene with male sex limitation. In those families in which gonadotropin levels have been investigated, hypogonadotropic hypogonadism was indicated. However, at this point, none of these families has been studied with measurements of response to LRF. It is apparent that hypogonadotropic hypogonadism in association with cerebellar ataxia is genetically heterogeneous and may be pathogenetically heterogeneous as well.

Associated anomalies have included pes cavus, spina bifida, pectus excavatum, and cardiac conduction defects (Bardin, 1971).

NEVOID BASAL CELL CARCINOMA SYNDROME. Several authors, including Simpson (1977) and Gorlin et al. (1976), have called attention to the occurrence of hypogonadism in males and females with the nevoid basal cell carcinoma syndrome. In males, the clinical features have included cryptorchidism, unilateral absence of a testis, and female hair distribution. Wallace et al. (1973) described a family in which the nevoid basal cell carcinoma syndrome was accompanied by hypogonadotropic hypogonadism and anosmia. Anosmia occurred in every affected member with the nevoid basal cell carcinoma syndrome and occurred in none who was not affected. The one affected member with hypogonadotropic hypogonadism was a female. Whether a single mutant gene was responsible for the entire spectrum of abnormalities or whether Kallmann syndrome was a chance concurrence in the family is unknown. In general, the nature of the relationship of hypogonadism with the autosomal dominant nevoid basal cell carcinoma syndrome is unknown.

BIEMOND SYNDROME. The syndrome described by Biemond (1934) includes coloboma of the iris, mental retardation, obesity, postaxial polydactyly, and hypogonadism, apparently of the hypogonadotropic variety. Its phenotype is quite similar to that of the Laurence-Moon-Bardet-Biedl syndrome, and, in fact, it may represent a variant form of this syndrome. The condition would appear to be inherited in an autosomal recessive manner.

CARPENTER SYNDROME. The Carpenter syndrome is one of the acrocephalosyndactyly syndromes and actually involves severe acrocephaly, syndactyly, and preaxial polydactyly (Temtamy, 1973). It is characterized further by facies with lateral displacement of medial canthi, epicanthal folds, downward slanting palpebral fissures, flat nasal bridge, broad cheeks, and micrognathia. The limb malformations are symmetrical. Soft-tissue syndactyly involves the third and fourth fingers and is associated with brachymesophalangy. The proximal phalanx of the thumb has two ossification centers that produce duplication of the thumb in the adult. Preaxial polydactyly and syndactyly characterize the feet. Coxa valga occurs along with pes varus, obesity, mental retardation, and abdominal hernias.

The hypogonadism is said by Rimoin and Schimke (1971) to be similar to that in the Laurence-Moon-Bardet-Biedl syndrome. Temtamy (1973) indicates that Carpenter syndrome is inherited in an autosomal recessive manner, but Palacios and Schimke (1969) have reported two-generation transmission.

CRANDALL SYNDROME.   Crandall et al. (1973) described three brothers with slowly progressive neurosensory deafness, alopecia with pili torti, and hypogonadotropic hypogonadism. The brothers had three unaffected full siblings, and their mother had seven unaffected children by her second husband. Despite the suggestion that the three affected males might indicate X-linked inheritance, the condition in the family reported by Crandall was most likely inherited in an autosomal recessive manner.

ICHTHYOSIS-HYPOGONADISM SYNDROME.   Lynch et al. (1960) described a combination of congenital ichthyosis with apparent hypogonadotropic hypogonadism. Their proband has a eunuchoid habitus, sparse pubic and axillary hair, a small penis, and an immature scrotum. The voice was high pitched, and the skin showed changes typical of congenital ichthyosis. The testes were small, and testicular biopsy revealed atrophy, absent spermatogenesis, virtual absence of Leydig cells, and scattered areas of hyalinization in the connective tissue. In addition to the proband, two maternal first cousins once removed were affected, and two other previous male relatives may have been affected. Congenital ichthyosis may be inherited in an X-linked manner, and the authors concluded that the pedigree of their proband also supported such a genetic mode for the combination of ichthyosis and hypogonadotropic hypogonadism seen in their patient. Associated anomalies included pectus excavatum, a prominent cleft between the first and second toes, and kyphosis or scoliosis or both. In addition, Bardin (1971) observed a single patient with hypogonadotropic hypogonadism, ichthyosis, and anosmia. These authors called attention to the similarity of their patients to the rather ill-defined Rüd syndrome (MacGillivray, 1954), which is characterized by congenital ichthyosis, hypogonadism, severe mental retardation, epilepsy, anemia, polyneuritis, gigantism, and retinitis pigmentosa.

KRAUS-RUPPERT SYNDROME.   Kraus-Ruppert (1956) reported three brothers, the offspring of consanguineous parents, whose phenotypes were characterized by severe mental retardation and microcephaly, syndactyly of the second to fourth toes, and hypogonadism. At autopsy, widespread hypoplasia of hypothalamic nuclei was shown and may well have been responsible for the hypogonadism. The testes lacked Leydig cells and showed no spermatogenesis. It would appear that the constellation of anomalies in this family was inherited in an autosomal recessive manner (Rimoin and Schimke, 1971).

LAURENCE-MOON-BARDET-BIEDL SYNDROME. In 1866, two British ophthalmologists, Laurence and Moon, reported four cases of retinitis pigmentosa, accompanied by "several imperfections of development." Bardet, as cited by Bell (1958), added the presence of polydactyly to the description, and Biedl (1922) emphasized other features of the, syndrome.

The classic features of the Laurence-Moon-Bardet-Biedl syndrome include retinitis pigmentosa, mental retardation, polysyndactyly, obesity, progressive renal disease, and hypogonadotropic hypogonadism. The hypogonadism occurs in 75 to 86 percent of affected males and in 45 to 53 percent of affected females. According to Rimoin and Schimke (1971), several females have had offspring, but no documented case of male fertility exists. Marked intrafamilial variability exists in this condition, which is inherited in an autosomal recessive manner.

The similarity of the Laurence-Moon-Bardet-Biedl syndrome to the Biemond syndrome has been mentioned previously, and Rimoin and Schimke (1971) call attention to its similarities to Alström syndrome and Prader-Willi syndrome. Endo et al. (1976) reported the questionable coexistence of a brother with the Laurence-Moon-Bardet-Biedl syndrome (without polydactyly) and a sister said to have Prader-Willi syndrome. Interestingly, neither sib had hypogonadotropism and both responded normally to LRF. The absence of hypogonadotropism makes the diagnosis of the Laurence-Moon-Bardet-Biedl syndrome questionable.

Gonadal in Origin. A number of syndromes exist in which there are intrinsically abnormal testes along with somatic features involving other than the reproductive system. They are summarized in Table 5. These conditions have been studied in more or less detail, and that detail is reflected in the table.

CONCLUSIONS AND PROSPECTS

Gonadal dysfunction can be first manifest at the earliest stage of gonadal differentiation, later during sex differentiation, at the time of puberty, or in later adult life. The genetic influences on gonadal differentiation and function are myriad, and the gonadal abnormality may be basically intrinsic or part of a more generalized syndrome. Exciting advances have elucidated previously poorly understood aspects of gonadal function and have opened the door to future investigation on many fronts. The causes of gonadal changes in the multiple anomaly syndromes deserve intensive investigation relative to the level of the defect, using recently refined or developed techniques for LH and FSH measurement and response to LRF.

Table 5. Syndromes That Include Primary Gonadal Failure in the Male

CONDITION	ABNORMALITIES INVOLVING GONADS	SOMATIC FEATURES	MODE OF INHERITANCE
Alström syndrome (Alström et al., 1973)	Germinal cell aplasia with varying degrees of tubular sclerosis and slight immaturity. Normal sexual development. Elevated gonadotropin levels.	Obesity beginning in infancy, nystagmus, sensitivity to light, progressive visual impairment with blindness by age 7, retinal degeneration, cataracts, neurosensory hearing loss, diabetes mellitus with onset after puberty.	Autosomal recessive
Ataxia-telangiectasia (Ammann, 1973)	Absence of hypoplasia of gonads, cryptorchidism. Elevated gonadotropin levels.	Cerebellar ataxia, choreoathetosis, nystagmus, recurrent sinopulmonary infections, telangiectasias of skin and bulbar conjunctiva, IgA deficiency, defects in cellular immunity, chromosome breakage.	Autosomal recessive
Borjeson syndrome (Borjeson et al., 1962)	Cryptorchidism, micropenis, sexual infantilism, germinal aplasia, interstitial fibrosis. Decreased gonadotropin levels.	Mental retardation, obesity, grotesque facies, dwarfism, seizures.	X-linked recessive
Fanconi syndrome (Rimoin and Schimke, 1971)	Small, firm testes, tubular hypoplasia, decreased spermatogenesis.	Pancytopenia, bone marrow hypoplasia, skin hyperpigmentation, short stature, upper limb malformations, chromosome damage.	Autosomal recessive
Fraser syndrome (Rimoin and Schimke, 1971)	Cryptorchidism, hypospadias, micropenis.	Cryptophthalmus, hypoplastic eyebrows, coloboma of alae nasi, midfacial cleft, cleft lip and palate, ankyloglossia, small ears, hearing loss, syndactyly, umbilical hernia, laryngeal stenosis, nipple displacement, renal malformations.	Autosomal recessive

Syndrome			Inheritance
Geminne syndrome (Rimoin and Schimke, 1971)	Seminiferous tubule failure, normal Leydig cell function, cryptorchidism.	Congenital torticollis keloids, renal dysplasia, cutaneous nevi, varicose veins.	X-linked recessive
Multiple lentigines syndrome (Gorlin, 1973)	Small or absent testes, hypospadias.	Multiple lentigines, pulmonary stenosis, short stature, hypertelorism, sensorineural deafness, EKG changes.	Autosomal dominant
Myotonic dystrophy (Rimoin and Schimke, 1971; Sagel et al., 1975)	Normal gonadal function until young adult life, with later testicular atrophy, involving primarily the seminiferous tubules. Germinal aplasia or tubular fibrosis. Elevated basal FSH level with exaggerated LRF response. Normal LH level with exaggerated LRF response.	Muscle atrophy, myotonia, cataracts, frontal balding, diabetes mellitus.	Autosomal dominant
Noonan syndrome (Summitt, 1973)	Complete absence of testicles, cryptorchidism, germinal aplasia. Gonadal function may be normal.	Short stature, mental retardation, cardiac defect, ear abnormalities, epicanthal folds, ptosis, downward slanting palpebral fissures, anterior open bite, micrognathia, webbed neck, pectus excavatum, cubitus valgus, vertebral anomalies, renal anomalies, lymphedema.	? Autosomal dominant. (We have recently seen definitely affected father and son.)
Osteochondritis dissecans syndrome (Rimoin and Schimke, 1971)	Eunuchoid habitus, high-pitched voice, sparse facial and axillary hair.	Osteochondritis dissecans in multiple joints, hypertelorism, ptosis, pectus excavatum. (Relationship to Noonan syndrome?)	Uncertain

(Continued)

Table 5. Syndromes That Include Primary Gonadal Failure in the Male (*Continued*)

CONDITION	ABNORMALITIES INVOLVING GONADS	SOMATIC FEATURES	MODE OF INHERITANCE
Prader-Willi syndrome (Rimoin and Schimke, 1971; Tolis et al., 1974)	Sterility, sexual infantilism, testicular atrophy, deficient spermatogenesis, cryptorchidism, hypoplastic scrotum, small penis. Variable basal LH and FSH levels, variable response to LRF.	Mental retardation, obesity, short stature, infantile hypotonia, delicate facial features.	Uncertain
Ruthmund-Thomsen syndrome (Rimoin and Schimke, 1971)	Cryptorchidism, delayed puberty and/or deficient masculinization.	Erythema, telangiectasia, skin atrophy and irregular pigmentation, short stature, juvenile cataracts, saddle nose, small hands and feet, sparse hair, mental retardation.	Autosomal recessive
Russell-Silver syndrome (Rimoin and Schimke, 1971)	Cryptorchidism, hypospadias. Variable gonadotropin levels.	Low birthweight, dwarfism, triangular face, asymmetry, macrocephaly (relative).	Uncertain
Sohval-Soffer syndrome (Rimoin and Schimke, 1971; Sohval and Soffer, 1953)	Small, soft testes, small penis, defective secondary sex development, azoospermia, gynecomastia, germinal aplasia, tubular fibrosis. Elevated gonadotropin levels.	Mental retardation, multiple skeletal anomalies involving cervical spine and ribs.	Uncertain

Van Benthem syndrome (Rimoin and Schimke, 1971)	Cryptorchidism, testicular agenesis.	Chest deformities, muscle hypoplasia, deficient subcutaneous fat, dolichocephaly, mental retardation.	Autosomal or X-linked recessive ?
Weinstein syndrome (Weinstein et al., 1969)	Small, soft testes, small hyalinized tubules, germinal hypoplasia, normal Leydig cell function, normal virilization, thick lamina propria. Low plasma testosterone levels unresponsive to HCG.	Blindness, neurosensory deafness, cataract, retinal degeneration, hyperuricemia, hypertriglyceridemia, obesity, short stature.	Uncertain
Werner syndrome (Rimoin and Schimke, 1971)	Small testes and penis, decreased pubic hair, diminished libido, sterility, testicular atrophy, hyalinized tubules, absent spermatogenesis.	Premature aging, short stature, cataracts, sclerodermatous skin changes, mild diabetes mellitus.	Autosomal recessive
Xerodermic idiocy syndrome (Reed, 1973)	Small testes, cryptorchidism.	Xeroderma pigmentosa, cutaneous malignancy, progressive mental retardation, microcephaly, dwarfism, ataxia, athetosis, retarded bone age, sensorineural deafness. Defective DNA repair.	Autosomal recessive

The classification of hypogonadism used in this discussion is fluid and doubtless will be changed repeatedly, probably even before this book is published. Any nosologic consideration must be constantly open to change on the basis of new insights into the diseases involved, their genetic bases, and their pathogenetic mechanisms. The goal of any such classification is specificity, and the author's hope is that the classification presented in this discussion reflects as accurately and completely as possible the currently available knowledge.

References

Alström, C. H. 1973. Alström Syndrome. In Birth Defects Atlas and Compendium, Bergsma, D. (Ed.) pp. 153–154. White Plains, The National Foundation.

Alvarez, M. N., M. D. Cloutier, and A. B. Hayles. 1973. Male pseudohermaphroditism due to 17α-hydroxylase deficiency in two siblings. Pediat. Res. 7:325.

Ammann, A. J. 1973. Ataxia-telangiectasia. In Birth Defects Atlas and Compendium, Bergsma, D. (Ed.), pp. 192–193. White Plains, The National Foundation.

Amrhein, J. A., G. J. Klingensmith, P. C. Walsh, V. A. McKusick, and C. J. Migeon. 1977. Partial androgen insensitivity. The Reifenstein syndrome revisited. New Eng. J. Med. 297:350–356.

Amrhein, J. A., W. J. Meyer, III, H. W. Jones, and C. J. Migeon. 1976. Androgen insensitivity in man: Evidence for genetic heterogeneity. Proc. Nat. Acad. Sci. U.S.A. 73:891–894.

Anderson, C. T., Jr., and I. H. Carlson. 1975. Elevated plasma testosterone and gonadal tumor in two 46,XY "sisters." Arch. Path. 99:360–363.

Balodimos, M. C., H. Lisco, I. Irwin, W. Merrill, and J. F. Dingman. 1966. XYY karyotype in a case of familial hypogonadism. J. Clin. Endocr. Metabol. 26:443–452.

Baraket, A. Y., Z. L. Papadopolou, R. S. Chandra, C. E. Hollerman, and P. L. Calcagno. 1974. Pseudohermaphroditism, nephron disorder and Wilms tumor: A unifying concept. Pediatrics 54:366–369.

Bardin, C. W. 1971. Hypogonadotropic Hypogonadism in Patients with Multiple Congenital Defects. In Birth Defects: Original Article Series, Bergsma, D. (Ed.), Vol. 7:6, pp. 175–178. White Plains, The National Foundation.

Bell, J. 1958. The Laurence-Moon Syndrome. In The Treasury of Human Inheritance, Penrose, L. D. (Ed.), Vol. 5, p. 3. London, Cambridge University Press.

Bell, J., I. Spitz, A. Slonim, A. Perlman, S. Segal, Z. Palti, and D. Rabinowitz, 1973. Heterogeneity of gonadotropin response to LH-RH in hypogonadotropic hypogonadism. J. Clin. Endocr. Metabol. 36:791–794.

Bergada, C., W. W. Cleveland, H. W. Jones, and L. Wilkins. 1962. Variants of embryonic testicular dysgenesis: Bilateral anorchia and the syndrome of rudimentary testes. Acta Endocr. 40:521–536.

Berger, R., D. Abonyi, A. Nodot, J. Vialatte, and J. Lejeune. 1970. Hermaphroditisme vrai et <<Garcon XX>> dans une fratrie. Rev. Eur. Etud. Clin. Biol. 15:330–333.

Berger, R., M. Binoux, E. Chassen, and J. Lejeune. 1972. Dysgénésie gonadique pure familiale. Ann. Endocr. (Paris) 33:35–40.

Berthezène, F., M. G. Forest, J. A. Grimaud, B. Claustrat, and R. Mornex. 1976. Leydig-cell agenesis. A cause of male pseudohermaphroditism. New Eng. J. Med. 295:969–972.

Biedl, A. 1922. Ein Geschwisterpaar mit adiposo-genitaler Dystrophie. Dtsch. Med. Worchenschr. 68:1630.

Biemond, A. 1934. Het syndroom van Laurence-Biedl en een aanverwant, nieuw syndroom. Ned. Tijdschr. Geneeskd. 78:1801–1814.

Boczkowski, K., J. Teter, and Z. Sternadel. 1972. Sibship occurrence of XY gonadal dysgenesis with dysgerminoma. Am. J. Obstet. Gynec. 113:952–955.

Bongiovanni, A. M. 1961. Unusual steroid pattern in congenital adrenal hyperplasia: Deficiency of 3β-hydroxy dehydrogenase. J. Clin. Endocr. Metabol. 21:860–862.

Bongiovanni, A. M. 1962. The adrenogenital syndrome with deficiency of 3β-hydroxysteroid dehydrogenase. J. Clin. Invest. 41:2086–2092.

Bongiovanni, A. M., and W. R. Eberlein. 1961. Defects in steroidal metabolism in subjects with the adrenogenital syndrome. Metabolism 10:917–935.

Böök, J. A., B. Eilon, I. Halbrecht, L. Komlos, and F. Shabtay. 1973. Isochromosome Y [46,X,1(Yq)] and female phenotype. Clin. Genet. 4:410–414.

Borgaonkar, D. S., E. Mules, and F. Char. 1970. Do the 48,XXYY males have a characteristic phenotype? Clin. Genet. 1:272–293.

Borjeson, M., H. Forssman, and O. Lehmann. 1962. An X-linked recessively inherited syndrome characterized by grave mental deficiency, epilepsy, and endocrine disorder. Acta Med. Scand. 171:13–21.

Bowen, P., C. S. N. Lee, C. J. Migeon, N. M. Kaplan, P. J. Whalley, V. A. McKusick, and E. C. Reifenstein. 1965. Hereditary male pseudohermaphroditism with hypogonadism, hypospadias and gynecomastia (Reifenstein's syndrome). Ann. Intern. Med. 62:252–270.

Bradbury, J. T., R. G. Bunge, and R. A. Boccabella. 1956. Chromatin test in Klinefelter's syndrome. J. Clin. Endocr. Metabol. 16:689.

Bray, P., and A. Josephine. 1963. An XXXYY sex-chromosome anomaly. Report of a mentally deficient male. JAMA 184:179–182.

Brook, C. G. D., H. Wagner, M. Zachmann, A. Prader, S. Armendares, S. Frenk, P. Alemán, S. S. Najjar, M. S. Slim, N. Genton, and C. Bozic. 1974. Familial occurrence of persistent müllerian structures in otherwise normal males. Brit. Med. J. 1:771–773.

Brown, D. M., Markland, C., and Dehner, L. P. 1978. Leydig cell hypoplasia: a cause of male pseudohermaphroditism. J. Clin. Endocr. Metabol. 46:1–7.

Bullock, L. M., C. W. Bardin, and S. Ohno. 1971. The androgen insensitive mouse: Absence of intranuclear androgen retention in the kidney. Biochem. Biophys. Res. Commun. 44:1537–1543.

Camacho, A. M., A. Kowarski, C. J. Migeon, and A. J. Brough. 1968. Congenital adrenal hyperplasia due to a deficiency of one of the enzymes involved in the biosynthesis of pregnenolone. J. Clin. Endocr. Metabol. 28:153–161.

Carr, D. H., R. A. Haggar, and A. G. Hart. 1968. Germ cells in the ovaries of XO female infants. Am. J. Clin. Pathol. 49:521–526.

Casey, M. D., L. J. Segall, D. R. K. Street, and C. E. Blank. 1966. Sex chromosome abnormalities in two state hospitals for patients requiring special security. Nature 209:641–642.

Castaneda, E., A. E. Perez, M. A. Guillen, S. Ramirez-Robles, C. Gaul, and G. Perez-Palacios. 1971. Metabolic studies in a patient with testicular feminization syndrome. Am. J. Obstet. Gynec. 110:1002–1007.

Cattanach, B. M., C. E. Pollard, and S. G. Hawkes. 1971. Sex-reversed mice: XX and XO males. Cytogenetics 10:318–337.

Chemke, J., R. Carmichael, J. M. Stewart, R. H. Geer, and A. Robinson. 1970. Familial XY gonadal dysgenesis. J. Med. Genet. 7:105–111.

Chen, A. T. L., and A. Falek. 1969. Centromeres in human meiotic chromosomes. Science 166:1008–1010.

Christian, J. C. 1973. Hypertelorism-Hypospadias Syndrome. In Birth Defects Atlas and Compendium, Bergsma, D. (Ed.), p. 509. White Plains, The National Foundation.

Christiansen, P. 1972. Urinary gonadotrophins in nine fertile eunuchs. Acta Endocr. (Kbh.) 71:454–468.

Clements, J. A., F. I. Reyes, J. S. D. Winter, and C. Faiman. 1976. Studies on human sexual development. III. Fetal pituitary and serum, and amniotic fluid concentrations of LH, CG and FSH. J. Clin. Endocr. Metabol. 42:9–19.

Court Brown, W. M. 1968. Review Article: Males with an XYY sex chromosome complement. J. Med. Genet. 5:341–359.

Crandall, B. F., L. Samec, R. S. Sparkes, and S. W. Wright. 1973. A familial syndrome of deafness, alopecia and hypogonadism. J. Pediat. 82:461–465.

Davidoff, F., and D. D. Federman. 1973. Mixed gonadal dysgenesis. Pediatrics. 52:725–742.

Degenhart, H. J., H. K. A. Visser, H. Boon, and N. J. O'Doherty. 1972. Evidence for deficient 20α-cholesterol-hydroxylase activity in adrenal tissue of a patient with lipoid adrenal hyperplasia. Acta Endocr. 71:512–518.

de la Chapelle, A. 1972. Analytic review: Nature and origin of males with XX sex chromosomes. Am. J. Hum. Genet. 24:71–105.

de la Chapelle, A., H. Hortling, R. Sanger, and R. R. Race. 1964. Successive nondisjunction at first and second meiotic division in spermatogenesis: Evidence of chromosomes and Xg. Cytogenetics 3:334–341.

de la Chapelle, A., J. Schröder, J. Murros, and G. Tallqvist. 1977. Two XX males in one family and additional observations bearing on the etiology of XX males. Clin. Genet. 11:91–106.

Del Castillo, E. B., A. Trabucco, and F. A. De La Baize. 1947. Syndrome produced by absence of the germinal epithelium without impairment of the Sertoli or Leydig cells. J. Clin. Endocr. 7:493–507.

De Morsier, G. 1954. Etudes sur les dysraphies cranioencephaliques. I. Agénésie des lobes olfactifs (télencéphaloschizis latéral) et des commisures calleuse et anterieure (télencéphaloschizis médian). La dysplasie olfacto-génitale. Schweiz. Arch. Neurol. Neurochir. Psychiat. 74:309–361.

Dorland's Illustrated Medical Dictionary. 1974. 25th Ed., Friel, J. P. (Ed.), p. 750. Philadelphia, W. B. Saunders Company.

Dosik, H., D. P. Madashor, F. Khan, and G. Spergel. 1975. The XX male: Apparent translocation of Y chromosome material to chromosome 17. Clin. Res. 23:261A.

Dosik, H., S. S. Wachtel, F. Khan, G. Spergel, and G. C. Koo. 1976. Y-chromosomal genes in a phenotypic male with a 46,XX karyotype. JAMA 236:2505–2508.

Edwards, J. A., and R. M. Bannerman. 1971. Familial Gynecomastia. In Birth Defects: Original Article Series, Bergsma, D. (Eds.), Vol. 7:6, pp. 193–195, White Plains, The National Foundation.

Edwards, J. H. 1971. On the distribution of phenotypes in XXY males and their parents. J. Med. Genet. 8:434–437.

Elsahy, N. I., and W. R. Walters. 1971. The brachio-skeleto-genital syndrome. Plast. Reconstr. Surg. 48:542–550.

Endo, M., Y. Tasaka, N. Matsuura, and I. Matsuda. 1976. Laurence-Moon-Biedl syndrome (?) and Prader-Willi syndrome (?) in a single family. Eur. J. Pediat. 123:269–276.

Faiman, C., D. L. Hoffman, R. J. Ryan, and A. Albert. 1968. The "fertile eunuch" syndrome: Demonstration of isolated leuteinizing hormone deficiency by radioimmunoassay technique. Mayo Clin. Proc. 43:661–667.

Federman, D. D. 1967. Abnormal Sexual Development. A Genetic and Endocrine Approach to Differential Diagnosis, pp. 82–84. Philadelphia, W. B. Saunders Company.

Ferguson-Smith, M. A. 1958. Chromatin-positive Klinefelter's syndrome (primary microrchidism) in a mental deficiency hospital. Lancet 1:928–931.

Ferguson-Smith, M. A. 1963. Chromosome studies in Klinefelter's syndrome. Proc. R. Soc. Med. 56:577–578.

Ferguson-Smith, M. A. 1966. Klinefelter's Syndrome and Mental Deficiency. In The Sex Chromatin, Moore, K. L. (Ed.), p. 277. Philadelphia, W. B. Saunders Company.

Ferrier, P. E., and E. F. Stone. 1969. Familial pituitary dwarfism associated with an abnormal sella turcica. Pediatrics 43:858–865.

Fleishmann, P. R., M. Berlin, and M. M. Dana. 1976. Gonadal dysgenesis in two siblings. Am. J. Obstet. Gynec. 124:208–209.

Francke, U., K. Benirschke, and O. W. Jones. 1975. Prenatal diagnosis of trisomy 9. Humangenetik 29:243–250.

French, F. S., B. Baggett, J. J. Van Wyk, L. M. Talbert, W. R. Hubbard, F. R. Johnston, R. P. Weaver, E. Forchielli, G. S. Rao, and I. R. Sarda. 1965. Testicular feminization: Clinical, morphological and biochemical studies. J. Clin. Endocr. Metabol. 25:661–677.

French, F. S., J. J. Van Wyk, B. Baggett, W. F. Easterling, L. M. Talbert, F. R. Johnston, E. Forchielli, and A. C. Dey. 1966. Further evidence of a target organ defect in the syndrome of testicular feminization. J. Clin. Endocr. Metabol. 26:493–503.

Friedrich, U., and J. Nielsen. 1973. Chromosome studies in 5,049 consecutive newborn children. Clin. Genet. 4:333–343.

German, J., J. L. Simpson, R. S. K. Chaganti, R. L. Summitt, L. B. Reid, and I. R. Merkatz. 1978. Genetically determined sex-reversal in 46,XY humans. Science 202:53–56.

German, J., J. L. Simpson, and G. McLemore. 1973. Abnormalities of human sex chromosomes. I. A ring Y without mosaicism. Ann. Genet. (Paris) 16:225–231.

Gilbert-Dreyfus, S., C. I. A. Sébaoun, and J. Belaisch. 1957. Étude d'un cas familial d'androgynoidism avec hypospadias grave, gynécomastie et hyperoestrogénie. Ann. Endocr. (Paris) 18:93–101.

Givens, J. R., W. L. Wiser, R. L. Summitt, I. J. Kerber, R. N. Andersen, D. E. Pittaway, and S. A. Fish. 1974. Familial male pseudohermaphroditism without gynecomastia due to deficient testicular 17-ketosteroid reductase activity. New Eng. J. Med. 291:938–944.

Goebelsmann, U., R. Horton, J. H. Mestman, J. J. Arce, Y. Nagata, R. M. Nakamura, I. H. Thorneycroft, and D. R. Mishell, Jr. 1973. Male pseudohermaphroditism due to testicular 17β-hydroxysteroid dehydrogenase deficiency. J. Clin. Endocr. Metabol. 36:867–879.

Goebelsmann, U., M. Zachmann, V. Davajan, R. Israel, J. H. Mestman, and D. R. Mishell. 1976. Male pseudohermaphroditism consistent with 17,20-desmolase deficiency. Gynec. Invest. 7:138–156.

Goldberg, E. H., E. A. Boyse, D. Bennett, M. Scheid, and E. A. Carswell, 1971. Serological demonstration of H-Y (male) antigen on mouse sperm. Nature 232:478–480.

Goldman, A. S. 1970. Production of congenital lipoid adrenal hyperplasia in rats and inhibition of cholesterol side-chain cleavage. Endocrinology 86:1245–1251.

Goldsmith, O., D. H. Solomon, and R. Horton. 1967. Hypogonadism and mineralocorticoid excess. The 17-hydroxylase deficiency syndrome. New Eng. J. Med. 277:673–677.

Gorlin, R. J. 1973. Multiple Lentigines Syndrome. In Birth Defects Atlas and Compendium, Bergsma, D. (Ed.), p. 643. White Plains, The National Foundation.

Gorlin, R. J., J. J. Pindborg, and M. M. Cohen, Jr. 1976. Syndromes of the Head and Neck, pp. 520–526. New York, McGraw-Hill Book Company.

Greenstein, R. M., D. J. Harris, L. Luzzatti, and H. M. Cann. 1970. Cytogenetic analysis of a boy with the XXXY syndrome: Origin of the X-chromosome. Pediatrics 45:677–686.

Griffin, J. E., K. Punyashthiti, and J. D. Wilson. 1976. Dihydrotestosterone binding by cultured human fibroblasts. Comparison of cells from control subjects and from patients with hereditary male pseudohermaphroditism due to androgen resistance. J. Clin. Invest. 57:1342–1351.

Grumbach, M. M., J. C. Roth, S. L. Kaplan, and R. P. Kelch. 1974. Hypothalamic-Pituitary Regulation of Puberty in Man: Evidence and Concepts Derived from Clinical Research. In Control of the Onset of Puberty, Grumbach, M. M., G. D. Grave, and F. E. Mayer (Eds.), pp. 115–166. New York, John Wiley & Sons, Inc.

Hambert, G. 1971. Males with Positive Sex Chromatin. Göteborg, Akademiforlaget.

Hamerton, J. L. 1971. Human Cytogenetics, Vol. 2. New York, Academic Press.

Hamerton, J. L., N. Canning, M. Ray, and S. Smith. 1975. A cytogenetic survey of 14,069 newborn infants. I. Incidence of chromosome abnormalities. Clin. Genet. 8:223–243.

Hamerton, J. L., J. M. Dickson, C. E. Pollard, S. A. Grieves, and R. V. Short. 1969. Genetic intersexuality in goats. J. Reprod. Fertil. Suppl. 7:25–51.

Heremans, G. F. P., A. J. Moolenar, and H. H. Gelderen. 1976. Female phenotype in a male child due to 17-α-hydroxylase deficiency. Arch. Dis. Child. 51:721–723.

Herrman, J., and J. M. Opitz, 1969. The Lenz Microphthalmia Syndrome. In Birth Defects: Original Article Series, Bergsma, D. (Ed.), Vol. 5:2, pp. 138–143. White Plains, The National Foundation.

Hertig, A. T., J. Rock, and E. C. Adams. 1956. A description of 34 human ova within the first 17 days of development. Am. J. Anat. 98:435–493.

Hook, E. B., and J. L. Hamerton. 1977. The Frequency of Chromosome Abnormalities Detected in Consecutive Newborn Studies — Differences Between Studies — Results by Sex and by Severity of Phenotypic Involvement. In Population Cytogenetics. Studies in Humans, Hook, E. B., and I. H. Porter (Eds.), pp. 63–79. New York, Academic Press.

Howard, R. P., R. C. Sniffen, F. A. Simmonds, and F. Albright. 1950. Testicular deficiency: A clinical and pathologic study. J Clin. Endocr. 10:121–186.

Huhtaniemi, I., M. Ikonen, and R. Vihko. 1970. Presence of testosterone and other neutral steroids in human fetal testis. Biochem. Biophys. Res. Commun. 38:715–720.

Imperato-McGinley, J., L. Guerrero, T. Gautier, and R. E. Peterson. 1974a. An unusual form of male pseudohermaphroditism. A model of 5α-reductase deficiency in man. J. Clin. Invest. 53:35a.

Imperato-McGinley, J., L. Guerrero, T. Gautier, and R. E. Peterson. 1974b. Steroid 5α-reductase deficiency in man. An inherited form of male pseudohermaphroditism. Science 186:1213–1215.

Imperato-McGinley, J., and R. E. Peterson. 1976. Male pseudohermaphroditism: The complexities of male phenotypic development. Am. J. Med. 61:251–272.

Isurugi, K., Y. Aso, H. Ishida, T. Suzuki, T. Kakizoe, T. Motegi, T. Nishi, and H. Aoki. 1977. Prepubertal XY gonadal dysgenesis. Pediatrics 59:569–573.

Jacobs, P. A., and A. Ross. 1966. Structural abnormalities of the Y chromosome in man. Nature 210:352–354.

Jacobs, P. A., W. H. Price, W. M. Court Brown, R. P. Brittain, and P. B. Whatmore. 1968. Chromosome studies on men in a maximum security hospital. Ann. Hum. Genet. 31:339–358.

Jacobs, P. A., and J. A. Strong. 1959. A case of human intersexuality having a possible XXY sex-determining mechanism. Nature 183:302–303.

Jirasek, J. E. 1977a. Morphogenesis of the Genital System in the Human. In Morphogenesis and Malformation of the Genital System. Birth Defects: Original Article Series, Blandau, R. J., and D. Bergsma (Eds.), Vol. 13:2, pp. 13–39. White Plains, The National Foundation.

Jirasek, J. E. 1977b. Principles of Reproductive Embryology. In Disorders of Sexual Differentiation, Simpson, J. E. (Ed.), pp. 51–110. New York, Academic Press.

Josso, N., J.-Y. Picard, and D. Tran. 1977. The Anti-müllerian Hormone. In Morphogenesis and Malformation of the Genital System. Birth Defects: Original Article Series, Blandau, R. J., and D. Bergsma, (Eds.), Vol. 13:2, pp. 59–84. White Plains, The National Foundation.

Jost, A. 1953. Problems of fetal endocrinology. The gonadal and hypophyseal hormones. Recent Prog. Horm. Res. 8:379–418.

Jost, A. 1970. Hormonal factors in the sex differentiation of the mammalian foetus. Philos. Trans. R. Soc. Lond. (Biol.) 259:119–131.

Kallmann, F., W. A. Schonfeld, and S. E. Barrera. 1944. The genetic aspects of primary eunuchoidism. Am. J. Ment. Defic. 48:203–236.

Kaplan, E., H. Schwachman, A. D. Perlmutter, A. Rule, K.-T. Khaw, and D. S. Holsclaw. 1968. Reproductive failure in males with cystic fibrosis. New Eng. J. Med. 279:65–69.

Kasdan, R., H. R. Nankin, P. Troen, N. Wald, S. Pan, and T. Yanaihara. 1973. Paternal transmission of maleness in XX human beings. New Eng. J. Med. 288:539–545.

Kase, N., and J. M. Morris. 1965. Steroid synthesis in the cryptorchid testes of three cases of the "testicular feminization" syndrome. Am. J. Obstet. Gynec. 91:102–105.

Kaufman, M., C. Straisfield, and L. Pinsky. 1976a. Specific 5α-dihydrotestosterone binding in labial skin fibroblasts cultured from patients with male pseudoher-maphroditism. Clin. Genet. 9:567–574.

Kaufman, M., C. Straisfield, and L. Pinsky. 1976b. Heterogeneity of complete testicular feminization (CTF) revealed by different levels of 5α-dihydrotestosterone (DHT) binding in cultured skin fibroblasts. Pediat. Res. 10:340.

Keenan, B. S., W. J. Meyer, A. J. Hadjian, H. W. Jones, and C. J. Migeon. 1974. Syndrome of androgen insensitivity in man: Absence of 5α-dihydrotestosterone binding protein in skin fibroblasts. J. Clin. Endocr. Metabol. 38:1143–1146.

Kershnar, A. K., D. Borut, M. D. Kogut, E. G. Biglieri, and M. Schambelan. 1976. Studies in a phenotypic female with 17-α-hydroxylase deficiency. J. Pediat. 89:395–400.

Kirkland, R. T., J. L. Kirkland, C. M. Johnson, M. Horning, L. Librik, and G. W. Clayton. 1973. Congenital lipoid adrenal hyperplasia in an eight-year-old phenotypic female. J. Clin. Endocr. Metabol. 36:488–496.

Klinefelter, H. F., Jr., E. C. Reifenstein, Jr., and F. Albright. 1942. Syndrome character-ized by gynecomastia, aspermatogenesis without A-Leydigism and increased ex-cretion of follicle-stimulating hormone. J. Clin. Endocr. 2:615–627.

Knudson, A. G., L. C. Strong, and D. E. Anderson. 1973. Heredity and cancer in man. Prog. Med. Genet. 9:113–158.

Kraus-Ruppert, R. 1956. Zur Frange Vererbter diencephaler Storungen; infantiler Eun-uchoidismus sowie Mikrocephalie bei recessivem Erbgang. Z. Mensch. Vererb. 34:643–656.

Laron, Z., and I. H. Hochman. 1971. Small testes in prepubertal boys with Klinefelter's syndrome. J. Clin. Endocr. Metabol. 32:671–672.

Laurence, J. Z., and R. C. Moon. 1866. Four cases of retinitis pigmentosa occurring in the same family and accompanied by general imperfections of development. Ophthal. Rev. 2:32–41.

Lecluse-van der Bilt, F. A., A. Hagemeijer, E. M. E. Smit, H. K. A. Visser, and G. J. Vaandrager. 1974. An infant with XXXYY karyotype. Clin. Genet. 51:263–270.

Leshin, M., J. E. Griffin, and J. D. Wilson. 1978. 5α-reductase deficiency: Evidence for genetic heterogeneity. Clin. Res. 26:47A.

Lubs, H. A., Jr., O. Vilar, and D. M. Bergenstal. 1959. Familial male pseudoher-maphroditism with labial testes and partial feminization: Endocrine studies and genetic aspects. J. Clin. Endocr. Metabol. 19:1110–1120.

Lynch, H. T., F. Ozer, C. W. McNutt, J. E. Johnson, and N. A. Jampolsky. 1960. Secondary male hypogonadism and congenital ichthyosis: Association of two rare genetic diseases. Am. J. Hum. Genet. 12:440–447.

Lyon, M. F. 1974. Mechanism and evolutionary origins of variable X-chromosome activity in mammals. Proc. Roy. Soc. Lond. (Biol.) 187 (1088): 243–268.

Lyon, M. F., and S. G. Hawkes. 1970. An X-linked gene for testicular feminization in the mouse. Nature 227:1217–1219.

MacGillivray, R. C. 1954. The syndrome of Rud. Am. J. Ment. Defic. 59:62–72.

MacLean, N., W. M. Court Brown, P. A. Jacobs, D. J. Mantle, and J. A. Strong. 1968. A survey of sex chromatin abnormalities in mental hospitals. J. Med. Genet. 5:165–172.

Madden, J. D., P. C. Walsh, P. C. McDonald, and J. D. Wilson. 1975. Clinical and endocrinologic characterization of a patient with the syndrome of incomplete tes-ticular feminization. J. Clin. Endocr. Metabol. 41:751–760.

Mallin, S. R. 1969. Congenital adrenal hyperplasia secondary to 17-hydroxylase defi-ciency. Two sisters with amenorrhea, hypokalemia, hypertension and cystic ovaries. Ann. Intern. Med. 70:69–75.

Mantero, F., B. Busnardo, A. Riondel, R. Veyrat, and M. Austoni. 1971. Hypertension artérielle, alcalose hypokaliemique et pseudohermaphrodisme male par deficit en 17α-hydroxylase. Schweiz. Med. Wochenschr. 101:38–43.

Matte, R., P. D'Amour, C. Faiman, and J. S. D. Winter. 1974. Familial hypothalamic hypogonadotropic hypogonadism. Canad. Med. Assoc. J. 110:509–512.

McCullagh, E. P., G. C. Beck, and C. A. Schaffenburg. 1951. A syndrome of eunuchoidism with spermatogenesis, normal urinary FSH and low or normal ICSH (fertile "eunuchs"). J. Clin. Endocr. Metabol. 11:612–620.

McDonough, P. G., J. O. Ellegood, J. R. Byrd, and V. B. Mahesh. 1976. Ovarian and peripheral venous steroids in XY gonadal dysgenesis and gonadoblastoma. Obstet. Gynec. 47:351–355.

Meckel, S., and E. Passarge. 1971. Encephalocele, polycystic kidneys, and polydactyly as an autosomal recessive trait simulating certain other disorders: The Meckel syndrome. Ann Genet. 14:97–103.

Merriam, G. R., I. Z. Beitins, and H. H. Bode. 1977. Father-to-son transmission of hypogonadism with anosmia. Kallmann's syndrome. Am. J. Dis. Child. 131:1216–1219.

Meyer, W. J., III, B. R. Migeon, and C. J. Migeon. 1975. Locus on human X chromosome for dihydrotestosterone receptor and androgen insensitivity. Proc. Nat. Acad. Sci. U.S.A. 72:1469–1472.

Mittwoch, U. 1973. Genetics of Sex Differentiation. New York, Academic Press.

Miyashita, A., K. Isurugi, and H. Aoki. 1976. Infantile XX male: A case report. Clin. Genet. 10:208–213

Monteleone, J. A., C. L. Witzleben, P. L. Monteleone, and J. Giangiacomo. 1975. Male Pseudohermaphroditism and Degenerative Renal Disease. In Birth Defects: Original Article Series, Bergsma, D. (Ed), Vol. II:4, p. 155. White Plains, The National Foundation.

Morris, J. M. 1953. The syndrome of testicular feminization in male pseudohermaphrodites. Am. J. Obstet. Gynec. 65:1192–1211.

Morris, J. M., and V. B. Mahesh. 1963. Further studies on the syndrome, "testicular feminization." Am. J. Obstet. Gynec. 87:731–748.

Naftolin, F., G. W. Harris, and M. Bobrav. 1971. Effect of purified luteinizing hormone releasing factor on normal and hypogonadotropic anosmic men. Nature 232:496–497.

Naftolin, F., and H. L. Judd. 1973. Testicular feminization. Obstet. Gynec. Ann. 2:25–53.

Najjar, S. S., R. J. Takla, and V. H. Nassar. 1974. The syndrome of rudimentary testes: Occurrence in five siblings. J. Pediat. 84:119–122.

Neuhaüser, G., and J. M. Opitz. 1975. Autosomal recessive syndrome of cerebellar ataxia and hypogonadotropic hypogonadism. Clin. Genet. 7:426–434.

Neumann, F., and W. Elger, 1966. The effect of the anti-androgen 1,2-alpha-methylene-6-chloro-delta-[4,6]-pregnadiene-17-alpha-ol-3,20-dione-17-alpha-acetate (cyproterone acetate) on the development of the mammary glands of male foetal rats. J. Endocr. 36:347–352.

New, M. I., and L. Suvannakul. 1970. Male pseudohermaphroditism due to 17α-hydroxylase deficiency. J. Clin. Invest. 49:1930–1941.

Niebuhr, E. 1974. Triploidy in man. Cytogenetical and clinical aspects. Humangenetik 21:103–125.

Nielsen, J. 1969. Klinefelter's syndrome and the XYY syndrome. A genetical, endocrinological and psychiatric-psychological study of thirty-three severely hypogonadal male patients and two patients with karyotype 47,XYY. Acta Psychiatr. Scand. (Suppl.) 209:1–353.

O, W.-S., and R. V. Short. 1977. Sex Determination and Differentiation in Mammalian Germ Cells. In Morphogenesis and Malformation of the Genital System. Birth Defects: Original Article Series, Blandau, R. J., and D. Bergsma (Eds.), Vol. 13:2, pp. 1–12. White Plains, The National Foundation.

Oettinger, M., D. W. Bruneteau, A. Psaroudakis, and R. B. Greenblatt. 1976. FSH and LH response to LHRF in Kallmann's syndrome. Obstet. Gynec. 47:233–236.

Ohno, S. 1976a. Major regulation genes for mammalian sexual development. Cell 7:315–321.

Ohno, S. 1976b. Sexual differentiation and testosterone production. New Eng. J. Med. 295:1011–1012.

Ohno, S. 1977. Testosterone and Cellular Response. In Morphogenesis and Malformation of the Genital System. Birth Defects: Original Article Series, Blandau, R. J., and D. Bergsma (Eds.), Vol. 13:2, pp. 99–106. White Plains, The National Foundation.

Ohno, S. 1978. The role of H-Y antigen in primary sex determination. JAMA 239:217–220.

Ohno, S., U. Tettenborn, and R. Dofuku. 1971. Molecular biology of sex differentiation. Hereditas 69:107–124.

Opitz, J. M. 1973. Gonosomal Intersexuality. In Birth Defects Atlas and Compendium, Bergsma, D. (Ed.), pp. 451–452. White Plains, The National Foundation.

Opitz, J. M., R. I. DeMars, S. L. Inhorn, and B. R. Elejalde. 1977. Follow-up on a Human X-Autosome Translocation. In Annual Review of Birth Defects, Birth Defects: Original Article Series 14:6c, Summitt, R. L., and D. Bergsma (Eds.), pp. 365–375. New York, Alan R. Liss, Inc.

Opitz, J. M., J. L. Frias, J. E. Gutenberger, and J. R. Pellett. 1969. The G Syndrome of Multiple Congenital Anomalies. In Birth Defects: Original Article Series, Bergsma, D. (Ed.), Vol. 5:2, pp. 95–101. White Plains, The National Foundation.

Opitz, J. M., and J. J. Howe. 1969. The Meckel Syndrome (Dysencephalia Splanchnocystica, the Gruber Syndrome). In Birth Defects: Original Article Series, Bergsma, D. (Ed.), Vol. 5:2, pp. 167–179. White Plains, The National Foundation.

Opitz, J. M., J. L. Simpson, G. E. Sarto, R. L. Summitt, M. I. New, and J. German. 1971. Pseudovaginal perineoscrotal hypospadias. Clin. Genet. 3:1–26.

Overzier, C., and H. Linden. 1956. Echter Agonadismus (Anorchismus) bei Geschwistern. Gynaecologica 142:215–233.

Palacios, E., and R. N. Schimke. 1969. Craniosynostosis-syndactylism. Am. J. Roentgen. 106:144–155.

Parks, G. A., J. A. Bermudez, C. S. Anast. A. M. Bongiovanni, and M. I. New. 1971. Pubertal boy with 3β-hydroxysteroid dehydrogenase defect. J. Clin. Endocr. Metabol. 33:269–278.

Paulsen, C. A. 1974. The Testes. In Textbook of Endocrinology, 5th Ed., Williams, R. H. (Ed.), pp. 323–367. Philadelphia, W. B. Saunders Company.

Paulsen, C. A., D. L. Gordon, R. W. Carpenter, H. W. Gandy, and S. D. Drucker. 1968. Klinefelter's syndrome and its variants: A hormonal and chromosomal study. Recent Prog. Horm. Res. 24:321–363.

Pearson, P. L., and M. Bobrow, 1970. Definitive evidence for the short arm of the Y chromosome associating with the X chromosomes during meiosis in the human male. Nature 226:959–961.

Peterson, R. E., J. Imperato-McGinley, T. Gautier, and E. Sturla. 1977. Male pseudohermaphroditism due to steroid 5α-reductase deficiency. Am. J. Med. 62:170–191.

Pfeiffer, R. A., G. Körver, R. Sanger, and R. R. Race. 1966. Paternal origin of an XXYY anomaly. Lancet 1:1427–1428.

Pfeiffer, R. A., and R. Sanger. 1973. Origin of 48,XXXY. The evidence of the Xg blood groups. J. Med. Genet. 10:142–143.

Pinsky, L. 1978. The Nosology of Male Pseudohermaphroditism Due to Androgen Insensitivity. In Annual Review of Birth Defects. Birth Defects: Original Article Series, 14:6c, Summitt, R. L., and D. Bergsma (Eds.), pp. 73–95. New York, Alan R. Liss.

Pinsky, L., R. Finkelberg, C. Straisfield, B. Zilahi, M. Kaufman, and G. Hall. 1972. Testosterone metabolism by serially subcultured fibroblasts from genital and nongenital skin of individual human donors. Biochem. Biophys. Res. Commun. 46:364–369.

Pion, R. J., W. J. Dignam, E. J. Lamb, J. G. Moore, M. V. Frankland, and H. H. Simmer. 1965. Testicular feminization. Am. J. Obstet. Gynec. 93:1067–1075.

Plunkett, E. R., and M. L. Barr. 1956. Testicular dysgenesis affecting the seminiferous tubules principally, with chromatin-positive nuclei. Lancet 2:853–857.

Prader, A., and G. J. P. A. Anders. 1962. Zur Genetik der kongenitalen Lipoidyperplasie der Nebennieren. Helv. Pediat. Acta 17:285–289.

Prader, A., and H. P. Gurtner. 1955. Das Syndrom des Pseudohermaphroditismus masculinis bei kongenitaler Nebennierenrinden-Hyperplasie ohne Androgenüberproduktion (adrenaler Pseudohermaphroditismus masculinis). Helv. Pediat. Acta 10:397–412.

Prader, A., and R. E. Siebenmann. 1957. Nebenniereninsuffizienz bei kongenitaler lipoid Hyperplasie der Nebennieren. Helv. Pediat. Acta 12:569–595.

Rabin, D. 1975. The Syndromes of Isolated Gonadotropin Deficiency. In Birth Defects: Original Article Series, Bergsma, D. (Ed.), Vol. 10:4, pp. 73–80. White Plains, The National Foundation.

Reed, W. B. 1973. Xeroderma and Mental Retardation. In Birth Defects Atlas and Compendium, Bergsma, D. (Ed.), p. 898. White Plains, The National Foundation.

Reyes, F. I., J. S. D. Winter, and C. Faiman. 1973. Studies on human sexual development. I. Fetal gonadal and adrenal sex steroids. J. Clin. Endoc. Metabol. 37:74–78.

Richards, G., and A. M. Neville. 1974. Formation and Metabolism of 5α-reduced steroids by gonadal tissue in testicular feminization. J. Endocr. 62:405–406.

Rimoin, D. L. 1971. Genetic Forms of Pituitary Dwarfism. In Birth Defects: Original Article Series, Bergsma, D. (Ed.), Vol. 7:6, pp. 12–20. White Plains, The National Foundation.

Rimoin, D. L., and R. N. Schinke. 1971. Genetic Disorders of the Endocrine Glands. St. Louis, C. V. Mosby Company.

Robinson, J. A., and K. E. Buckton. 1971. Quinacrine fluorescence of variant and abnormal human Y chromosomes. Chromosoma 35:342–352.

Root, A. W. 1973. Endocrinology of puberty. I. Normal sexual maturation. J. Pediat. 83:1–19.

Rosenfield, R. L., A. M. Laurence, S. Liao, and R. L. Lindau. 1971. Androgens and androgen responsiveness in the feminizing testis syndrome. Comparison of complete and "incomplete" forms. J. Clin. Endocr. Metabol. 32:625–632.

Rosewater, S., G. Gwinup, and G. J. Hamwi. 1965. Familial gynecomastia. Ann. Intern. Med. 63:377–385.

Roth, J. C., M. M. Grumbach, and S. L. Kaplan. 1973. Effect of synthetic luteinizing hormone-releasing factor on serum testosterone and gonadotropins in prepubertal, pubertal and adult males. J. Clin. Endocr. Metabol. 37:680–686.

Rundle, A. T., and P. E. Sylvester. 1962. Endocrinological aspects of mental deficiency. II. Maturational status of adult males. J. Ment. Defic. Res. 3:87–93.

Saez, J. M., E. de Peretti, A. M. Morera, M. David, and J. Bertrand. 1971. Familial male pseudohermaphroditism with gynecomastia due to testicular 17-ketosteroid reductase defect. I. Studies in vivo. J. Clin. Endocr. Metabol. 32:604–610.

Saez, J. M., A. M. Morera, E. de Peretti, and J. Bertrand. 1972. Further in vivo studies in male pseudohermaphroditism with gynecomastia due to a testicular 17-ketosteroid reductase defect (compared to a case of testicular feminization). J. Clin. Endocr. Metabol. 34:598–600.

Sagel, J., L. A. Distiller, J. E. Morley, and H. Isaacs. 1975. Myotonia dystrophica: Studies on gonadal function using luteinizing-hormone-releasing hormone (LRH). J. Clin. Endocr. Metabol. 40:1110–1113.

Sanger, R., P. Tippett, and J. Gavin. 1971. Xg groups and sex abnormalities in people of Northern European ancestry. J. Med. Genet. 8:417–426.

Santen, R. J., and C. A. Paulsen. 1973. Hypogonadotropic eunuchoidism. I. Clinical study of the mode of inheritance. J. Clin. Endocr. Metabol. 36:47–54.

Sarto, G. E., and J. M. Opitz. 1973. The XY gonadal agenesis syndrome. J. Med. Genet. 10:288–293.

Saunders, D. M., J. Barrett, and G. Grudzinskas. 1975. Feminization in gonadal dysgenesis associated with ovarian gonadoblastoma. Obstet. Gynec. 46:93–97.

Schimke, R. N., J. J. Spaulding, and J. G. Hollowell. 1971. X-linked Congenital Panhypopituitarism. In Birth Defects: Original Article Series, Bergsma, D. (Ed.), Vol. 7:6, pp. 21–23. White Plains, The National Foundation.

Scully, R. E. 1970. Gonadoblastoma — a review of 74 cases. Cancer 25:1340–1356.

Siiteri, P. K., and J. D. Wilson. 1974. Testosterone formation and metabolism during male sexual differentiation in the human embryo. J. Clin. Endocr. Metabol. 38:113–125.

Similä, S., E. Jukarainen, R. Herva, and E. S. Heikinen. 1974. Gonadoblastoma associated with pure gonadal dysgenesis. Clin. Pediat. 13:177–180.

Simpson, J. L. 1977. Disorders of Sexual Differentiation. New York, Academic Press.

Simpson, J. L., A. C. Christakos, M. Horwith, and F. S. Silverman. 1971. Gonadal Dysgenesis in Individuals with Apparently Normal Chromosomal Complements: Tabulation of cases and compilation of genetic data. In Birth Defects: Original Article Series, Bergsma, D. (Ed.), Vol. 7:6, pp. 215–228. White Plains, The National Foundation.

Simpson, J. L., and G. Photopulos. 1976. The Relationship of Neoplasia to Disorders of Abnormal Sexual Differentiation. In Birth Defects: Original Article Series, Bergsma, D. (Ed.), Vol. 12:1, pp. 15–50. White Plains, The National Foundation.

Simpson, J. L., R. L. Summitt, J. German, and I. R. Merkatz. 1976. Etiology of XY gonadal dysgenesis. Gynec. Invest. 7:37.

Singh, R. P., and D. H. Carr. 1966. The anatomy and histology of XO human embryos and fetuses. Anat. Rec. 155:369–384.

Smith, D. W., L. Lemli, and J. M. Opitz. 1964. A newly recognized syndrome of multiple congenital anomalies. J. Pediat. 64:210–217.

Smith, G. F., and J. M. Berg. 1976. Down's Anomaly. New York, Churchill Livingstone.

Sohval, A. R. 1963. "Mixed" gonadal dysgenesis: A variety of hermaphroditism. Am. J. Hum. Genet. 15:155–158.

Sohval, A. R., and L. J. Soffer. 1953. Congenital familial testicular deficiency. Am. J. Med. 14:328–348.

Soller, M., B. Padeh, M. Wysoki, and N. Ayalon. 1969. Cytogenetics of Saanen goats showing abnormal development of the reproductive tract associated with the dominant gene for polledness. Cytogenetics 8:51–67.

Sperling, K., R. Kaden, and W. Hirsch. 1973. A causistic contribution to the XX male problem. Humangenetik 17:145–154.

Stearns, P. E., K. E. Droulard, and F. H. Sahhar. 1960. Studies bearing on fertility of male and female mongoloids. Am. J. Ment. Defic. 65:37–41.

Sternberg, W. H., D. L. Barclay, and H. W. Kloepfer. 1968. Familial XY gonadal dysgenesis. New Eng. J. Med. 278:695–700.

Strickland, A. L., and F. S. French. 1969. Absence of response to dihydrotestosterone in the syndrome of testicular feminization. J. Clin. Endocr. Metabol. 29:1284–1286.

Summitt, R. L. 1970. The role of the cytogeneticist in the team approach to primary amenorrhea. Southern Med. J. 63:628–632.

Summitt, R. L. 1973. Noonan Syndrome. In Birth Defects Atlas and Compendium, Bergsma, D. (Ed.), pp. 670–671. White Plains, The National Foundation.

Summitt, R. L. 1975. Sex Determination, Differentiation and Development. In Synopsis of Pediatrics, Hughes, J. G., (Ed.), pp. 572–613. St. Louis, C. V. Mosby Company.

Summitt, R. L. 1977. Disorders of Sex Differentiation. In Gynecologic Endocrinology, Givens, J. R. (Ed.), pp. 69–92. Chicago, Year Book Medical Pubs., Inc.

Summitt, R. L. 1978. Autosomal syndromes. Pediat. Ann. (In press).

Swyer, G. J. M. 1955. Male pseudohermaphroditism: A hitherto undescribed form. Brit. Med. J. 2:709–712.

Talerman, A. 1971. Gonadoblastoma and dysgerminoma in two siblings with dysgenetic gonads. Obstet. Gynec. 38:416–426.

Temtamy, S. 1973. Acropolysyndactyly. In Birth Defects Atlas and Compendium, Bergsma, D. (Ed.), p. 141. White Plains, The National Foundation.

Tolis, G., W. Lewis, M. Verdy, H. G. Friesen, S. Solomon, G. Pagalis, F. Pavlatos, P. Fessas, and J. G. Rochefort. 1974. Anterior pituitary function in the Prader-Willi syndrome. J. Clin. Endocr. Metabol. 39:1061–1066.

Tysyachnyuk, S. P. 1974. The variant of chromatin-positive Klinefelter's syndrome with the karyotype 46,XX. Genetika 10:156–162.

Vague, J., J. Guidon, J. F. Mattei, J. M. Luciani, and S. Angeletti. 1977. Les hommes à caryotype 46,XX. Ann. Endocr. (Paris) 38:311–321.

Valman, H. B., and N. E. France. 1969. The vas deferens in cystic fibrosis. Lancet 2:566–567.

Volpe, R., W. S. Metzler, and M. W. Johnston. 1963. Familial hypogonadotrophic eunuchoidism with cerebellar ataxia. J. Clin. Endocr. Metabol. 23:107–115.

Wachtel, S. S. 1977. H-Y antigen and the genetics of sex determination. Science 198:797–799.

Wachtel, S. S., G. C. Koo, W. R. Breg, H. T. Thaler, G. M. Dillard, I. M. Rosenthal, H. Dosik, P. S. Gerald, P. Saenger, M. New, E. Leiber, and G. N. Miller. 1976. Serologic detection of a Y-linked gene in XX males and XX true hermaphrodites. New Eng. J. Med. 295:750–754.

Wallace, D. C., K. J. Murphy, L. Kelly, and W. H. Ward. 1973. The basal cell nevus syndrome. Report of a family with anosmia and a case of hypogonadotrophic hypogonadism. J. Med. Genet. 10:30–33.

Walsh, P. C., J. D. Madden, M. J. Harrod, J. L. Goldstein, P. C. McDonald, and J. D. Wilson. 1974. Familial incomplete male pseudohermaphroditism, type 2. Decreased dihydrotestosterone formation in pseudovaginal perineoscrotal hypospadias. New Eng. J. Med. 291:944–949.

Wegenke, J. D., D. T. Uehling, J. B. Wear, Jr., E. S. Gordon, J. G. Bargman, J. S. R. Deacon, J. P. R. Herrmann, and J. M. Opitz. 1975. Familial Kallmann syndrome with unilateral renal aplasia. Clin. Genet. 7:368–381.

Weinstein, R. L., B. Kliman, and R. E. Scully. 1969. Familial syndrome of primary testicular insufficiency with normal virilization, blindness, deafness, and metabolic abnormalities. New Eng. J. Med. 281:969–977.

Weyeneth, R. 1956. Etiopathogenic et diagnostic de la stérilité masculine. Praxis 45:21–34.

Wilkins, L. 1957. The Diagnosis and Treatment of Endocrine Disorders in Childhood and Adolescence, p. 276. Springfield, Ill., Charles C Thomas.

Wilson, J. D., M. J. Harrod, J. L. Goldstein, D. L. Hemsell, and P. C. McDonald. 1974. Familial incomplete male pseudohermaphroditism, type 1. Evidence for androgen resistance and variable clinical manifestations in a family with the Reifenstein syndrome. New Eng. J. Med. 290:1097–1103.

Winter, J. S. D., I. A. Hughes, F. I. Reyes, and C. Faiman, 1976. Pituitary-gonadal relations in infancy: 2 patterns of serum gonadal steroid concentrations in man from birth to two years of age. J. Clin. Endocr. Metabol. 42:679–686.

Winter, J. S. D., and C. Faiman. 1972. Pituitary-gonadal relations in male children and adolescents. Pediat. Res. 6:125–135.

Winter, J. S. D., C. Faiman, and F. I. Reyes. 1977. Sex Steroid Production by the Human Fetus: Its Role in Morphogenesis and Control by Gonadotropins. In Morphogenesis and Malformation of the Genital System, Birth Defects: Original Article Series, Blandau, R. J., and D. Bergsma (Eds.), Vol. 13:2, pp. 41–58. White Plains, The National Foundation.

Witschi, E., W. D. Nelson, and S. J. Segal. 1956. Genetic developmental and hormonal aspects of gonadal dysgenesis and pseudohermaphroditism. J. Clin. Endocr. Metabol. 16:922–923.

Zachmann, M., J. A. Völlmin, W. Hamilton, and A. Prader. 1972. Steroid 17,20-desmolase deficiency: A new cause of male pseudohermaphroditism. Clin. Endocr. 1:369–385.

Zarate, A., A. J. Kastin, J. Soria, E. S. Canales, and A. V. Schally. 1973. Effect of synthetic luteinizing hormone-releasing hormone (LH-RH) in two brothers with hypogonadotropic hypogonadism and anosmia. J. Clin. Endocr. Metabol. 36:612–614.

Zollinger, H. 1969. Das XXXY-Syndrom. Zwei neue Beobachtungen im Kleinkindesalter und eine Literaturübersicht. Helv. Pediat. Acta 24:589–599.

2

The Role of Twin Studies in Human Quantitative Genetics

WALTER E. NANCE

Professor and Chairman, Department of Human Genetics, Medical College of Virginia

INTRODUCTION

Twins have long been the subject of awe and curiosity, and they became the subject of scientific inquiry in 1876 when Galton published his treatise *The History of Twins As a Criterion of the Relative Powers of Nature and Nurture.* Although twins have been widely used for genetic research since Galton's time, increased understanding of the biology of twinning has raised many issues concerning the interpretation of data from twins. The purpose of this review is to consider those aspects of the biology of twins that are relevant to their use in the classic twin model and to describe a study design using data from the families of identical twins that holds great promise for permitting an incisive analysis of the genetic and environmental determinants of continuously distributed metric traits in man. More comprehensive reviews of various aspects of the biology of twins can be found in the books of Strong and Corney (1967), Bulmer (1970), MacGillivray et al. (1975), and Nance et al. (1978a), and in reviews by Allen (1965) and Benirschke and Kim (1973).

BACKGROUND

Variation is an essential quality of life, and two of the most fundamental ideas of biology — the gene theory and the theory of evolution — were formulated to account for variation within and among species. In his book *On the Origin of Species by Means of Natural Selection* (1859), Darwin clearly showed how variation, acting as the substrate for natural selection, could lead to biologic evolution. Although he accurately described the familial patterns of qualitative traits later shown to have recessive, dominant, and X-linked modes of inheritance, Darwin (1875) lacked a precise theoretical framework for understanding the distribution and hereditary transmission of variation in natural populations. Mendel (1866) recognized how the predictable phenotypic ratios observed among the progeny of experimental crosses could readily be interpreted in terms of the pairwise segregation and independent assortment of his multiple factors of heredity. In 1918, R. A. Fisher extended the mendelian theory of the inheritance of discrete qualitative traits by demonstrating that it could also account for the genetic determination of continuously distributed metric traits. His classic paper on *The Correlation Between Relatives under the Supposition of Mendelism* marks the beginning of modern quantitative genetics.

Fisher assumed that variation in continuous quantitative traits results in part from the combined effects of many genes and gene pairs, each of which has a small individual effect. Mendelian segregation in such a system leads to predictable genetic correlations between relatives, and Fisher showed how the observed correlations could in turn be used to estimate the magnitude of various sources of genetic and environmental variation.

The goal of human quantitative genetics is to infer accurately the causes of phenotypic variation in defined populations. The analytic strategy, as proposed by Fisher, is to express a sufficient number of distinct genetic relationships in terms of their unknown genetic and environmental variance components to permit estimation of these variables from empiric observations of the specified relationships. If at least as many statistically independent relationships, or equations, are available as there are unknown variables to be estimated, the system is said to be determinant, and a solution can be obtained. Fisher carefully distinguished between the causes of the phenotype and the causes of phenotypic variation in a population and warned against the use of "loose phrases about the 'percentage of causation' which obscure the essential distinction between the individual and the population." Unfortunately, as noted by Lewontin (1974) and Kempthorne (1978), confusion over these concepts has led to misunderstanding and misuse of the results of quantitative genetics studies. The contrast between causes and causes of variation may be illustrated by the expected results of a genetic analysis of a quantitative trait such as blood pressure in a highly inbred strain of mice. Since the mice are all genetically identical, one would expect to find no genetic variation in blood pressure within the population. This expectation does not imply that genes do not control the formation of the heart and blood vessels or the development and functioning of the renin-angiotensin system in inbred mice; rather, it simply indicates that the genes that influence blood pressure are monomorphic in that population. It should be equally clear from this example that any given estimate of the proportion of variation arising from either genetic or environmental causes is entirely dependent upon the particular population selected and the particular environment in which it is observed. As with any experimental result, extrapolation beyond the conditions of inference must be made with caution.

Genetic Variation

The variability in a population can be measured by the variance, or average squared deviation of individual measurements from the population mean. Under the simplest possible model, the total phenotypic variance in a population, V_T, may be partitioned into a genetic component, V_G, and an environmental component, V_E, giving

$$V_T = V_G + V_E. \tag{1}$$

As Fisher showed, using different symbolism, the genetic variance further subdivides into additive, V_A, dominant, V_D, and epistatic, V_P, components such that

$$V_G = V_A + V_D + V_P. \tag{2}$$

The additive genetic variance measures the direct effects of individual genes, whereas dominance and epistasis arise from pairwise interactions of alleles and nonalleles, respectively. If the effects of a gene are completely additive, a double dose of the gene will have twice as much effect on the measured trait as a single dose will, or, expressed in genetic terms, the phenotype of the heterozygote is exactly intermediate between the phenotypes of the two homozygous genotypes. Additive genetic effects account for the genetic resemblance of parents and offspring in natural populations, and they provide a measure of the extent to which the offspring's phenotype can be predicted from the parental phenotypes. When dominance is complete, the phenotype of the heterozygote, rather than being intermediate, is indistinguishable from one or the other of the two homozygous phenotypes, and, if there is overdominance, the phenotype actually falls outside the range of the two homozygous phenotypes. When dominance is present, measurements of the parents are poor predictors of the offspring's phenotype. Dominance contributes to both the similarities and differences of full siblings but not to the resemblance of parents and offspring or to the genetic similarity of half-siblings who are related to each other through only one parent. Epistasis refers to similar nonadditive interactions between nonallelic genes. Epistasis is difficult to measure in man, but it is of great importance conceptually as a potential explanation for extreme and clinically significant deviations in phenotypes, such as hypertension, mental deficiency, or hypercholesterolemia.

The genetic covariance of related individuals is composed of differing fractions of the genetic subcomponents shown in equation (2), depending upon the degree and type of their relationship. Since monozygotic twins possess identical sets of nuclear genes, they fully share the additive, dominance, and epistatic effects: Consequently the coefficient for these subcomponents in the expected value of the covariance is unity. In 1948, Malécot gave a general formula from which the coefficients of the additive and dominance genetic components can be calculated for the covariances of less closely related individuals. Considering only the additive and dominance components, Malécot showed that the covariance between two individuals is equal to

$$\tfrac{1}{2} (f + f') V_A + ff' V_D \tag{3}$$

where f and f' are the coefficients of relationship between alleles derived from the father and mother, respectively. The terms f and f' are the probabilities that one or the other allele at a given locus is identical by descent in a given pair of relatives and may be calculated from a pedigree showing the relationships between the two individuals. The coefficient of V_A, therefore, is equal to the average probability that a given gene in the two individuals is identical by descent or, alternatively, is equal to the proportion of all genes held in common. The coefficient for the dominance term is the product of the two probabilities. Thus, dominance contributes to the genetic covariance of relatives only when both probabilities are nonzero, i.e., when the individuals concerned are related to each other through both parents.

In his treatment of epistasis, Fisher (1918) considered only the additive pairwise interactions of nonalleles. Kempthorne (1954) subsequently extended the analysis to account for higher order interactions between an arbitrary number of genes as well as for interactions between the additive and dominance effects of nonallelic genes. Thus, for the interaction between additive genetic effects at r loci and dominance effects at s loci, Kempthorne gives the following as the epistatic variance:

$$[\tfrac{1}{2} (f + f')]^r (ff')^s V_P. \tag{4}$$

In the simple case of two-locus additive epistasis (V_{AA}) for the parent-offspring relationship where $f = f' = \tfrac{1}{2}$, the formula with $r = 2$ and $s = 0$ yields $\tfrac{1}{4} V_{AA}$ for V_P as derived by Fisher. Although it is conceivable that higher order interactions of the type $r > 2$, $s \geq 1$ may be of importance as a cause of deviant phenotypes in man, it seems unlikely that the conventional techniques used in quantitative genetic analysis will permit recognition of these effects, because of their proportionately small contribution to the phenotypic similarities of virtually all classes of relatives other than monozygotic twins.

Nongenetic Variation

The major limitation of Fisher's model was his treatment of environmental effects. Fisher allowed for the random effects of environment but (with the exception of assortative mating) made no provision for the possible effects of common environment on the correlation between relatives. If matings are assumed to be assortative by phenotype, Fisher showed how a positive marital correlation would increase the expected correlation among and the total variation of the offspring. Since the parental phenotypes are determined by both genetic and environmental factors, his model assumed that premarital environmental similarities could contribute to the correlation of spouses but not to the correlation of genetically related individuals.

Subsequent elaborations of Fisher's model have attempted to allow for the common family environment of relatives by incorporating additional parameters into the expressions for the predicted correlations of relatives of various degree (Falconer, 1960; Lange et al., 1976; Mather and Jinks, 1977; Martin and Eaves, 1977; Elston and Rao, 1978). However, in contrast to the genetic effects, no a priori theory specifies the functional relationships to be expected for the shared environments of various classes or relatives. One could argue that each distinct genetic relationship should be associated with a unique environmental similarity. However, if a new, unknown environmental parameter is required to describe each different relationship adequately, the attempt to achieve determinacy by including observations of additional genetic relationships in an analysis will be frustrated. Most of the current controversy over the specification of quantitative genetic models concerns the biologic plausibility of alternative attempts to restrict the number of estimated genetic and environmental sources of variation by assuming various functional relationships among the variables. Thus, with a given data set, it may be possible to obtain estimates of genetic and environmental variance components if all the genetic effects are assumed to be additive, if the environmental commonality of siblings is assumed to be identical to that between parents and offspring, or if the environmental similarities of identical and fraternal twins are assumed to be equal. Such assumptions should not be automatically rejected, since there may well be traits for which they are valid.

In addition to genetic and environmental effects, three other potential sources of variation should be considered in any genetic analysis of quantitative inheritance. Genetic environmental interactions, V_I, refer to nonadditive interactions between specific genotypes and environments. In their absence, the effects of a given environment will be uniform across all genotypes, and, similarly, the rank ordering of genotypes will be the same in all environments. When interactions exist, the rank ordering will change, depending upon the environment. Examples of genetic environmental interactions in man include all of the recognized pharmacogenetic traits (Vesell, 1973) and the sickle cell polymorphism. The concept provides a provocative model for the possible role of genetic factors in the predisposition to many common diseases.

Genetic environmental covariance, V_C, refers to the nonrandom distribution of genotypes over environments that may exist in natural populations. If "favorable" genotypes select or tend to occur in favorable environments, whereas less favorable genotypes are paired with unfavorable environments, the effect will be to increase the likelihood of extreme phenotypes and thereby augment the total variance of the population.

Maternal effects, V_M, are an important potential cause for phenotypic similarities of siblings. They can arise from the influence of nuclear genes in the mother or cytoplasmic factors in the embryo or from maternal environmental influences, acting either pre- or postnatally. Prenatal maternal effects are of documented importance in determining litter size and weight in laboratory mammals (Jinks and Broadhurst, 1963) and can have a profound effect on growth, in some cases persisting to adult life (Walton and Hammond, 1938). Diabetic embryopathy, birth weight, and the fetal response to maternal phenylketonuria (PKU) are familiar examples of maternal effects in man. Recent comparisons of maternal and paternal inbreeding suggest that genetically determined maternal effects may also be an important cause of fetal loss and cerebral palsy (Tanaka, 1977).

USE OF TWINS IN QUANTITATIVE GENETICS

Because of the limited number of genetic relationships that are available for analysis in nuclear family units, the identification and exploitation of unique relationships have been recurrent themes of research in human quantitative genetics. Twins have long been used in quantitative genetics as an adjunct to nuclear families and the adoption paradigm. The classic twin study method consists of comparing the variation observed within identical, or monozygotic (MZ), twin pairs with that observed within fraternal, or dizygotic (DZ), twin pairs. Since MZ twins arise from a single fertilized egg, they possess identical sets of nuclear genes, and differences within the pair must arise from pre- or postnatal environmental factors, cytoplasmic differences, or somatic mutations that occur during the course of development.

In contrast, DZ twins are genetically related to each other in the same way that full siblings are and, on the average, share one half of their genes. Differences within fraternal pairs arise, therefore, from both genetic and environmental causes. A basic assumption of the classic twin model is that the environmental similarities and differences will be the same for identical twins as they are for fraternal twins. If this assumption is correct, the difference between the two within pair variances will be a measure of the genetic variation within dizygotic twin pairs.

Under the simplest assumptions, an analysis of variance leads to

$$V_{MZW} = V_{EW}$$
$$V_{MZA} = V_{EA} + V_{G}$$
$$V_{DZW} = V_{EW} + V_{GW}$$
$$V_{DZA} = V_{EA} + V_{GA},$$

where V_{MZW} and V_{DZW} are the written pair variances of MZ and DZ twins respectively, V_{EW} is the environmental variance within pairs, V_{G} is the genetic variance, V_{MZA} and V_{DZA} are the among pair components of variance, V_{EA} is the among pair environmental variance, and V_{GA} and V_{GW} are the genetic variances among and within DZ twins.

In the twin model, like-sexed DZ twins are selected instead of siblings for comparison with MZ twins because the members of a pair are the same age and are the product of a multiple pregnancy — circumstances that should make them more comparable to the identical twins. In fact, however, many variables, such as maternal age, parity, race, family background, and fertility drugs, are known to influence the occurrence of DZ twins, possibly causing them to be a biased or stratified sample of the general population. Furthermore, unresolved questions about the biology of DZ twinning exist — whether some arise from fertilization of a polar body (Nance, 1977) and others from superfetation (Scrimgeour and Baker, 1974; Rhine and Nance, 1976) — and these mechanisms could falsely inflate the evidence for genetic effects derived from a classic twin study by increasing the intrapair variance of the DZ twins. Alternatively, the biased ascertainment of phenotypically similar pairs, a common occurrence with self-selected twin samples, can lead to a

Table 1. Placentation in 295 Consecutive Liveborn Twin Pairs at Four Hospitals

	RACE					
	White		Black		Total	
TYPE OF PLACENTATION	No.	%	No.	%	No.	%
Monozygotic Twins						
Monochorionic, monoamnionic	4	6	3	6	7	6
Monochorionic, diamnionic	44	65	26	55	70	61
Dichorionic, diamnionic	20	29	18	39	38	33
Total	68	(44)°	47	(34)	115	(39)
Dizygotic Twins						
Dichorionic, diamnionic – fused	34	39	31	34	65	36
Dichorionic, diamnionic – separate	54	61	61	66	115	64
Total	88	(56)	92	(66)	180	(61)
Grand Total	156	(100)	139	(100)	295	(100)

° Numbers in parentheses give percentages of all twins in category.

spurious reduction in the average genetic variation within DZ twins.

Other important biologic biases may affect data from monozygotic twins. It is generally believed that monozygotic twinning may occur at any time during about the first 10 days of embryonic life and that differences in timing of the event cause the distinctive differences in placentation that are observed among monozygotic pairs (Corner, 1955). In Table 1, the placental findings in a series of 295 personally examined twin placentae are given. About one third of the MZ pairs had two separate placentas and birth sacs. These dichorionic pairs are assumed to originate in early embryonic life, when the twinning occurs prior to implantation. More commonly, there is a single placental mass with only one chorion and one or two inner birth sacs, or amnions. This type of placentation presumably arises when the twinning process occurs after implantation. Monoamnionic placentation is the rarest type, being found in about 6 per cent of all MZ pairs. Further delay in the twinning process results in conjoined, or Siamese, twins. Vascular anatomoses can almost invariably be demonstrated in the placentae of monochorionic twins. In some cases, unequal sharing of the common blood supply can lead to striking differences in birth weight and other traits —the so-called twin transfusion syndrome (Aherne et al., 1968). Acardia, a rare malformation that occurs almost exclusively in MZ twin pregnancies, is thought to represent an extreme expression of this phenomenon (Price, 1950). It is difficult to generalize about the significance of placental differences in MZ twins. For example, monochorionic pairs show greater intrapair differences in birth weight (Corey et al., 1976), but dichorionic pairs have been reported to display a 5-fold greater within pair variation in cord blood cholesterol levels (Corey et al., 1976). When the weights of MZ twins differ by more than 25 per cent at birth, persistent discordance in stature and in tests of mental ability are frequently observed (Babson and Phillips, 1973). How long the placental effect on cholesterol-level variation persists is not known with certainty. These observations emphasize the importance of careful documentation of the placental findings in all twins, including histologic examination of the membranes by a competent obstetric pathologist. Although placental findings do not provide an absolute criterion for determining zygosity (except in the case of monochorionic pairs, which can be confidently classified as monozygotic), they are invaluable as a method of timing the twinning event in MZ pairs. For this reason, studies in a subpopulation of twins classified by placental type should permit assessment of the potential significance of prenatal biases on the trait in question. Since the intrapair variance of MZ twins may include variation resulting from competitive interactions that are unique to twins as well as from random environmental effects, it would seem reasonable, for most traits, to regard the intrapair differences as a conservatively large estimate of the extent to which random environmental effects can produce phenotypic differences in genetically identical individuals.

A facile approach to avoiding the potential biases caused by the common blood supply in monochorionic twins would be to employ only dichorionic MZ pairs, whose prenatal development should be more comparable to that of DZ twins. However, this approach would sacrifice data on the majority of MZ twins and would also retain any errors in zygosity determination that may have been made, since these errors would be confined to the dichorionic group. Even a relatively low rate of misclassification could have a disproportionately large effect if the most dissimilar MZ twins and the most similar DZ twins were systematically misclassified. In practice, however, misinformation about the significance of the placental findings appears to be the most common cause of mistaken zygosity in MZ twins whose parents were told at the time of the twins' birth that they must be dizygotic because there were two placentae. Finally, prenatal factors, such as twin transfusion, that are unique to MZ twins are often responsible for the differences in extremely discordant pairs. Misclassification of these pairs might therefore have the paradoxical effect of making the results of the analyses correspond more closely to the assumed genetic model.

Zygosity Determination

Several approaches to zygosity determination have been used in the past. The similarity method involves the analysis of multiple genetic markers, with the probability of monozygosity and dizygosity for twins with identical typing results being estimated from known gene frequencies or parental typing results or both (Emery, 1976). Objective anthropometric data, such as dermatoglyphic findings, and information on the type of placentation can be included in such calculations. Gaines and Elston (1969) have shown how information contained in the among pair as well as in the within pair variation can also be used to improve the resolution. With the addition of chromosomal markers (VanDyke et al., 1977) to existing isoenzyme and antigenic polymorphisms, zygosity determination is seldom a problem when extensive typing procedures are available. For example, in a recently reported co-twin control study involving 44 pairs of MZ twins who were extensively genotyped, the estimated number of misclassified pairs was 0.37, or less than 1 pair (Miller and Nance, 1977).

For large surveys, in which extensive genotyping is impractical, 95 per cent accuracy in zygosity determination can be achieved by questionnaire. Several discriminant function analyses of questionnaire responses have been reported (Jablon et al., 1967; Cohen et al., 1975), but they appear to provide surprisingly little improvement over the response to a single question first used by Swedish investigators: "When you were children, were you as alike as two peas in a pod?" (Cederlöf et al., 1961). In 1978, Kaprio et al. described an interesting alternative to complete reliance upon questionnaire responses for zygosity determinations in large twin samples. These authors devised a decision tree that classified twins into three groups of definite and uncertain zygosity. Genotyping could then be limited to the uncertain group, yielding near perfect zygosity determination at a greatly reduced cost.

Skin transplantation is another method that has been used for zygosity determination. Although a successful take has been accepted in a court of law as proof of monozygosity (McIndoe and Franceschetti, 1949), even this criterion can fail in the rare case of DZ blood group chimeras, in whom vascular mixing occurs prenatally, resulting in immune tolerance (Nichols et al., 1957).

The Classic Twin Model

The genetic variance of twins may be partitioned according to the relationships given in equations (3) and (4), and, as noted previously, the environmental variation may be partitioned into effects common to both members of a pair, V_{EA}, and effects peculiar to individual members of the pair, V_{EW}. The basic assumption of the twin model is that the V_{EW}'s for MZ and DZ twins are equal. The within pair environmental variations can be considered to include random environmental effects as well as variations arising from the unique embryology of twins. The latter effects are assumed to be either negligible or equivalent in MZ and DZ twins, an assumption that can be tested by comparing twins of known placental type. It also seems likely that the postnatal environments of MZ and DZ twins may differ in their similarities. Many authors have dealt with this possibility by assuming that the environmental covariance of twins augments the among pair variation and decreases the within pair variation to exactly the same extent, thus maintaining an identical total variance. Although this approach may be mathematically appealing, recent evidence suggests that it may not be biologically sound, Garrison et al. (1978) examined the effect of "environmental covariance" on the within and among pair variance of serum cholesterol measurements by classifying a sample of 214 adult MZ pairs into two groups depending upon the frequency of contact with one another. As expected, the among pair variance of the pairs who saw each other "often" was substantially greater than that of pairs who "seldom got together." However, rather than being smaller, the within pair variance in the former group was also slightly larger. These observations suggest that a more appropriate model might be to assume that when unique covariances arising from the "twin situation" exist (Zazzo, 1978), their major effect will be to augment the among pair component for MZ twins. Since these covariances will be encountered in exaggerated form only in genetically identical individuals, it would seem best to regard them as a form of genetic-environmental covariance, V_C, or a measure of the maximum extent to which genetically identical individuals tend to select similar environments. When MZ twin variances are combined with data from other relationships, a poor fit may be observed either because the among pair variance is "too large" or because the within pair variance is "too small," or both. To the extent that the total variance of MZ twins is greater than that of DZ twins, it seems reasonable to attribute the excess to a unique covariance that augments the among pair variance of MZ twins, as previously noted. This expanded interpretation of twin variances is summarized in the following equations:

$$V_{MZW} = V_{EW} \qquad (5)$$

$$V_{MZA} = V_A + V_{AA} + V_D + V_M + V_{EA} + V_C \qquad (6)$$

$$V_{DZW} = \tfrac{1}{2}\,V_A + \tfrac{3}{4}\,V_{AA} + \tfrac{3}{4}\,V_D + V_{EW} \qquad (7)$$

$$V_{DZA} = \tfrac{1}{2}\,V_A + \tfrac{1}{4}\,V_{AA} + \tfrac{1}{4}\,V_D + V_M + V_{EA} \qquad (8)$$

The model is admittedly heuristic, since the contribution of genetic-environmental covariances to the among pair variance of DZ twins is not specified. Strictly speaking, V_C should be regarded as the excess genetic-environmental covariance found in MZ twins greater than that observed in less closely related individuals. The remaining covariance is confounded with the among pair environmental effects. Clearly, the full model cannot be fitted unless data from twins are combined with observations from other sources. This interpretation of twin data exploits the unique relationship of MZ twins in order to identify the likely source of additional variation in situations in which the total variance of MZ pairs is greater than that of DZ pairs.

Several different approaches have been proposed for estimating the degree of genetic determination, or heritability, from data on twins, and the relative merits of several alternative methods have been reviewed by Jensen (1967). A disadvantage of the classic twin model is that direct and interactive genetic effects cannot be unambiguously resolved. Consequently, heritability estimates derived from twins include a fraction of the interactive effects as well as the additive effects and are referred to as broad heritability estimates, H^2, as opposed to narrow estimates, h^2, which are the ratio of the additive genetic variance to the total variance. In general, psychologists have favored the use of correlation coefficients, whereas quantitative geneticists have more often employed variance component analyses. Correlation coefficients can be readily adjusted for attenuation and for spousal correlation, factors that are of particular importance in the analysis of mental test scores. Conversely, since correlations are equivalent to the ratio between a covariance and a total variance, their use may tend to obscure potentially important differences between the total variance of MZ twins and other kinds of relatives, which, as we have seen, can point to the existence of genetic-environmental covariance (or interactions, see later discussion). In addition, when data from twins are combined with observations from other classes of relatives, correlation coefficients do not lend themselves readily to a more refined partitioning of the genetic variance into dominance, epistatic, and maternal components, even when sophisticated techniques such as path analysis are employed.

The F statistic, comparing the within pair variance of DZ and MZ twins, perhaps provides the simplest test for the existence of significant genetic variation in dizygotic twins, and if the assumptions of the twin model are met, the difference between the within pair variances of DZ and MZ twins is a maximum likelihood estimate of the genetic variation within DZ twins (Haseman, 1970). In 1955, Clark proposed that the proportion of the variance within fraternal twins that is determined by genetic factors be measured by the formula

$$H^2 = \frac{V_{WDZ} - V_{WMZ}}{V_{WDZ}}$$

One advantage of this estimate is that it is not sensitive to differences in the age and sex composition of the samples or to other potential sources of stratification that might bias either the total genetic or the total environmental variance of the two types of twins. Alternatively, Holzinger (1929) proposed the formula

$$H^2 = \frac{r_{MZ} - r_{DZ}}{1 - r_{DZ}},$$

where r is the intraclass correlative coefficients for MZ and DZ twins, respectively. Least squares and maximum likelihood procedures for estimating the genetic variance from the four mean squares associated with the within and among pair components have been described in detail by Haseman and Elston (1970), but these methods require the further assumptions that there is no dominance or epistasis, that the environmental covariances of MZ and DZ twins are absent or equal, and that the total genetic variances of MZ and DZ twins are equal.

Multivariate Analysis

Extension of the classic twin model to the multivariate case allows the identification of multiple independent dimensions of genetic variation that may affect distinct clusters of biologically related traits. Bock and Vandenberg (1968) showed how the covariance matrix of the intrapair differences of multiple interrelated metric traits in MZ twins could be combined with a similar matrix derived from measurements in a sample of DZ twins by a process they likened to a multivariate extension of the univariate F test. Factor analysis of the resulting covariance matrix of heritable components then permits identification of the minimum number of independent dimensions of genetic variation that are contained within the data. The method is illustrated by the results of an analysis of dermatoglyphic variables in Tables 2 and 3 (Nance et al., 1974). All the 16 individual dermatoglyphic traits that were studied in a sample of 80 MZ and 45 like-sexed DZ twin pairs showed evidence of genetically determined variation, in agreement with many previous studies (Table 2). However, the question arises whether some of the varia-

Table 2. Univariate Analysis of 16 Dermatoglyphic Variables in 80 Monozygotic and 45 Like-sexed Dizygotic Twins Pairs[*]

VARIABLE	$\dfrac{V_{WDZ}}{V_{WMZ}}$	$H^2 = \dfrac{V_{WDZ} - V_{WMZ}}{V_{WDZ}}$
Proximal triradial measurement		
left (L–pt)	2.43†	0.58
right (R–pt)	1.67‡	0.40
Distal triradial measurement		
left (L–dt)	2.52†	0.60
right (R–dt)	2.16†	0.53
atd angle		
left (L–atd)	2.70†	0.63
right (R–atd)	2.87†	0.65
Ridge count		
left thumb (L–t)	3.92†	0.74
right thumb (R–t)	3.26†	0.69
Ridge count		
left index finger (L–2)	4.06†	0.75
right index finger (R–2)	2.70†	0.62
Ridge count		
left middle finger (L–3)	5.02†	0.80
right middle finger (R–3)	4.75†	0.78
Ridge count		
left ring finger (L–4)	4.18†	0.76
right ring finger (R–4)	4.72†	0.78
Ridge count		
left little finger (L–5)	3.44†	0.70
right little finger (R–5)	3.09†	0.67

[*]Adapted from Nance, W. E. et al., 1974.
†$p < 0.01$
‡$p < 0.05$

Table 3. Factor Analysis of Heritable Component of Variation of 16 Dermatoglyphic Variables*

VARIABLE	LOADINGS (×100) ON EIGHT SIGNIFICANT ORTHAGONAL FACTORS†								TOTAL
	1	2	3	4	5	6	7	8	
L–pt					−95				
R–pt		29			−78	21	46		
L–dt	−22			94					
R–dt				98					
L–atd		24				94			
R–atd	−23				−36		88		
L-t	−27		−85		22	−27			
R-t	−50		81		20				
L–2	−47	−37	−20					−74	
R–2	−75	−39	−22				22	−37	
L–3	−82	−32	−33				24		
R–3	−87	−23	−32						
L–4	−62	−55	−20			−24	−29	−34	
R–4	−79	−35			23	−40			
L–5	−31	−90	−24						
R–5	−43	−86							
% of Heritable Variance	24.9	16.0	12.5	12.3	11.8	8.6	7.8	6.0	99.9
% by Bold Face Variables	18.7	9.6	8.6	11.5	9.4	5.5	4.8	3.4	71.5

*Adapted from Nance, W. E. et al., 1974.
†Loadings less than 0.2 omitted.

tion is determined jointly. The results of a rotated factor analysis of the covariance matrix of heritable components is shown in Table 3. Virtually all the heritable variation in the 16 variables could be accounted for by eight orthogonal factors, and there was a striking tendency for homologous measurements on the two sides of the body to be heavily weighted on the same factor. This tendency is particularly notable for the first five factors, which accounted for 77.5 per cent of the heritable variation. The following findings are of special interest: Three factors appeared to influence variation in the dermal ridge counts; the first predominantly affecting the middle fingers, the second predominantly affecting the little fingers, and the third predominantly affecting the thumbs. These results provide an impressive confirmation of the ability of the technique to detect biologically meaningful associations, since under virtually any reasonable model of genetic determination, one would assume that genes that influence the variation in a trait on one side of the body would also influence homologous contralateral measurements. The method of analysis has been described in detail elsewhere (Nakata et al., 1974). Similar studies have been performed using dental variables (Potter et al., 1976), cephalometric variables (Nakata et al., 1974), and psychologic variables (Vandenberg, 1965). More recently, Fulker (1978) and Iagolnitzer (1978) have extended these multivariate methods to utilize the among pair as well as the within pair covariance matrices of MZ and DZ twins. These methods provide a useful method for investigating the genetic determination of interrelated metric traits. Whether the independent factors detected by such an analysis result from the pleiotropic effects of major genes segregating at a few independent loci or are a consequence of the integrated effects of multiple clusters of genes is unknown, but a distinction between these possibilities could possibly be made by linkage studies.

KINSHIPS OF MONOZYGOTIC TWINS

Kinships consisting of monozygotic twins, their spouses, and their descendents contain individuals who share multiple genetic relationships that can be used to partition both the genetic and nongenetic variations into their constituent subcomponents (Fig. 1). Although the offspring of a twin are full sibs to each other, they are related in the same way as half-siblings are to the children of the co-twin. This simultaneous bi- and uniparental relationship permits

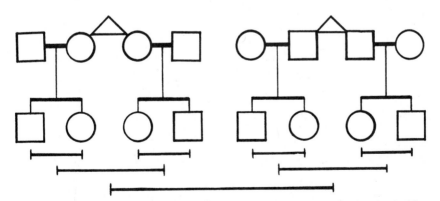

Figure 1. Pedigrees showing genetic relationships contained within the families of monozygotic twins. Lines under pedigree suggest how variation in the offspring may be partitioned by a nested analysis of variance in an among half-sibship, a between sibship within half-sibship, and a within sibship component.

the separation of additive, dominance, and epistatic effects from observations on individuals who are members of the same generation.
Maternal effects can be detected by contrasting the analyses for
male and female twins. If a trait is strongly influenced by either
genetic or environmental maternal effects, one would expect the
children of identical female twins to resemble one another to a
greater extent than would the children of identical male twins. Conversely, for the children of male twins who are born to genetically
unrelated mothers, there should be greater variation between sibships within each half-sibship than is observed in the families of
female twins. By contrasting the analyses for the identical twin
parents with those of their single-born offspring and spouses, the
model permits exploitation of the unique relationship of MZ twins
to detect genetic-environmental interactions and covariance. Finally, analysis of the spousal correlations permits resolution of the
usually confounded effects of common environment and assortative
mating.

The genetic interpretation of the relationships contained within
the MZ half-sib kinships is summarized in Tables 4 and 5. Data
from the offspring may be partitioned by a nested analysis of variance into an among half-sibship, a between sibship within half-
sibship, and a within sibship mean square (Nance and Corey, 1976).
The genetic and environmental expectations for the "among," "between," and "within" components associated with these mean
squares are given in Table 4. Since the expectations for the within
sibship components for male and female twins are the same, they
are pooled, giving a total of five relationships from the offspring
data. The coefficients for the genetic variance components in Table

Table 4. Genetic Interpretation of Variance Components and
Covariances Derived from the Families of Monozygotic Twins[*]

OBSERVED VARIANCE COMPONENT		COEFFICIENTS FOR CONSTITUENT SUBCOMPONENTS								
		V_A	V_D	V_{AA}	V_M	V_{EH}	V_{ES}	V_{EW}	V_I	V_C
[a] Among male half-sibships	A ♂	$1/4$	0	$1/16$	0	1	0	0	$1/4\, r$	0
[b] Between sibships within male half-sibships	B ♂	$1/4$	$1/4$	$3/16$	1	0	1	0	$1/4\, r$	0
[c] Within sibships	W	$1/2$	$3/4$	$3/4$	0	0	0	1	$1-1/2\, r$	0
[d] Between sibships within female half-sibships	B ♀	$1/4$	$1/4$	$3/16$	0	0	1	0	$1/4\, r$	0
[e] Among female half-sibships	A ♀	$1/4$	0	$1/16$	1	1	0	0	$1/4\, r$	0
[f] Among twin pairs	AT	1	1	1	1	1	0	0	0	1
[g] Within twin pairs	WT	0	0	0	0	0	1	1	0	0

[*] For definition of terms see pp. 95 and 96.

Table 5. Interpretation of Covariances Between Twins and
Their Spouses*

		Subcomponents		
Observed Covariance		V_{EH}	V_{EW}	V_T
[h] Husband-Wife	HW	1	1	α
[i] Spouse-Spouse	SS	1	0	α^2
[j] Twin-Spouse	TS	1	0	α

*For definition of terms see text.

4 can be derived from the relationships shown in equations (3) and (4). The among half-sibships component is equivalent to the covariance of half-siblings, whereas the sum of the "among" and "between" components is equal to the covariance of full siblings, and the sum of all three components is equal to the total genetic variance, or a coefficient of one for each subcomponent. Three environmental components are included in the model, corresponding to sources of environmental variation acting among half-sibships, V_{EH}, between sibships within half-sibships, V_{ES}, and within sibships, V_{EW}. A form of genetic-environmental interaction, V_I, can be detected by contrasting the analyses of the parent and the offspring data. Differences in age, sex, and parity of the offspring can give rise to genetic environmental interactions related to the growth process. Thus, even if measurements of the offspring are adjusted for age and sex, there may be residual variation resulting from the interaction of different genotypes with age or with differences in the childhood environment provided by parents when they are young in contrast to the environment they might provide when they are older. The present model assumes that these effects are transient, augmenting the total variance of the offspring but not of the parents, and the coefficients of V_I are estimated from the observed correlation in age among half-sibships, r. In theory, there should be no variation in the average age of offspring between sibships within half-sibships, since they are ascertained through twin parents of the same age and sex. Nevertheless, the variation in age among half-sibships contributes to interactions in both the "between" and "among" components. Genetic environmental covariances, V_C, arise when individuals "select" specific environments depending on their genotype. In Table 4, it is assumed that the effect of these covariances will be to augment the among pair variation of the adult twin parents who have identical genotypes. Finally, maternal effects, V_M, augment the among half-sibship component

for female twins and the between sibship among half-sibship component for male twins.

Observations on the twins and their spouses permit the estimation of the husband-wife covariance, cov HW, the covariance between the spouses of the twins, cov SS, and the covariance between a twin and the spouse of the co-twin, cov TS, in addition to the among and within pair variance of the twins themselves. The genetic interpretations of these parameters, in terms of the variables of the model, are shown in Table 5. The covariance between husband and wife will be determined by the environmental factors they share in the home, V_{ES}, and the environmental factors common to the half-sibships, V_{EH}, as well as by a component attributable to nonrandom mating. If matings are assortative, and α is the marital correlation attributable to assortative mating, this effect will increase the husband-wife covariance by an amount equal to αV_T where V_T is the total variance. In the case of the covariance between the spouses of the twins, only the half-sibship environment is shared, and assortative mating makes a smaller contribution, $\alpha^2 V_T$, to the covariance. Note that regardless of whether matings are assortative or disassortative, the effect on the spouse covariance will be positive. Sex is an example of a phenotype in which matings are disassortative. Although husbands and wives are negatively correlated for this trait, the spouses of twins are positively correlated. Finally, both the half-sibship environment and assortative mating contribute to the covariance of twins with the spouses of their co-twin. Husband-wife correlations have been considered by some investigators to arise primarily from the effects of common environment (Sackett, 1975), whereas the same statistic is often regarded by others as providing evidence for assortative mating (Jensen, 1967). Use of the relationships shown in Table 5 permits the resolution of those usually confounded effects.

Five additional relationships can be derived from the parent-offspring covariances. Furthermore, by partitioning the data into half-fraternities and half-sororities, the independent effects of X-linked and autosomal genes can be separated. Finally, the model can be extended to include the grandchildren of identical twins, permitting a much more incisive analysis of maternal effects. These elaborations have been described in detail elsewhere (Nance et al., 1978), along with formulations of the model in terms of path coefficients that permit resolution of the individual contributions of males and females to assortative mating (Nance, 1979).

Data Analysis

Each of the relationships shown in Tables 4 and 5 gives rise to an equation of estimation, which can be combined to obtain estimates of the unknown genetic and environmental variables of interest. In practice, observed mean squares from the analysis of variance are used instead of the components shown in [a] to [g]. Since the mean squares are linear combinations of the components, the genetic expectations for the mean squares can be calculated from those of the components, using weights to take into account variation in family size within and among the half-sibships (Snedecor, 1956). Finally, estimates of the unknown variables can be obtained from the resulting equations by a least squares analysis. However, since the final estimates depend in part on the errors of the estimates, which in turn depend on the estimates themselves, the solution must proceed in an iterative manner; and because the observed mean squares are not known with equal precision, each must be weighted by its degrees of freedom. Finally, appropriate adjustments must be made for the fact that many of the observed variances and covariances are derived from related individuals rather than from independent samples. These complexities and the methods of dealing with them have been discussed in detail elsewhere (Nance and Corey, 1976).

With nine variables from which to select, a large number of causal solutions are theoretically possible. The process of model fitting involves selecting and testing alternative solutions that seem biologically plausible. Solutions that yield negative variance component estimates are rejected as not fitting the data. Some authors recommend rejecting solutions of this type only if a highly significant negative variance estimate is obtained. However, we have elected to reject all such solutions and, in addition, often ignore solutions yielding positive component estimates that are much smaller than their standard errors. The process involved in selecting biologically plausible models is more difficult to describe. In general, interactive genetic effects are not fitted unless there is evidence for additive genetic variance, and V_{EW} is included in most solutions, since the data sets in question usually include measurement error. Finally, if a univariate F test provides evidence for a significant maternal effect, models that include V_M are favored. A choice between alternative solutions, all of which fit the data, can be made by comparing the X^2 goodness of fit associated with each; and the significance of individual variables, in an acceptable solution, can be judged by the magnitude of the estimates in relation to their standard errors. The estimation procedure depends on large sample theory and the assumption that the measurements in question are normally distributed.

Other approaches to data analysis are possible. Morton (1978) has advocated the use of path analysis and has provided a formulary of equations describing the relationships contained in these families. However, since the parameters used were not defined specifically for the model, they provide an inadequate description of some of the relationships. Morton also advocates the use of Z transforms of the observed correlations because of their improved sampling properties (Morton and Rao, 1978), but in practice, according to Goldberger (1978), whether Z transforms are used or not, the actual results differ little.

Maximum likelihood estimation is a third approach to data analysis that should lead to comparable results (Lange et al., 1976). Hypothesis testing is possible by comparing the likelihood of full and restricted models, but by definition, no test of the goodness of fit and the full model is possible, since all the information available is used to obtain the estimates. Therefore, no residual degrees of freedom remain to test for goodness of fit. Another disadvantage of current maximum likelihood approaches is that for large data sets, the amount of computer time required for an analysis may become prohibitive.

Population Used in Study

In Indianapolis, Indiana, and in Richmond, Virginia, fertile MZ twins were ascertained through advertisement, self-referral, and referral by other twins who had participated in the study. The twins, their spouses, and their children were examined in an outpatient clinic setting or occasionally at home. The sample included only white twins who were generally from middle class backgrounds and cannot be regarded as a random or population-based sample of MZ twins. The possible effects of self-selection or stratification in distorting the range of genotypes or environments sampled in the study should be borne in mind in interpreting the results. Preliminary regression and data adjustment were performed with a statistical package (SAS), and the iterative weighted least squares solutions were obtained with REVAR — a series of programs specifically written for the analysis of MZ half-sib data on an IBM 370/158 computer.

Stature. The analysis was based on height measurements from 398 offspring of 28 male and 48 female twin pairs as well as the twins themselves and 104 of their spouses — a total of 654 individuals in all. Only families in which data were available on both twins and at least

Table 6.   Analyses of Stature: Observed and Expected Mean Squares

STATISTIC	DEGREES OF FREEDOM	VALUE OF MEAN SQUARE	
		Observed	Expected (VI)
[a] MS A ♂	27	3.1378	3.6096
[b] MS B ♂	28	1.6889	1.7932
[c] MS W	246	0.7458	0.7228
[d] MS B ♀	48	0.9521	1.2771
[e] MS A ♀	47	3.8034	4.2652
[f] MS AT	75	1.7020	1.6340
[g] MS WT	76	0.0862	0.0900
[h] Cov HW	103	0.0758	0.0930
[i] Cov SS	51	0.1590	0.1021
[j] Cov TS	103	0.1109	0.0930

one child in each sibship were included in the analysis. The subjects ranged in age from 18 months to 60 years, and to adjust the data for changes in the mean and variance of height that occur with age, each measurement was expressed as a standard score, using the population means and standard deviations given by Smith (1977) for males and females from birth to adult life. Finally, the resulting distribution of standard scores was adjusted to remove any remaining mean difference between the sexes in the sample. One child whose recorded height was more than six standard deviations above normal for his age was omitted from the analysis.

The observed mean squares and covariances that were used in the analysis are shown in Table 6. Note that the within sibship mean square is more than eight times as great as the within pair variance of MZ twins. The latter includes only environmental variation, whereas the former measures both genetic and environmental effects as well as genetic-environmental interactions. For stature, variation resulting from genetic differences in the timing of growth is not entirely removed by adjusting the original measurements for difference in age and sex, and it can be considered to be a form of genetic-environmental interaction (V_I) that contributes to variation in the offspring but not to variation in the twin parents who have achieved their adult stature. Also note that in the offspring data, the "among" mean square for the children of female twins is greater than that for the children of male twins, whereas the "between" mean square for the families of male twins is greater than that observed among the families of female twins. This is a pattern of variation that is consistent with the presence of a maternal effect, and a sensitive univariate test for the significance of the effect is provided by the ratio of the "between" mean squares for male and female twins. For the data given in

Table 7. Stature: Estimated Variance Components

| | GENETIC MODELS[*] | | | | | | | VI % Total Variance | |
VARIANCE COMPONENT	I Est. ±SE	II Est. ±SE	III Est. ±SE	IV Est. ±SE	V Est. ±SE	VI Est. ±SE	VII Est. ±SE	Children & Adults	
V_A			1.19 ±0.08	0.79 ±0.13	0.70 ±0.14	0.45 ±0.19	0.04 ±0.59	30	52
V_D							0.32 ±0.44		
V_I				0.46 ±0.14	0.50 ±0.15	0.64 ±0.17	0.60 ±0.18	42	
V_M						0.22 ±0.13	0.32 ±0.18	15	26
V_{EH}		0.44 ±0.10			0.12 ±0.08	0.10 ±0.08	0.11 ±0.08	7	12
V_{ES}		0.07 ±0.07							
V_{EW}	0.95 ±0.05	0.69 ±0.06	0.09 ±0.01	0.08 ±0.01	0.09 ±0.01	0.09 ±0.02	0.09 ±0.02	6	10
X^2	118	39.9	14.6	8.47	4.93	1.97	1.44		
df	8	6	7	6	5	4	3		
p	<0.001	<0.001	0.041	0.206	0.42	0.741	0.696		

[*]See text for explanation of genetic models.

Table 6, $F = (ms\ B\ \male) / (ms\ B\ \female) = 1.774$, df, 28, 48, p = 0.0397. Finally, note that when the data are expressed as standard scores, the spousal covariances are small in magnitude and the spouse-spouse covariance, cov SS, actually exceeds the husband-wife covariance, cov HW. This is a pattern of variation one would expect for a trait in which marriages tend to be assortative among cohorts but are disassortative within cohorts. To determine the appropriate coefficients for V_I in Table 4, the half-sibship intraclass correlation in age, r, was calculated and was found to be 0.72.

In Table 7, the results of fitting several solutions to equations for [a] to [i] in Table 6 are given, ignoring the effects of assortative mating in [h] and [i] in the initial analysis. Environmental effects alone cannot account for the observed variation, since both the simple (I) and the full (II) environmental models yielded large X^2 values, indicating a poor fit of the model to the data. A simple genetic model assuming additive genetic and random environmental effects (III) gave a markedly improved fit but could also be rejected at the 5 per cent level. The addition of V_I, V_{EH}, and V_M in Models IV to VI resulted in a progressive improvement in fit. Dominance could also be included in the solution, as shown in Model VII, without further improvement in fit, but the addition of epistasis, or V_{ES}, led to negative component estimates. Although the component estimates in Model VI are all larger than their standard errors, additional observation will be required to determine whether the data have been "over-fitted."

The values for cov HW and cov TS provide independent evidence for the absence of a significant V_{ES} component, since the latter is somewhat larger — not smaller — than the former. Equations for [h] and [j] can therefore be combined to give a pooled estimate of (V_{EH} + αV_T) and solved simultaneously with [i], giving $\alpha = -0.006$ and V_{EH} = 0.15. This value for V_{EH} is in reasonable agreement with the estimate derived from the previous analysis (Table 7; Model VI) and indicates that in our sample, when factors common to the half-sibship environment were appropriately accounted for, the spousal covariances actually provided little evidence for assortative mating; in fact, the data suggest that the matings were, to a small extent, disassortative with respect to stature.

The analysis reveals that despite adjustment of the data for age and sex, the total variance of the offspring was 74 per cent greater than that of the parents — an effect that is quite likely related to genetic-environmental interactions involving the timing of growth. This factor accounted for 42 percent of the variation in the offspring. The common half-sibship environmental variance, V_{EH}, that was identified in the analysis may well include the effects of ethnic, cultural, and socioeconomic homogamy among half-sibships, as well as cohort effects resulting from variation in the mean parental age among half-sibships. Random environmental effects, V_{EW}, made a relatively small contribution to the observed variation in stature among both the offspring and the parents. Perhaps the most startling result of the analysis is the evidence provided by the data that maternal effects make a significant contribution to variation in stature, accounting for more than one seventh of the total variance in the offspring and one quarter of the variance in adults. Although it cannot be determined from the present data whether the maternal influences arise from nuclear or cytoplasmic effects of the maternal genome or from pre- or postnatal environmental effects, they raise the possibility that a significant part of the dramatic increase in stature that has occurred in western societies during the past century may be attributable to improved maternal health — a hypothesis that could possibly be tested by observations of the effects of prenatal starvation on adult stature.

Expected values for the observed mean squares can be calculated from the component estimates of Model VI, using the relationships given in Tables 4 and 5 and the component weights calculated from the distribution of sibship sizes. The agreement between the observed and the expected mean squares is shown in Table 6, yielding the weighted goodness of fit X^2 given in Table 7.

Birth Weight. The analysis was based on data on the birth weights of 339 offspring of 23 male and 39 female MZ twins of unknown placental type. Only families in which the mother could give what was considered to be a reliable estimate of gestational age were included in the analysis, and because of the well-known effect of placental vascular anastomoses in exaggerating the birth weight differences of monochorionic twins, the study was based entirely upon the offspring equations. The normative data of Lubchenco et al. (1963) were used to adjust the weights for sex and gestational age, and separate analyses of the raw and adjusted birth weights were compared. The mean squares used for the analysis are given in Table 8. A univariate F test provided evidence for a significant maternal effect acting on both the raw (F = 2.149, df 22, 38, p = 0.019) and adjusted birth weights (F = 2.075, df 22, 38, p = 0.001).

In Table 9, the results of fitting several models to the data are summarized. For both the raw and the adjusted birth weight data, the simple and full environmental models were rejected. A simple additive genetic–random environmental model was also rejected for the adjusted birth weight data but yielded a marginal fit (X^2 = 5.97, 3df, p = 0.11) for raw birth weight. However, in both cases, the goodness of fit was substantially improved by the inclusion of V_M, as shown in Model I of Table 9. Models in which V_A is replaced by V_{AA} also fit the data well, and for raw birth weight, V_{AA} could be added to the vari-

Table 8. Analysis of Birth Weight: Observed and Expected Mean Squares Expressed in Centigrams^2

		VALUE OF MEAN SQUARE			
		Raw Birth Weight		Adjusted Birth Weight	
STATISTIC	DEGREES OF FREEDOM	OBSERVED	EXPECTED (I)	OBSERVED	EXPECTED (I)
[a] MS A ♂	21	79.25	70.20	43.53	50.34
[b] MS B ♂	22	55.25	49.24	52.65	40.38
[c] MS W	205	18.34	18.30	12.82	13.00
[d] MS B ♀	38	25.71	26.12	17.12	15.82
[e] MS A ♀	37	83.36	94.09	69.14	75.43

Table 9. Birth Weight: Estimates of Variance Components Derived
from Analyses of Offspring Data

VARIANCE COMPONENT	GENETIC MODEL I				GENETIC MODEL II			
	Raw Wt.		Adjusted Wt.		Raw Wt.		Adjusted Wt.	
	EST. ±SE	% OF TOTAL	EST. ±SE	% OF TOTAL	EST. ±SE	% OF TOTAL	EST. ±SE	% OF TOTAL
V_A	12.2 ±8.6	36	4.4 ±5.4	18	29.5 ±6.0	89	23.7 ±4.5	96
V_M	9.4 ±4.4	28	9.9 ±3.1	39				
V_{EW}	12.2 ±5.0	36	10.8 ±3.3	43	3.5 ±3.8	11	1.0 ±2.8	4
Equations	[a], [b], [c], [d], [e]				[a + e], [b + d], [c]			
X^2	0.63		1.68		0.03		0.19	
df	2		2		1		1	
p	0.73		0.43		0.86		0.66	

ables in Model I but without improvement in fit. Although adjustment
of the data for gestational age resulted in a 35 percent decrease in the
total variance, the variance attributable to maternal factors (expressed
in centigrams^2) increased slightly in the analysis of adjusted birth
weight, resulting in a substantial increase from 28 to 39 percent in the
proportion of the total variance attributable to the maternal effect.
These observations suggest that the maternal effect acts primarily on
fetal growth, whereas gestational age at birth may be influenced to a
greater extent by genetic effects. These results confirm previous evidence for a maternal effect on birth weight in man (Robson, 1954,
1955; Morton, 1955) and are consistent with the hypothesis of Oun-
stead (1972) that the tendency to bear small-for-dates babies is a
maternal effect.

The findings in Model II are of particular interest because they
show that when the "among" and "between" mean squares for male
and female twins are pooled for the raw and adjusted birth weights
(yielding three equations, respectively), the simple genetic model
provides a good fit to both sets of data. Thus, when relationships are
used that do not permit the separation of genetic, environmental, and
maternal effects, maternal variation may be erroneously confounded
with the genetic variance. As was true for stature, the nature of the
maternal influence is unknown, but it is possible that a nuclear,
cytoplasmic, or environmental source for the variation could be iden-

tified by studies of the grandchildren of monozygotic twins (Corey et al., 1978).

Total Ridge Count. The total dermal ridge counts were measured in 362 offspring of 30 male and 44 female twin pairs as well as in the twins themselves — a total of 510 individuals. The total ridge count is the sum of the ridge counts of the ten fingers, and the method of Holt (1968) was used to obtain the individual ridge counts. Since males are known to have a higher ridge count than females, prior to the analysis, a linear adjustment of the scores was made to remove the effect of sex. The mean squares used for the study are shown in Table 10. Preliminary monovariate analysis of the offspring data showed no hint of a maternal effect. The results of fitting several alternative solutions to the data are shown in Table 11. As with stature and birth weight, the simple and full environmental models could be rejected as an explanation for the data, but a surprising number of two-variable genetic models fit the data well. In Table 11, the two best-fitting three-variable models are given. The standard errors of the estimates of V_A and V_{AA} in Model II are large when they are estimated simultaneously because of the degree to which these effects are confounded. In an attempt to further substantiate the existence of additive epistatic effects on total ridge count, the kinships were rank-ordered separately for male and female twins by twin pair mean and partitioned into lower (Model III), middle (Model IV), and upper (Model V) thirds. The epistatic model was then fitted to the subdivided data sets, giving the results shown in Models III to V. Since the data were truncated by selection through the twin pair mean, the among twin pair equation was omitted, and the analysis was based only on the five offspring equations and the within twin pair equation. Model III shows that there was increased evidence for epistasis in the families of twins with low ridge counts and reduced evidence in the families of

Table 10. Analysis of Total Ridge Count: Observed and Expected Mean Squares

| | | VALUE OF MEAN SQUARE | |
STATISTIC	DEGREE OF FREEDOM	Observed	Expected (II)
[a] MS A ♂	29	4313	3680
[b] MS B ♂	30	1853	2110
[c] MS W	214	1261	1212
[d] MS B ♀	44	1742	2187
[e] MS A	43	3734	3834
[f] MS AT	73	4250	4863
[g] MS WT	74	104	105

Table 11. Total Ridge Count: Estimates of Genetic and Environmental Variance Components

VARIANCE COMPONENTS	GENETIC MODELS[*]							
	I Est. ±SE	II Est. ±SE	% Total	III Est. ±SE	% Total	IV Est. ±SE	% Total	V Est. ±SE
V_A	2007 ±513	1051 ±978	54	533 ±727	31	1960 ±876	86	2107 ±927
V_{AA}		775 ±783	40	1078 ±635	64	181 ±694	8	−624 ±685
V_{EH}	65 ±388							
V_{EW}	107 ±18	105 ±17	6	65 ±40	5	144 ±14	6	64 ±35
X^2	1.75	1.84		0.98		1.04		0.81
df	4	4		3		3		3
p	0.78	0.76		0.81		0.79		0.85

[*] See text for explanation of genetic models.

twins with intermediate ridge counts. In the high ridge count families, the model failed, providing no evidence for epistasis. This approach suggests a way in which to explore the possibility that epistasis could account for extreme deviations in phenotype, and the results of the analysis raise the possibility that low ridge count may, in fact, represent an example of additive epistasis in man.

SUMMARY AND CONCLUSIONS

Twin studies have been subjected to intensive criticism on biologic, epidemiologic, and methodologic grounds (Rao et al., 1976; Elston and Boklage, 1978; Goldberger, 1978). Although the prenatal development of twins and singletons differs substantially, and there are also many important differences in the biology of MZ and DZ twins, the significance of these variations can be evaluated in appropriately designed studies and, as noted by Fulker (1978), have seldom been shown to constitute an important source of bias in the genetic analysis of the quantitative traits for which twins have actually been used. Unique prenatal effects can be the cause of extreme and persistent discordance in twins. However, markedly aberrant pairs can usually be recognized and excluded if necessary, and, in samples in which accurate observations of the afterbirth are available, the placental differences in MZ twins can be exploited to identify less extreme sources of variation that must clearly have their origin in prenatal life. Although observations of this type in twins cannot prove that similar effects exist in singletons, they can at least demonstrate the potential magnitude and duration of prenatal influences on later development. For traits such as birth weight, in which the classic twin model would seem to be inappropriate, longitudinal studies in MZ twins of known placental type could provide a crude assessment of the potential significance of an adverse prenatal environment.

Although twin births occur in only about 1 per cent of all confinements, there are compelling advantages in the use of twins for research that compensate for their relative rarity. The systematic recording of twin births in vital records has greatly facilitated the development of population-based Twin Registries in many countries, particularly in Scandinavia (Kaprio et al., 1978; Kringlen, 1978; Cederlöf and Lorich, 1978). In the United States, the most ambitious twin panel is the NAS–NRC Veterans Twin Registry, which includes almost all U.S. twins who were veterans of World War II (Hrubec and Neel, 1978). More recently, Friedman and his colleagues (1978) have initiated a Registry that includes more than 7000 twin pairs of both sexes who are members of the Kaiser-Permanente Medical Care Program. The availability of large, population-based Registries mitigates the relative rarity of twin births. Twins and their parents instinctively perceive the way in which the twin relationship constitutes a unique "experiment of nature." In an era of increasing concern about informed consent, twin studies could become one of the most effective strategies for obtaining a compliant group of research subjects who can be considered to represent a random sample of genotypes in the population. Both conventional and opportunistic research designs have provided remarkably little insight into the genetic epidemiology of many important health problems such as heart disease, mental illness, and birth defects. It is surprising, therefore, that despite the potential value of twin studies and the great efficiency of the co-twin control design, Twin Registries have not been fully exploited in this country as a sampling frame for epidemiologic research.

When applied with good judgment, classic twin studies remain a very powerful tool for the investigation of complex human traits, particularly interrelated metric traits. However, progressive refinement of the known and potential sources of phenotypic variation has made it clear that twin data alone are inadequate to separate genetic, environmental, and maternal effects or to partition the genetic variance into its causal elements. Consequently, data from twins have frequently been combined with observations on other relationships. The major objection to this approach is the unavoidable heterogenity that may occur when the results of separate studies, possibly conducted by different investigators on separate populations at varying times, are pooled (Rao et al., 1976). The MZ half-sib design provides a versatile solution to this dilemma, since all the relationships required for an incisive resolution of the phenotypic variation are contained within each kindred. By focusing on MZ twins, the design avoids some of the shortcomings of classic twin studies (Nance, 1977) and exploits the unique relationship of twins through observations on their normal offspring — children who have been raised in their own homes by their biologic parents. Even genetic-environmental covariance or interactions, or both, can be detected by contrasting the analysis of data from the twin parents with that from the offspring. The design permits the separation of the effects of common environment and assortative mating and can readily be extended to detect variations resulting from X-linked genes by dividing the families into half-fraternities and half sororities. In addition to the variables reported here, the results of preliminary analyses of serum cholesterol levels, uric acid levels, blood pressure, immunoglobulin levels, and mental test scores have been reported elsewhere (Campbell et al., 1976; Nance et al., 1978; Escobar et al., 1978; Ewell et al., 1978, Rich et al., 1978).

Recent discoveries in the area of molecular biology have tended to divert the science of genetics from its early preoccupation with variation to the more glamorous study of causes. Some contemporary scientists have even questioned the value of the analysis of variation in a species such as man, in which selective breeding is not a realistic goal (Lewontin, 1974). However, it is becoming increasingly apparent that even a rather complete knowledge of the causes of a "normal" or an "average" phenotype may not lead to an understanding of those variations in phenotype that we characterize as disease. Because of its immediate and compelling health relevance, perhaps it is time to reorder our biomedical research priorities to include a greater emphasis on the analysis of clinically significant phenotypic variation. Twin studies could provide a useful approach toward achieving this goal.

ACKNOWLEDGMENTS: This is paper No. 77 from the Department of Human Genetics of the Medical College of Virginia and was supported in part by USPHS Grant HD 10291. It is a pleasure to acknowledge the helpful advice of L. A. Corey, L. J. Eaves, and J. Boughman, the aid of P. Winter, P. Bader, G. Bingle, and J. Christian with the data collection, and the assistance of L. Ewell, W. Crown, and T. Spangler in data processing, computer analysis, and typing of the manuscript.

References

Aherne, W., S. J. Strong, and G. Corney. 1968. The structure of the placenta in the twin transfusion syndrome. Biol. Neonat. 12:121–135.

Allen, G. 1965. Twin research: problems and prospects. Prog. Med. Genet. 4:242–269.

Babson, S. G., and D. S. Phillips. 1973. Growth and development of twins dissimilar in size of birth. New Eng. J. Med. 289:937–940.

Benirschke, K., and C. K. Kim. 1973. Multiple pregnancy. New Eng. J. Med. 288:1276–1284.

Bock, R. D., and S. G. Vandenberg. 1968. Components of Heritable Variation in Mental Test Scores. In Progress in Human Behavior Genetics, Vandenberg, S. G., (Ed.), pp. 233–260. Baltimore, Johns Hopkins Press.

Bulmer, M. G. 1970. The Biology of Twinning in Man, p. 205. Oxford, Clarendon Press.

Campbell, J. B., L. A. Corey, J. C. Christian, K. W. Kang, R. J. Rose, and W. E. Nance. 1976. Application of the MZ twin half-sib model in analyzing quantitative traits. Behav. Genet. 6:101.

Cederlöf, R., L. Friberg, E. Jonsson, and L. Kaij. 1961. Studies on similarity diagnosis in twins with the aid of mailed questionnaires. Acta Genet. (Basel) 11:338–362.

Cederlöf, R. and U. Lorich. 1978. The Swedish Twin Registry. In Progress in Clinical and Biological Research: Twin Studies, Nance, W. E., G. Allen, and P. Parisi (Eds.), Part B, pp. 189–196. New York, Alan R. Liss, Inc.

Clark, P. J. 1955. The heritability of certain anthropometric characteristics as ascertained from measurements of twins. Am. J. Hum. Genet. 8:49–54.

Cohen, D. J., E. Dibble, J. M. Grawe, and W. Pollin. 1975. Reliably separating identical from fraternal twins. Arch. Gen. Psychiat. 32:1371–1375.

Corey, L. A., K. W. Kang, J. C. Christian, J. A. Norton, R. E. Harris, and W. E. Nance. 1976. Effects of chorion type on variation in cord blood cholesterol of monozygotic twins. Am. J. Hum. Genet. 28:433–441.

Corey, L. A., W. E. Nance, and K. Berg. 1978. A New Tool in Birth Defect Research: The MZ Half-sib Model and Its Extension to Grandchildren of Identical Twins. In Birth Defects Original Article Series, Summitt, R. (Ed.). New York, Alan R. Liss, Inc., Vol. XIV:6A, pp. 193–220.

Corner, G. W. 1955. The observed embryology of human single ovum twins and other multiple births. Am. J. Obstet. Gynec. 70:933–951.

Darwin, C. 1875. The Variation of Animals and Plants Under Domestication. London, John Murray.

Darwin, C. 1859. On the Origin of Species by Means of Natural Selection. London, John Murray.

Elston, R. C., and C. E. Boklage. 1978. An Examination of Fundamental Assumptions of the Twin Method. In Progress in Clinical and Biological Research: Twin Studies, Nance, W. E., G. Allen, and P. Parisi (Eds.), Part A, pp. 189–200. New York, Alan R. Liss, Inc.

Elston, R. C., and D. C. Rao. 1978. Statistical modeling and analysis in human genetics. Ann. Rev. Biophys. 7:253–286.

Emery, A. E. H. 1976. Methodology in Medical Genetics, pp. 77–83. Edinburgh, Churchill Livingstone.

Escobar, V., W. E. Nance, D. Bixler, A. Biegel, and L. A. Corey. 1978. Inheritance of Immunoglobulin Levels. In Progress in Clinical and Biological Research: Twin Studies. Nance, W. E., G. Allen, and P. Parisi (Eds.), Part C, pp. 171–176. New York, Alan R. Liss, Inc.

Ewell, L. W., L. A. Corey, P. M. Winter, J. A. Boughman, W. E. Nance. 1978. Blood Pressure Studies on Monozygotic Twins and Their Families. In Progress in Clinical and Biological Research: Twin Studies. Nance, W. E., G. Allen, and P. Parisi (Eds.), Part C, pp. 29–38, New York, Alan R. Liss, Inc.

Falconer, D. S. 1960. Introduction to Quantitative Genetics, pp. 1–365. New York, Ronald Press Co.

Fisher, R. A. 1918. The correlation between relatives on the supposition of mendelian inheritance. Trans. R. Soc. Edin. 52:399–433.

Friedman, G. D., and A. M. Lewis. 1978. The Kaiser-Permanente Twin Registry. In Progress in Clinical and Biological Research: Twin Studies, Nance, W. E., G. Allen, and P. Parisi (Eds.), Part B, pp. 173–178. New York, Alan R. Liss, Inc.

Fulker, D. W. 1978. Multivariate Extensions of a Biomedical Model of Twin Data. In Progress in Clinical and Biological Research: Twin Studies, Nance, W. E., G. Allen, and P. Parisi (Eds.), Part A, pp. 217–236. New York, Alan R. Liss, Inc.

Gaines, R. E., and R. C. Elston. 1960. On the probability that a twin pair is monozygotic. Am. J. Hum. Genet. 21:457–465.

Garrison, R. J., D. L. DeMets, R. Fabsitz, and M. Feinleib. 1978. A Likelihood Ratio Test for Shared Environmental Variance in Twin Studies. In Progress in Clinical and Biological Research: Twin Studies, Nance, W. E., G. Allen, and P. Parisi (Eds.) New York, Alan R. Liss, Inc. (In press).

Goldberger, A. S. 1978. Models and Methods in the I.Q. Debate, Part I. (Revised). Social Science Research Institute Workshop Paper 7801, p. F9. Madison, University of Wisconsin Press.

Harvald, B., and M. Hauge. 1963. Heredity of cancer elucidated by a study of unselected twins. J.A.M.A. 186:749–753.

Haseman, J. K. 1970. The Genetic Analysis of Quantitative Traits Using Twin and Sib Data, Ph.D. Thesis, pp. 1–136. Chapel Hill, University of North Carolina Press.

Haseman, J. K., and R. C. Elston. 1970. The estimation of genetic variance from twin data. Behav. Genet. 1:11–19.

Holt, S. B. 1968. The Genetics of Dermal Ridges. Springfield, Charles C Thomas.

Holzinger, K. J. 1929. The relative effect of nature and nurture influences on twin differences. J. Educ. Psychol. 20:241–248.

Hrubec, Z., and J. V. Neel. 1978. National Academy of Sciences–National Research Council Twin Registry: Ten Years of Operation. In Progress in Clinical and Biological Research: Twin Studies, Nance, W. E., G. Allen, and P. Parisi (Eds.), Part B, pp. 153–172. New York, Alan R. Liss, Inc.

Iagolnitzer, R. 1978. Component Pair Analysis: A Multivariate Approach to Twin Data with Application to Dermatoglyphics. In Progress in Clinical and Biological Research: Twin Studies, Nance, W. E., G. Allen, and P. Parisi (Eds.), Part C, pp. 211–222. New York, Alan R. Liss, Inc.

Jablon, S., J. V. Neel, H. Gershowitz, and G. F. Atkinson, 1967. The NAS–NRC twin panel: methods of construction of the panel, zygosity diagnosis, and proposed use. Am. J. Hum. Genet. 19:133–161.

Jensen, A. R. 1967. Estimation of the limits of heritability of traits by comparison of monozygotic and dizygotic twins. Proc. Nat. Acad. Sci. 58:149–156.

Jinks, J. L., and P. L. Broadhurst. 1963. Diallel analysis of litter size and body weight in rats. Heredity (Lond.) 18:319–336.

Kaprio, J., S. Sarna, M. Koskenvuo, and J. Rantosalo. 1978. The Finnish Twin Registry: Formation and Compilation, Questionnaire Study, Zygosity Determination Procedures and Research Program. In Progress in Clinical Biological Research: Twin Studies, Nance, W. E., G. Allen, and P. Parisi (Eds.), Part B, pp. 179–184. New York, Alan R. Liss, Inc.

Kempthorne, O. 1954. The correlations between relatives in a random mating population. Proc. R. Soc. Lond. (Biol.). 143:103–113.

Kempthorne, O. 1978. Logical, epistemological and statistical aspects of nature-nurture data interpretation. Biometrics 34:1–23, 1978.

Kringlen, E. 1978. Norwegian Twin Registers. In Progress in Clinical and Biological Research: Twin Studies, Nance, W. E., G. Allen, and P. Parisi (Eds.), Part B, pp. 185–188. New York, Alan R. Liss, Inc.

Lange, K. L., J. Westlake, and M. A. Spence. 1976. Extensions to pedigree analysis. III. Variance components by the scoring method. Ann. Hum. Genet. 39(4):485–491.

Lewontin, R. C. 1974. The analysis of variance and the analysis of causes. Am. J. Hum. Genet. 26:400–401.

Lubchenco, L. O., C. Hansman, M. Dressler, and E. Boyd. 1963. Intrauterine growth as estimated from liveborn birth-weight data at 24 to 42 weeks of gestation. Pediatrics 32:793–800.

MacGillivray, I., P. P. S. Nylander, and G. Corney. 1975. Human Multiple Reproduction, pp. 1–238. Philadelphia, W. B. Saunders Company.

Malécot, G. 1948. Les Mathématiques de l'Hérédité. Paris, Masson et Cie.

Martin, H. G., and L. J. Eaves. 1977. The genetical analysis of covariance structure. Heredity (Lond.) 38:79–96.

Mather, K., and J. L. Jinks. 1977. Introduction to Biometrical Genetics, pp.1–231. Ithaca, Cornell University Press.

McIndoe, A. H., and A. Franceschetti. 1949. Medico-legal identification with skin homografts. Brit. J. Plast. Surg. 2:283.

Mendel, G. 1866. Versuche über pflanzen-hybriden. Berh. Natarf. Verein. Brünn. 4:3–47.

Miller, J. Z., and W. E. Nance. 1977. Diagnosis of twin zygosity by dermatoglyphics. J.A.M.A. 237:2718–2719.

Morton, N. E. 1955. The inheritance of human birth weight. Ann. Hum. Genet. 20:125–134.

Morton, N. E. 1978. Discussion. In Genetic Epidemiology. Morton, N. E., and C. S. Chung (Eds.), New York, Academic Press, pp. 121–128.

Nakata, M., P. L. Yu, W. B. Davis, and W. E. Nance. 1974. Genetic determinants of cranio-facial morphology: a twin study. Ann. Hum. Genet. 37:431–443.

Nance, W. E. 1977. The Use of Twins in Clinical Research. In Birth Defects: Original Article Series, Bergsma, D. (Ed.), Vol. 13:6, pp. 19–44. White Plains, The National Foundation.

Nance, W. E. 1979. A Note on Assortative Mating and Maternal Effects. In The Genetic Analysis of Common Diseases: Applications to Predictive Factors in Coronary Heart Disease, Sing, C. F. and Skolnick, M. (Eds.). New York, Alan R. Liss, Inc. (In press).

Nance, W. E., G. Allen, and P. Parisi (Eds.). 1978. Progress in Clinical and Biological Research: Twin Studies, Part A, pp. 1–253; Part B, pp. 1–203, Part C, pp. 1–287. New York, Alan R. Liss, Inc.

Nance, W. E., and L. A. Corey. 1976. Genetic models for the analysis of data from the families of identical twins. Genetics 83:811–826.

Nance, W. E., L. A. Corey, and J. A. Boughman. 1978b. Monozygotic Twin Kinships: A New Design for Genetic Epidemiologic Research. In Genetic Epidemiology, Morton, N. E., and C. S. Chung (Eds.), pp. 87–132. New York, Academic Press.

Nance, W. E., M. Nakata, R. D. Paul, and P. L. Yu. 1974. The Use of Twin Studies in the Analysis of Phenotypic Traits in Man. In Congenital Malformations: New Directions in Research, Janerich, D. T., R. G. Skaldo, and I. H. Porter (Eds.), pp. 23–49. New York, Academic Press.

Nichols, J. W., W. J. Jenkins, and W. L. Marsh. 1957. Case of blood chimerism. Brit. Med. J. 1:1458.

Ounsted, M. 1972. Gender and Intrauterine Growth. In Genetic Differences: Ontogeny and Significance, Ounsted, C., and D. C. Taylor (Eds.), pp. 177–201. Edinburgh, Churchill Livingstone.

Potter, R. H., W. E. Nance, P. L. Yu, and W. B. Davis. 1976. A twin study of dental dimension. II. Independent genetic determinants. Am. J. Phys. Anthropol. 44(3):397–412.

Price, B. 1950. Primary biases in twin studies. Am. J. Hum. Genet. 2:293–352.

Rao, D. C., and N. E. Morton, 1978. IQ as a paradigm in genetic epidemiology. In Genetic Epidemiology, Morton, N. E., and C. S. Chung (Eds.). New York, Academic Press, pp. 145–181.

Rao, D. C., N. E. Morton, and S. Yee. 1976. Resolution of cultural and biological inheritance by path analysis. Am. J. Hum. Genet. 28:228–242.

Rhine, S. A., and W. E. Nance. 1976. Familial twinning: a case for superfetation in man. Acta Genet. Med. Gemellol. (Roma) 25:66–69.

Rich, R. L., L. A. Corey, and W. E. Nance. 1978. Genetic Analysis of Variance in Uric Acid Levels in Man. In Progress in Clinical and Biological Research: Twin Studies, Nance, W. E., G. Allen, and P. Parisi (Eds.), Part C, pp. 187–192. New York, Alan R. Liss, Inc.

Robson, E. B. 1955. Birth weight in cousins. Ann. Hum. Genet. 19:262–268.

Robson, E. B. 1954. A Study of Human Birth Weight, Ph.D. Thesis, London, University College.

Sackett, D. L. 1975. Blood Pressure Studies in Spouses. In Epidemiology and Control of Hypertension, Paul, O. (Ed.), pp. 21–39. New York, Symposia Specialists.

Scrimgeour, J. B., and T. G. Baker. 1974. A possible cause of superfetation in man. J. Reprod. Fertil. 36:69–73.

Smith, D. W. 1977. Growth and Its Disorders: Basics and Standards, Approach and Classifications, Growth Excess Disorders, Obesity, pp. 1–155. Philadelphia, W. B. Saunders Company.

Snedecor, G. W. 1956. Statistical Methods, 5th Ed., pp. 271–275. Ames, Iowa State University Press.

Strong, S. J., and G. Corney. 1967. The Placenta in Twin Pregnancy, pp. 1–134. New York, Pergamon Press.

Tanaka, K. 1977. Genetic effects of maternal inbreeding in man on congenital abnormality, mental defect, infertility and prenatal death. Jpn. J. Hum. Genet. 22:55–71.

Vandenberg, S. G. 1965. Multivariate Analysis of Twin Differences. In Methods and Goals in Human Behavior Genetics, Vandenberg, S. G. (Ed.), pp. 29–44. New York, Academic Press.

VanDyke, D. L., C. G. Palmer, W. E. Nance, and P. L. Yu. 1977. Chromosome polymorphism and twin zygosity. Am. J. Genet. 29:431–447.

Vesell, E. S. 1973. Advances in pharmacogenetics. Prog. Med. Genet. 9:291–367.

Walton, A., and J. Hammond. 1938. The maternal effects on growth and conformation in Shire Horse, Shetland pony crosses. Proc. Roy. Soc. Brit. 125:311–335.

Zazzo, R. 1978. Genesis and Peculiarities of the Personality of Twins. In Progress in Clinical and Biological Research: Twin Studies, Nance, W. E., G. Allen, and P. Parisi (Eds.), Part A, pp. 1–12. New York, Alan R. Liss, Inc.

3

The Immunogenetics of Sexual Development*

STEPHEN S. WACHTEL

Memorial Sloan-Kettering Cancer Center, New York, New York 10021

SUSUMO OHNO

City of Hope National Medical Center, Duarte, California 91010

*Supported in part by grants from the NIH: AF 00042, AI 11982, CA 08748, HD 00171, HD 10065, and a contract: CB 33907.

A HORMONE-LIKE ROLE OF H-Y ANTIGEN
XX/XY GONADS
    The Ontogenetic Strategy of Competitive Displacement
THE MAJOR HISTOCOMPATIBILITY COMPLEX (MHC) AND
ORGANOGENESIS
CELL LINEAGE ANTIGENS IN GONADAL DIFFERENTIATION
SUMMARY

INTRODUCTION

In 1955, Eichwald and Silmser noted that female C57BL mice reject skin grafts from males of the same highly inbred strain. These intrastrain male grafts were rejected slowly (in comparison with grafts from major histocompatibility complex (MHC)-incompatible donors, for example). For this reason, the reaction was attributed to the presence of a "weak" transplantation antigen, determined in this case by a "minor" histocompatibility locus on the Y chromosome. The locus became known as the H-Y (histocompatibility-Y) gene, and the antigen became known as the H-Y antigen (reviewed in Gasser and Silvers, 1972).

It was a limitation of transplantation biology that such a weak male-specific antigen could be studied only within inbred strains — i.e., genetically homogeneous populations developed by repeated generations of brother-sister mating. Thus, the demonstration of sex-specific transplantation antigens was confined to those species in which inbred strains were available (reviewed in Silvers and Wachtel, 1977). The study of H-Y antigen was released from the technologic confines of transplantation biology by Ellen Goldberg (1971), who found that male-grafted female mice produce antibody (H-Y antibody) that is cytotoxic for mouse sperm (and male epidermal cells [Scheid et al., 1972].) Shortly thereafter, Gloria Koo, of our laboratory, developed a mixed hemadsorption-hybrid antibody (MHA.HA) assay, in which mouse sperm or male epidermal cells were exposed to H-Y antiserum and were then labeled with a visual marker such as tobacco mosaic virus (TMV) (Koo et al., 1973) or sheep red blood cells (SRBC) (Koo et al., 1977a). Labeling was accomplished by using a rabbit synthetic hybrid antibody with two binding specificities: mouse immunoglobulin (H-Y antibody) on one arm and a label (e.g., SRBC) on the other arm.

Sperm and male epidermal cells were used because other cell types are not susceptible to H-Y antiserum-mediated lysis in the cytotoxicity test, and, for technical reasons, they are unsatisfactory targets in the MHA.HA test. Yet, H-Y antigen is present in perhaps all tissues of the male mouse (Gasser and Silvers, 1972). Its presence may be determined in any tissue (e.g., blood) by measuring the ability of cells from that tissue to "absorb" H-Y antibodies, thereby limiting the reactivity of H-Y antiserum with target cells in both the cytotoxicity and MHA.HA tests (Fig. 1).

The sperm and epidermal cytotoxicity test and the MHA.HA test proved to be valuable although difficult techniques, for they enabled us to study the expression of H-Y antigen in noninbred

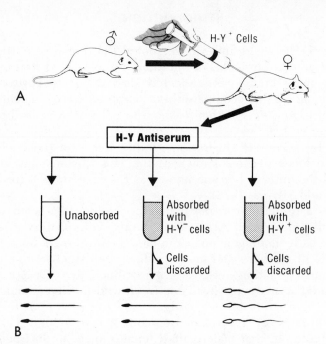

Figure 1. *A*, Preparation of H-Y antibody. Injection of male cells into female mice evokes production of H-Y antiserum. This contains H-Y antibodies that mediate killing of target cells (e.g., sperm) in the cytotoxicity test and labeling of target cells in the MHA.HA test. *B*, Absorption of H-Y antibody. Test cells are suspended in aliquots of H-Y antiserum. If these cells possess H-Y antigen on their membranes, they specifically remove H-Y antibodies from the serum, which then loses its ability to react with target cells. (See Wachtel (1977) for more detailed discussion of serological methods; see Tokuda et al. (1977) and Goldberg et al. (1978) for description of new techniques that demonstrate H-Y antigen on, respectively, mouse and human lymphocytes with *Staphylococcus aureus* marker.)

species such as the human. This led to the proposition that H-Y antigen functions in the primary determination of sex. In the following discussion, we shall review recent studies that substantiate this proposition and shed light on the genetics and modus operandi of this cell membrane component.

PHYLOGENETIC CONSERVATION OF H-Y ANTIGEN: A ROLE IN PRIMARY SEX DETERMINATION

Shortly after the demonstration by Silvers and Yang (1973) that male rat cells sensitize female mice to skin grafts from male mice of the same highly inbred strain, we noted that male rat cells also absorb mouse H-Y antibody. In subsequent studies, male cells but not female cells absorbed mouse H-Y antibody in mammalian species as divergent as the human (Wachtel et al., 1974), the mole vole (Nagai and Ohno, 1977), and the dog (Selden and Wachtel, 1977). However, mouse H-Y antibody is exquisitely specific for mouse H-Y antigen. This means that in each of these mammalian species, and perhaps in all mammalian species, male cells possess a plasma membrane component that is either identical to or highly cross-reactive with mouse H-Y antigen. The discovery that conservation of H-Y structure extended beyond mammals was even more striking. In avians, the sex-determining mechanism is reversed. It is the female that is the heterogametic sex (XY, or "ZW" as it is called in avians). It is the female whose cells bear sex-specific ("H-W") antigen (Gilmour, 1967), and it is the female whose cells absorb mouse H-Y antibody (Wachtel et al., 1975b).

In teleosts and amphibians, both the male scheme of heterogamety (XX/XY) and the female scheme (ZZ/ZW) operate side-by-side. Consider, for example, the common American leopard frog, *Rana pipiens*, which is a male-heterogametic species, and the South African clawed toad, *Xenopus laevis*, which is a female-heterogametic species: In both species H-Y antigen occurs in the heterogametic sex (Wachtel et al., 1975b). Thus, it would appear that mammals, the inheritors of male heterogamety, have also inherited the male-specific mode of H-Y antigen expression, whereas avians, the inheritors of female heterogamety, have inherited the female-specific mode of H-W antigen expression.

An important lesson of recent years is that genes of fundamental importance seldom undergo evolutionary change with respect to the active sites of the proteins for which they code. From this perspective, conservation of H-Y structure through several hundred million years of evolution must signify persistence of a vital function, and the invariable association of H-Y antigen with the Y (or W) chromosome must signify that the function is sex related.

In mammals, the inherent tendency of the embryo is to differentiate as a female. For example, embryos with the XO sex chromosomal constitution develop ovaries, and castrated embryos become phenotypic females irrespective of their gonadal sex (Jost, 1970). The mammalian Y chromosome exerts its male-determining influence against this inherent tendency by directing the indifferent embryonic gonad to organize a testis. The pivotal role of the Y chromosome is limited to the induction of the male gonad; subsequent masculinization of the embryo is the function of newly secreted androgens to which both male and female cells can respond. Indeed, androgen responsiveness is determined by the *Tfm* locus, which is situated on the X chromosome, and not by a gene on the Y chromosome (Lyon and Hawkes, 1970). In the special case of mutationally induced androgen unresponsiveness known as the testicular feminization syndrome (TFS) (see Morris, 1953), the gonads of the XY embryo become testes, and the testes secrete androgens. Yet, there is no response, and further differentiation is female (Gehring et al., 1971 [in mice]; Bardin et al., 1973 [in rats]; Keenan et al., 1974 [in humans]).

These considerations led us to conclude that the phylogenetically conserved plasma membrane component that is recognized serologically as H-Y antigen is in reality the product of the mammalian testis-determining gene (Wachtel et al., 1975c) (Fig. 2). An inevitable corollary is that this same cell surface component is ovary-inducing in female-heterogametic species.

Our hypothesis regarding the sex-determining role of H-Y (H-W) antigen predicted that expression of this cell surface component should always be associated with development of at least the rudimentary heterogametic gonad, irrespective of apparent karyotype or phenotypic sex. This prediction has allowed us to test our proposal by studying H-Y antigen expression in exceptional

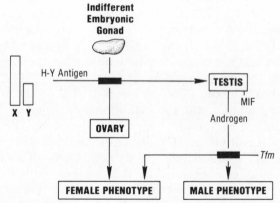

Figure 2. Mammalian sex determination. In normal XX embryos the indifferent embryonic gonad becomes an ovary, and further development is female. In XY embryos H-Y antigen blocks female development by inducing the gonad to differentiate as a testis. Sertoli cells of the newly formed testis secret müllerian inhibition factor (MIF), which prevents differentiation of müllerian derivatives (fallopian tubes, uterus, and cephalad portion of the vagina). Testicular Leydig cells secrete testosterone, which induces differentiation of wolffian derivatives (vasa deferentia, seminal vesicles, and epididymides). Some of the testosterone is converted enzymatically into dihydrotestosterone; this induces orderly differentiation of the penis and scrotum in the same tissues that would otherwise give rise to the clitoris, labia minora, and labia majora. The *Tfm* mutation blocks responsiveness to androgen; this leads to development of the female phenotype, but does not affect müllerian duct regression, in the H-Y+ chromosomal male.

mammalian individuals whose gonadal sex and chromosomal (or phenotypic) sex did not coincide. In every case, our expectation was fulfilled. Thus, XX males of the mouse (Bennett et al., 1977) and human (Wachtel et al., 1976a) were typed H-Y antigen positive, fertile XY females of the wood lemming were typed H-Y antigen negative (Wachtel et al., 1976b), and XY female mice and humans exhibiting the testicular feminization syndrome were typed H-Y antigen positive, despite total absence of extragonadal male development (Bennett et al., 1975; Koo et al., 1977c). Moreover, H-Y antigen was prominent in the testis-like gonads of bovine freemartin embryos, even though these gonads consisted almost entirely of XX cells (Ohno et al., 1976).

MAPPING THE LOCUS OF THE H-Y GENE ON THE Y CHROMOSOME

The observations presented are all perfectly consistent with the proposed sex-determining role of H-Y antigen, but the presence of H-Y antigen in XX males and its absence in XY females raise questions about the linkage of H-Y genes and the putative sex-determining role of the mammalian Y chromosome. Is it possible that the testis-determining (H-Y) gene normally resides on an autosome or X chromosome (Erickson, 1977)?

Early experiments relating to the location of H-Y genes were inconclusive, but they indicated a correlation between the expression of H-Y antigen and the presence of the Y chromosome. Thus, H-Y antigen was present in the spleen cells of XXY male mice, but it was absent from the spleen cells of XO female mice (Welshons and Russell, 1959) and from mouse testicular teratoma cells that had lost their Y chromosome (Bunker, 1966). Retention of the H-Y antigen positive cellular phenotype by subjects with the testicular feminization syndrome also argues in favor of a Y-chromosomal locus for H-Y genes. If the genes were autosomal or X-linked, they would be present in females, and they would require a male hormonal environment for their male-specific operation. However, we have already seen that H-Y antigen persists in the TFS despite insensitivity to androgen.

Convincing evidence for Y-situated H-Y genes was provided by the demonstration of excess H-Y antigen in the cells of human males with two Y chromosomes (48,XXYY and 47,XYY) (Wachtel et al., 1975c). The exact position of the H-Y genes remained to be determined, however. As a first step in more precise localization, we initiated a study of H-Y antigen in subjects exhibiting various Y-chromosomal structural abnormalities and deletions. By correlating expression or nonexpression of H-Y antigen with presence or absence of particular portions of the Y chromosome, Koo et al. (1977b) identified two H-Y loci — one on the short arm in 16 patients, and one on the long arm in at least 1 patient. Both loci were mapped near the Y centromere (Fig. 3). The long arm locus was assigned on the basis of a Y-to-X translocation in an H-Y antigen positive phenotypic female with a karyotype of 46,X,der(X)t(X;Y). Almost the entire long arm (Yq) appeared to have been transferred in the cells of this patient (Case 8, Table 1). Chromosome banding techniques (C banding and silver staining) indicated that the centromeric portion of the translocation chromosome was derived from the X chromosome, not the Y. A reciprocal translocation chromosome was not identified. In another female, with Turner's syndrome and a karyotype of 46,X,i(Yq), the short arm of the Y chromosome was absent, and there was an isochromosome (duplication) of the long arm, but in this instance, H-Y antigen was absent (Case 5, Table 1). This means that the long arm H-Y locus does not occur in all individuals; if it did, we would have expected (on the basis of our previous experience with XXYY and XYY males) an *excess* of H-Y antigen in the cells of this patient.

These data are consistent with the proposed sex-determining role of H-Y antigen, as the loci mapped correspond to male-determining regions that have been identified in earlier studies — on the short arm and on the long arm of the human Y chromosome (reviewed by Simpson, 1975). The data do not rule out the possibility of both long and short arm loci in some individuals nor do they preclude the likelihood of multiple copies of the H-Y gene clustered near or around the Y centromere (see later discussion).

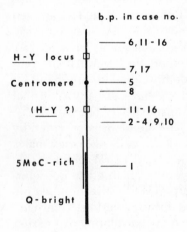

Figure 3. Cytogenetic map of the human Y chromosome, showing approximate short arm H-Y locus based on study of H-Y antigen in most of the 17 cases listed in Table 1, and approximate long arm H-Y locus based on H-Y antigen expression in Case 8. Approximate breakpoint (b.p.) in each case is indicated by line to right of "chromosome." Positions of centromere, 5-methylcytosine-rich region, and quinacrine-bright region are indicated to left. (From Koo, G. C. et al. 1977. Mapping the locus of the *H-Y* gene on the human Y chromosome. Science 198:940–942. Copyright 1977 by the American Association for the Advancement of Science.)

Table 1. Karyotype, Expression of H-Y Antigen, and Appearance of Gonads in Subjects with Abnormal Y Chromosome*

Case No.	Karyotype	H-Y Antigen	Sex	Gonads
1	46,X,Yq−	+	Male	testes
2	45,X/46,X,der(Y)t(Y;?)	+	Male, 1° hypospadias	testes
3	45,X/46,X,der(Y)t(Y;?)	+	Intersex	undifferentiated
4	45,X/46,X,der(Y)t(Y;?)	+	Female	streaks
5	46,X,i(Yq)	−	Female Turner	streaks
6	46,X,dup(Yq)	−	Female Turner	?
7	45,X/45,X,der(22)t(22;Y)	+	Male	testes
8	46,X,der(X)t(X;Y)	+	Female	?
9	45,X/46,X,Yq−	+	Male, 4° hypospadias	testes
10	45,X/46,X,Y minute	+	Female Turner	?
11	46,X,r(Y)	+	Male	testes
12	45,X/46,X,r(Y)	+	Male	testis, right, ? left
13	45,X/46,X,r(Y)	+	Intersex	?
14	45,X/46,X,r(Y)	+	Intersex	abdominal testes
15	45,X/46,X,r(Y)	+	Female Turner	?
16	45,X/46,X,r(Y)	+	Female Turner	?
17	45,X/46,X,r(X or Y)	−	Female Turner	?

*From Koo, G. C. et al. 1977. Mapping the locus of the *H-Y* gene on the human Y chromosome. Science 198:940–942. Copyright 1977 by the American Association for the Advancement of Science. (See Figure 3.)

Yq−, deletion of long arm (q) of Y chromosome; 45,X/46,X, etc., mosaic karyotypes: one cell line having 45 chromosomes including the X, another having 46 chromosomes including the X and . . .; der(Y)t(Y;?), derivative of Y translocation involving Y and unknown chromosome; i(Yq), isochromosome of long arm of Y chromosome; dup(Yq), duplication involving Yq; (22), autosome No. 22; r(Y), ring chromosome (of Y-chromosomal origin).

THE Y-CHROMOSOMAL H-Y GENES ARE STRUCTURAL

In the context of our foregoing discussion the question is raised whether H-Y loci that are situated on the Y chromosome are structural genes that determine the sequence of residues (amino acids?) in the H-Y molecule or regulatory genes that may activate or modify the function of H-Y structural elements on other chromosomes. Almost certainly, the H-Y loci situated on the Y chromosome are structural; increased expression of H-Y antigen in the cells of males with two Y chromosomes is not easily reconciled with the presence of an excess number of activating genes unless what we recognize serologically as H-Y antigen is in reality a set of discrete antigenic specificities, each coded by a discrete structural gene and activated by a specific regulator.

It can be determined unambiguously whether the Y-chromosomal H-Y genes are structural or regulatory by crossing two highly inbred stains, "AA" and "BB," and then injecting cells or grafting skin from a male of the maternal strain to a male of the F_1 hybrid generation:

$$X^A Y^A \rightarrow X^A Y^B$$

Since the only known incompatibility in this donor-host combination involves the disparate origin of the two Y chromosomes, antibody formation or graft rejection (Hildemann et al., 1970 [in the mouse]; Mullen and Hildemann, 1972 [in the rat]) must indicate not only that there are alleles of the H-Y structural locus but also that these alleles are located on the Y chromosome.

H-Y allelism superimposed against a background of serologic cross-reactivity suggests that H-Y is a complex system comprising both public and private specificities (Wachtel, 1977). Nevertheless, H-Y polymorphism is not demonstrable serologically so far, and this brings us to the intriguing possibility that serologically detectable H-Y antigen is not the same as H-Y transplantation antigen (Melvold et al., 1977).

THE H-Y GENE EXISTS IN MULTIPLE COPIES: EVIDENCE IN *Sxr* MICE

Perhaps the best-known example of male development in conjunction with a female sex chromosome constitution is the XX male mouse, sex-reversed by the autosomal dominant gene *Sxr* (Cattanach et al., 1971). Thus, *Sxr* determines the expression of H-Y antigen and the formation of testes, but to date there is no evidence of an intact or even partial Y chromosome in the cells of *Sxr* males. Accordingly, it has been suggested that *Sxr* might represent a constitutive mutation of an autosomal testis-determining gene, or alternatively, mutational acquisition of Y-chromosomal function by an autosomal locus (see Cattanach, 1975).

If, as we have indicated in the previous section, the testis-determining H-Y gene is normally situated on the Y chromosome, *Sxr* must represent a Y-to-autosome translocation too small to be detected by current cytologic methods. However, this view introduces new complications. There is a dominant autosomal gene *P* (*"polled"*) that causes hornlessness in goats without affecting sex differentiation. In the homozygous state, however, this gene causes the development of testis. Thus, chromosomal female goats (XX)

that are homozygous for *polled (P/P)* have testes and exhibit varying degrees of masculinity culminating in nearly normal male external genitalia (Hamerton et al., 1969). If it is a Y-to-autosome translocation that gives rise to an autosomal gene that is able to organize
testes in the absence of the Y chromosome, why is it that such a
gene behaves as a dominant in the mouse *(Sxr)* and as a recessive in
the goat *(P)*?

Moreover, XX males that are sex-reversed by *Sxr* are sterile,
so that the *Sxr* gene can be transmitted only by *Sxr*,XY carrier
males and only with the Y chromosome that was involved in the
original translocation event. If *Sxr* originated as a Y-to-autosome
translocation, why is it that this Y chromosome has retained its
testis-determining ability even after "giving away" its testis-
determining gene? To resolve this difficulty, Cattanach et al. (1971),
who first described the *Sxr* mutant, suggested that *Sxr* may have
arisen as a *chromatid* and not as a chromosome translocation. However, there is another explanation.

The grossly heteromorphic X and Y sex chromosomes of mammals must have evolved from a homomorphic and essentially homologous pair of chromosomes. This differentiation was accomplished
exclusively at the expense of the Y chromosome, which underwent
genetic degeneration to become a specialized testis-determiner,
while the X chromosome remained invariant. It has been argued
that as a result of this specialization, the mammalian Y chromosome
came to contain the testis-determining gene in multiple copies
(Ohno, 1967). Once this multiple copy hypothesis is introduced, it
is easy to reconcile Y-linkage of testis-determining H-Y genes with the
Y-to-autosome origin of *Sxr* in mice and the *P* in goats. Thus, translocation of a particular number of H-Y gene copies could result in both
transfer and retention of testis-determining function and, depending
on whether or not the number of copies translocated falls below a critical lower threshold, the newly arisen autosomal testis-determining
locus could behave either in a dominant manner as in the mouse or in
a recessive manner as in the goat (Fig. 4, and see Wachtel et al., 1978).

We have now discussed three hypotheses regarding the normal
locus of the H-Y structural gene and the origin of *Sxr*. Each of these
hypotheses makes distinct predictions concerning the amount of H-Y
antigen to be found in the males of an *Sxr* mutant stock: the noncarrier male, XY; the fertile carrier male, *Sxr*,XY; and the sterile sex-
reversed male, *Sxr*,XX. These hypotheses are schematically illustrated
in Figure 5.

The Y-linked Single Copy Hypothesis (Fig. 5A). As previously
noted, this scheme involves a transfer of one of the two chromatids

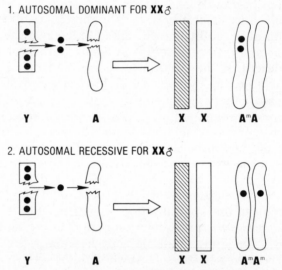

Figure 4. Translocation of a critical minimum (e.g., two fifths) of H-Y gene copies (small dark circles) from Y chromosome to autosome (A) leads to XX male condition that is transmitted as an autosomal dominant trait. Translocation of subcritical minimum (e.g., one fifth) of H-Y gene copies does not significantly alter female differentiation in XX subjects. In this case two such mutant autosomes (A^m), one from the mother (XXAA^m) and one from the father (XYAA^m), must combine in XX zygote to generate sufficient H-Y antigen for testicular differentiation in XX male condition that is inherited as a recessive trait.

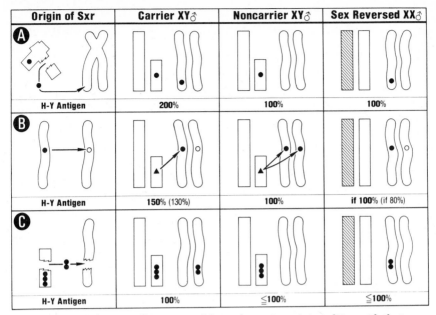

Origin of Sxr	Carrier XY♂	Noncarrier XY♂	Sex Reversed XX♂
Ⓐ			
H-Y Antigen	200%	100%	100%
Ⓑ			
H-Y Antigen	150% (130%)	100%	if 100% (if 80%)
Ⓒ			
H-Y Antigen	100%	≤100%	≤100%

Figure 5. Schematic illustration of three alternative origins of *Sxr*, with their predictable consequences regarding H-Y antigen levels (percent shown) in carrier XY males, noncarrier XY males, and sex-reversed XX males. The X chromosome is depicted as a long rectangle, the Y is a short rectangle, and the relevant autosomes are vermiform.

A. Y-linked single copy hypothesis. Duplication and transfer of H-Y gene (dark circle) during chromatid phase. Inheritance of autosomal duplicate causes sex reversal of XX embryo.

B. Autosomally linked single copy hpothesis. Autosomal H-Y gene is present in both males and females but is normally under control of Y-chromosome activator gene (triangle). When autosomal H-Y gene undergoes constitutive mutation (white circle), normal (regulated) production of H-Y antigen coexists with constitutive production in carrier male.

C. Y-linked multiple copy hypothesis. "Normal male level" of H-Y antigen is produced in carrier XY males. Assuming that H-Y genes are distributed about evenly between the Y chromosome and the translocation autosome, noncarrier XY males and sex-reversed XX males show equal (if reduced) expression of H-Y antigen.

of both the Y chromosome and the relevant autosome. According to this scheme, carrier males are the equivalent of XYY males in that they have a double "dose" of the H-Y gene.

Autosomally Inherited Single Copy Hypothesis (Fig. 5B). If this scheme were correct, *Sxr* would be a constitutive mutation of a pre-existing H-Y locus, and the cells of sex-reversed males should produce the single gene constitutive level of H-Y antigen. Unless this constitutive level were as low as 50 percent of the level of H-Y antigen expression found in normal males, one should expect to find considerably more antigen in carrier XY males than in noncarrier XY males. Thus, carrier males would express half the normal level plus the constitutive level (e.g., 130 percent if the constitutive level were 80 percent and 150 percent if the constitutive level were 100 percent).

The Y-linked Multiple Copy Hypothesis (Fig. 5C). In sharp contrast to the hypotheses just discussed, this hypothesis predicts that only carrier XY males possess the original number of H-Y gene copies and that they are now divided between the Y chromosome and an autosome. The fact that both the Y chromosome and *Sxr* of this stock still demonstrate full testis-determining capacity indicates that, if this scheme is correct, the mutational event that divided the original number of gene copies situated on the Y chromosome resulted in a more or less even distribution between the Y chromosome and the relevant autosome.

Our preliminary data, showing decreased expression of H-Y antigen in *Sxr* XX males and "normal" expression in *Sxr* XY carrier males, are consistent with the model depicted in the third scheme. Thus, we infer that under normal circumstances, there are multiple copies of the testis-determining H-Y gene on the Y chromosome — not only in the mouse but in the other mammalian species as well (see Bennett et al., 1977).

It is perhaps appropriate to mention here that repeated DNA sequences that are specific for the human Y chromosome have recently been identified (Cooke, 1976). Yet, this family of DNA has undergone very rapid evolutionary changes, whereas the H-Y gene has been highly conserved. Moreover, analysis of Y chromosome–specific reiterated DNA in patients with abnormal Y chromosomes and comparison with H-Y antigen expression in these patients indicated no relationship between these DNA sequences and H-Y genes (Kunkel et al., 1977). In contrast, the W chromosome–specific repeated DNA sequences identified in snakes and birds may be relevant to our present discussion. In view of their phylogenetic conservation, these sequences may correspond to multiple copies of the putative ovary-determining H-W gene (Singh et al., 1977).

ABNORMAL INHERITANCE OF H-Y GENES: XX SEX REVERSAL AND XX TRUE HERMAPHRODITISM

Human males with a female karyotype (46,XX) were first reported in 1964. Although the condition is relatively uncommon, 45 cases were chronicled by de la Chapelle in 1972, and several other cases have been discovered subsequently (reviewed in Simpson,

1976). Clinically, these males resemble patients with Klinefelter's syndrome (XXY). Like sex-reversed XX male mice, human XX males have small, characteristically aspermatogenic testes; however, immature spermatogonia have been observed. Although most human XX males represent a sporadic occurrence of this condition, familial occurrence is known (see Nicolis et al., 1972 and de la Chapelle et al., 1977), and it is perhaps noteworthy that XX males have also been reported in the same family as XX true hermaphrodites i.e., individuals possessing both ovarian and testicular tissue (Berger et al., 1970; Kasdan et al., 1973).

Theories concerned with the etiology of human XX male syndrome and XX true hermaphroditism generally propose the conservation of Y-chromosomal function — as a translocation, an undetected Y-bearing cell line (mosaicism), or a mutational acquisition of testis-determining ability by autosomal (or X-linked) genes. We have now studied white blood cells and cultured fibroblasts from 12 human XX males and 6 XX true hermaphrodites, and H-Y antigen was indeed present in every case. In a statistical analysis, cells from four XX males and three XX true hermaphrodites were found to absorb significantly less H-Y antibody than the same number of cells from normal XY males, indicating a decreased expression of H-Y antigen (Wachtel et al., 1976a). This could certainly imply Y-to-autosome (or Y-to-X) translocation of a subnormal quantity of H-Y gene copies (see Table 2 and Figures 4 and 5C), but the fact is that cytologic evidence for a Y-to-autosome translocation in human XX males is lacking. The phenomenon itself is known. Koo et al. (1976) have reported evidence for a Y-to-autosome translocation in the cells of a 45,X/45,X 22q+ male patient (H-Y antigen positive), a case that is perhaps analogous to the situation observed in the Sxr/XO male mouse (Cattanach et al., 1971).

In 1966, Ferguson-Smith suggested that the physical association of X and Y chromosomes during meiosis might facilitate the exchange of genetic material between them. A transfer of the critical testis (H-Y)-determining region from the Y to the X chromosome could thus account not only for XX males but also for XX true hermaphrodites. According to this scheme, the random inactivation of one X chromosome would leave the normal X chromosome functional in some cells (ovarian differentiation) and the X^Y functional in others (testicular differentiation). In support of Ferguson-Smith's proposal, a minute additional band has been observed on the short arm of one X chromosome in the cells of a human XX male (Fig. 6).

These studies do not rule out mutation or cryptic mosaicism as other possible causes of XX sex reversal in man. For example,

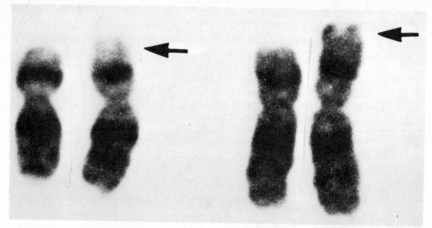

Figure 6. Y-X interchange? Arrows point to additional band identified on one X chromosome in two metaphase cells from human XX male. (From Wachtel, S. S. et al. 1976. Serological detection of a Y-linked gene in XX males and XY true hermaphrodites. N. Eng. J. Med. 255:750–754. Photo by O. J. Miller.)

Dosik et al. (1976) detected a single XXY cell among 201 XX lymphocytes from the blood of a phenotypic male. Characteristically, blood cells from the patient absorbed less H-Y antibody than the same number of blood cells from normal XY males, but it is open to question whether such a small minority of Y-bearing blood cells is detectable by current serologic means. Thus, it may be asked whether the reduced levels of H-Y antigen that are characteristic of the XX male syndrome and XX true hermaphroditism reflect, in general, the presence of a minority of Y-bearing cells, or, alternatively, a minority of translocated H-Y genes in XX cells. Also, it may be asked whether the small minority of Y-bearing blood cells in Dosik's patient represented a corresponding minority in the gonad and, indeed, whether H-Y typing of blood cells accurately reflects the karyotype of gonadal cells in any case.

Males with the XX karyotype occur frequently among certain breeds of dogs, notably the cocker spaniel (Haire, 1976). In the study of one cocker family by Selden and his colleagues (1978) histologic examination of the gonads taken from the XX *mother* of an XX male revealed prominent testicular tubules as well as mature ovarian follicles (Fig. 7). In other words, the mother was a true hermaphrodite. Cells from both the XX male and the XX hermaphrodite mother absorbed "normal" amounts of H-Y antiserum, indicating the presence of normal male levels of H-Y antigen. However, cells from the father of the true hermaphrodite (grandfather of the XX male) absorbed higher than normal amounts of H-Y antiserum,

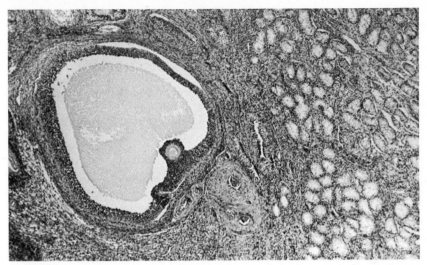

Figure 7. Photomicrograph of cross-section from canine ovotestis (magnification 84×). Note prominent Graafian follicle and testicular tubules separated by a zone of connective tissue. Spermatogenesis did not occur, but oogenesis was normal, and this dog functioned as a fertile female. (From Selden, J. R. et al. 1978. Genetic basis of XX male syndrome and XX true hermaphroditism: evidence in the dog. Science 201:644–646, 1978. Photo by Mark E. Haskins.)

indicating the presence of excess H-Y antigen (see Table 2). Although preliminary cytologic studies showed a normal male karyotype (78,XY) in the cells of the father, subsequent studies revealed the possibility of a Y-to-autosome translocation involving the entire Y chromosome in the cells of all three dogs — father, XX true hermaphrodite, and XX male pup.

Selden's observations are remarkable. Not only do they show that the XX male syndrome and XX true hermaphroditism are related conditions associated with abnormal inheritance of H-Y genes (in this case Y-to-autosome translocation), but they also confirm our earlier observation that excess H-Y antigen on the cell membrane is correlated with the presence of supernumerary H-Y genes in the nucleus. Moreover, Selden's study supports our contention that the H-Y genes situated on the Y chromosome are structural.

The point is that the father of the true hermaphrodite has sired normal 78,XY males in addition to the 78,XX (H-Y antigen positive) hermaphrodite. This signifies presence in his genome of normal H-Y genes on the Y chromosome and supernumerary H-Y genes on an autosome. If we assume that the Y-chromosomal H-Y genes are regulatory, the excess H-Y antigen in the cells of the father and the presence of testicular tissue in his XX true hermaphrodite

Table 2. Abnormal Inheritance of H-Y Genes

SEX CHROMOSOMES	SEX PHENOTYPE	H-Y PHENOTYPE	ETIOLOGY
		HUMAN	
XX	Male	±	Translocation
XX	True hermaphrodite	±	Translocation
XY	Male	±	H-Y gene loss
XY	Female (gonadal dysgenesis)	−	H-Y gene loss
		CANINE	
XY (father)	Male	++	Translocation
XX (mother)	True hermaphrodite	+	Translocation
XX (pup)	Male	+	Translocation

Human: XX male syndrome and XX true hermaphroditism, in man, associated with Y-to-autosome (or Y-to-X) translocation of threshold number of H-Y gene copies. XY female with gonadal dysgenesis, a reciprocal condition, results from the loss of a critical majority of H-Y gene copies. Normal ovaries fail to develop in the absence of second X chromosome. Another reciprocal condition, XY male with "moderate" gene loss and intermediate levels of H-Y antigen (±), has not been identified (see Figure 4).

Canine: Anomalous inheritance of "normal male" levels of H-Y antigen in Selden's cocker spaniel family. Excess H-Y antigen (++) in father of true hermaphrodite caused by presumptive Y-to-autosome translocation involving a second intact Y chromosome. Normal H-Y antigen phenotype (H-Y+) in true hermaphrodite "daughter" and her XX male pup results from the inheritance of translocation chromosome.

"daughter" would have to represent two abnormal events: (1) the duplication of H-Y structural genes and (2) the activation of these genes in the absence of a normal Y chromosome. Alternatively, if the Y-chromosomal H-Y genes are structural, a single event (viz. Y-to-autosome translocation) could account for both these conditions. (In this case we need not invoke a chromatid exchange as in *Sxr* sex reversal of the mouse. Because of the fertility of the hermaphrodite, new, intact Y chromosomes could be introduced into the cocker pedigree.)

FUNCTIONAL SEX REVERSAL IN NONMAMMALIAN VERTEBRATES

In lower vertebrates, sex reversal occurs in the absence of apparent chromosomal or genetic change. In the male-heterogametic Japanese cyprinodont fish *Oryzias latipes* ("Medaka"), the sex-determining locus is closely linked to one of the body color loci; X^rX^r white females and X^rY^R ruby-colored males can be distinguished at a glance. Exposure of the larvae to androgenic or estrogenic steroids readily causes sex reversal, producing X^rX^r white males and X^rY^R ruby-colored females, respectively — both of which are fertile. By mating ordinary X^rY^R males with sex-reversed X^rY^R females, one can obtain Y^RY^R males. When these males are mated with ordinary X^rX^r females, all of the progeny are X^rY^R ruby-colored males (Yamamoto, 1961).

Functional sex reversal is not limited to fish. In the South African clawed toad *Xenopus laevis,* addition of female steroid hormone to the water of developing tadpoles causes ZZ chromosomal male larvae to become females. Conversely, implantation of small testes causes ZW chromosomal female larvae to become males. When sex-reversed ZW males are mated with ordinary ZW females, WW females are produced, and these females can be sex-reversed to become functional males (Mikamo and Witschi, 1964).

In chickens and pheasants, surgical removal or accidental destruction (e.g., by shotgun pellets) of the left ovary often initiates testicular transformation of the right residual gonad in ZW hens. The result is a fertile, if impotent, cock, viz. the old English saying, "A whistling woman and a crowing hen are neither good for gods nor men."

We have said that H-Y antigen occurs in heterogametic ZW females (but not in homogametic ZZ males) of the clawed toad and chicken, and our preliminary observations now indicate its presence in XY males (but not in XX females) of the fish *Oryzias latipes.* Certainly, this implies that the H-Y structural locus is on the Y (or W) chromosome. Yet, the fact that it is possible to functionally reverse the sex of the homogametic XX (or ZZ) members of these species introduces a paradox: Either the H-Y structural locus is not restricted to the Y (W) chromosome, or H-Y antigen expression is not an essential feature in the sex-determining scheme of lower vertebrates. If H-Y antigen is critical to the differentiation of the heterogametic gonad, it would seem that in fish, in amphibians, and possibly in birds, members of both sexes retain at least the potential to produce H-Y antigen as well as the potential to suppress its production.

H-Y antigen expression is apparently free from this kind of regulation in the higher vertebrates. In the mouse, for example, H-Y antigen expression is not suppressed on fetal XY cells that are raised in a female hormonal environment (Wachtel et al., 1973b) nor is it induced in female cells following their transient sojourn in the male environment (Silvers et al., 1968; Polackova, 1969), but see Engelstein (1967). In addition, H-Y antigen expression is not induced in the cells of tolerant females bearing grafted testes (Weissman, 1973). In this context, it will be recalled that H-Y antigen occurs on the plasma membrane of perhaps all cell types of the male mouse. The assignment of a specific function in organogenesis to a plasma membrane component of all cells may seem rather unusual, but to direct a particular step in organogenesis, the relevant plasma membrane component must be present before commencement of that step. Indeed, in the ontogeny of the mouse, gonadal differentiation does not commence until the twelfth day of embryonic life (Peters, 1970). Yet H-Y antigen is detected 10 days earlier in male embryos of the eight-cell stage (Krco and Goldberg, 1976). Ubiquitous expression of H-Y antigen may thus be viewed as a mere reflection of its need for occurrence so early in development and its corresponding escape from the inducing and suppressing influences that are so obviously present in nonmammalian vertebrates. However, as the following section will show, H-Y structural genes of the mammal are not entirely free of regulation.

REGULATION OF H-Y STRUCTURAL GENES: AN X-LINKED ACTIVATOR

XY Gonadal Dysgenesis in Man

If the mammalian Y chromosome is male-determining (and all our experience implies it is), ovarian differentiation and subsequent female development in the presence of a Y chromosome must signify functional deletion of the male-determining portion of that Y chromosome. The absence of H-Y antigen from the cells of fertile XY females of the wood lemming *(Myopus schisticolor)* is a case in point (Wachtel et al., 1976b). In this rodent species, there is a skewed sex ratio with a preponderance of females; many embryos develop ovaries and mature as fertile females despite the presence of a normal male sex chromosome constitution (XY) (Fredga et al., 1976). If this skewing were due to the absence or mutation of Y-chromosomal H-Y genes, XY female wood lemmings could arise only from XY mothers. Yet, it is not the Y chromosome that is deficient in these animals. To the contrary, XY female wood lemmings do not transmit their Y chromosome; they produce only X-bearing eggs, and, in fact, the XY female (H-Y antigen negative) condition is inherited as an X-linked trait (Fredga et al., 1977).

These observations imply the existence of a regulatory element on the X chromosome — a gene that activates or modulates H-Y structural genes on the Y chromosome. In view of the extreme phylogenetic stability of the mammalian X chromosome (Ohno, 1967), corresponding regulatory elements probably exist in other mammalian species, such as the human. When these X-linked modulators become over-restraining due to mutation, the production of H-Y antigen is completely or almost completely suppressed (Fig. 8), and the result is the development of an XY female, which is fertile as in the wood lemming or sterile as in the human. Sterility in the human XY female is due to the apparent requirement of two X chromosomes to sustain normal ovarian development. XY subjects resemble XO subjects with respect to the number of X chromosomes, and whereas XO rodents are fertile females, XO humans develop the stigmata of Turner's syndrome, including undifferentiated (streak) gonads containing dense ovarian-like stroma but no oocytes (gonadal dysgenesis). Thus, the human analog of the XY female wood lemming condition should be an X-linked trait characterized by the suppression of H-Y antigen and the corresponding presence of undifferentiated gonads (postnatally). (The short stature and other somatic anomalies associated with Turner's syndrome need not be present in 46,XY gonadal dysgenesis because the human Y chromosome apparently contains genes that, in conjunction with similar genes on the X chromosome, obviate the development of these stigmata; see next section.)

Although often occurring as a spontaneous condition, XY gonadal dysgenesis is known in at least 15 human pedigrees (reviewed by Simpson, in press). In three of these, the mode of inheritance is consistent with presence of an X-linked mutant gene (Sternberg et al., 1968; Espiner et al., 1970; Simpson, in press).

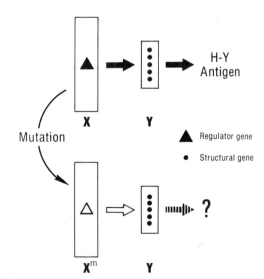

Figure 8. Regulator gene on mammalian X chromosome activates production of H-Y antigen by structural genes on the Y chromosome. After mutation of the regulator gene (white triangle), H-Y antigen production is suppressed or shut off, leading to development of XY female. Transmission of mutant X chromosome (X^m) by carrier females (XX^m) leads to heritable XY female condition.

H-Y GENE LOSS

An alternative mode of XY sex reversal could result from the actual physical loss of H-Y gene copies from the Y chromosome, e.g., as the reciprocal product of a Y-to-autosome translocation. In this condition (assuming noninheritance of the relevant autosome), H-Y antigen expression would be more or less deficient, depending on the number of H-Y gene copies lost, and gonadal development would range accordingly from undifferentiated streaks (in man) to almost normal testes (see Table 2).

A putative example of H-Y gene loss in human gonadal dysgenesis was provided in the recent study of a 46,XY phenotypic female (Rosenfeld et al., 1978). This patient exhibited several features of Turner's syndrome, including undifferentiated gonads, despite the absence of a 46,XO cell line in blood or fibroblasts cultured from skin or "gonads." In fact, the Y chromosome was present in all cells studied, yet H-Y antigen was not detected in skin fibroblasts, and its expression was considerably depressed in blood leukocytes. Subsequent careful analysis of the patient's karyotype revealed a small arm deletion of the Y chromosome compared with the intact Y chromosome of her father, observations that are consistent with a model in which both "Turner-suppressing" genes and a critical majority of structural H-Y gene copies have been lost (Fig. 9).

It is perhaps noteworthy that gonadal dysgenesis in XY human females is associated with a high incidence of gonadal tumors, most of which are testicular in nature (Manuel et al., 1976). It would appear that whereas XO females initially organize an ovary that may remain

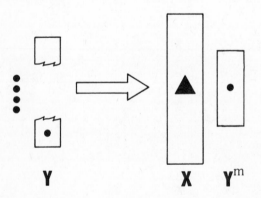

Figure 9. Through loss of a critical majority of H-Y gene copies (due for example to Y-to-autosome translocation), mutant Y-chromosome (Y^m) cannot sustain testicular differentiation. The result is an XY female, but this condition is heritable in neither the wood lemming nor man (see Table 2).

Y   X Y^m

normal until birth, XY females may initially organize a testis that later degenerates, often developing as a tumor (gonadoblastoma, dysgerminoma) (see Schellhas, 1974).

A HORMONE-LIKE ROLE OF H-Y ANTIGEN

The establishment of chorionic vascular anastomoses between bovine twin fetuses of opposite sex is associated with masculine development of the female, or freemartin twin (Short, 1970). In extreme cases, the gonads of the freemartin resemble small testes, which may produce considerable amounts of androgen. Common circulation would indicate a blood-borne etiology for this condition, yet, until recently, testicular organization of the freemartin gonad has remained enigmatic. Androgens cannot be responsible because they do not affect differentiation of the bovine ovary. XX/XY chimerism has been implicated, but the fact is that masculine differentiation of the freemartin gonad has occurred despite presence of a majority of XX cells. How, then, can a minority of XY cells induce a majority of XX cells to engage in testicular differentiation?

In birds, vascular anastomosis between heterosexual twin embryos is associated with feminization of the male (Lutz and Lutz-Ostertag, 1958). It would appear that in female-heterogametic species, ZW cells exercise dominance over ZZ cells of the presumptive testis, inducing them to engage in ovarian differentiation. Akram and Weniger (1968) have reported that mammalian fetal testes induce ovarian differentiation in co-cultured avian testes. Viewed from this perspective, the seemingly disparate observations in chimeric twins of the mammal and bird have a similar basis: A common hormone-like factor secreted by cells of the heterogametic gonad can induce the tissues of the homogametic gonad to develop toward the heterogametic mode, which may be male (XY) or female (ZW), depending on the species.

Yet, H-Y antigen is common to the heterogametic sex of birds and mammals. Moreover, we now recognize the presence of high levels of H-Y antigen in the embryonic freemartin gonad, even in the absence of a corresponding high proportion of XY cells. By inference, H-Y antigen is disseminated as a hormone-like factor at a critical stage in development (Ohno et al., 1976). Accordingly, it is H-Y antigen, disseminated by XY cells and bound by neighboring XX cells, that subverts ovarian differentiation and induces male differentiation in the freemartin gonad, and it is H-Y antigen, disseminated by ZW cells, that leads to the intersexual development of the ZZ gonad in heterosexual twin embryos of the bird.

XX/XY GONADS

The Ontogenetic Strategy of Competitive Displacement

Accidents are bound to occur at various stages during ontogeny. Accordingly, Nature must have devised various accommodations either to negate or to minimize the effect of these mishaps. It would be folly, for example, to assign the role of primordium for an entire cell type to a single embryonic cell; accidental death of that cell would deprive the embryo of an entire tissue. Wisely, each differentiative commitment in mammalian ontogeny is made by a group of cells rather than by a single cell (McLaren, 1976).

Similarly, accidental mix-ups between cells committed to alternative differentiative pathways are bound to occur at territorial junctions during organogenesis. What if a diverticulum of the primitive gut destined to be liver accidentally incorporated a number of stray cells that had already made an initial commitment to be intestinal cells? Purely autonomous organogenesis by irreversibly committed cells would produce an island of intestinal tissue in the midst of liver. However, mosaic organs of this kind are seldom encountered, and this indicates existence of a developmental strategy that avoids their formation.

This strategy is implicit in the development of XX/XY mosaic or chimeric gonads. Random fusions of two mouse blastocysts result in the formation of XX/XY chimeras 50 per cent of the time. If XX and XY gonadal cells were each to follow their inherent organogenetic dictate, the overall sex ratio of chimeric mice would be one XX/XX female to one XY/XY male to two XX/XY true hermaphrodites. However, true hermaphrodites seldom occur among chimeric mice. In fact, a survey of the literature reveals that of 550 chimeras described, only 8 were true hermaphrodites − an incidence of 1.4 per cent Most often, XX/XY gonads develop as testes, less often they develop as ovaries, and they seldom develop as ovotestes (McLaren, 1976). In one fertile BALB XX/C3H XY chimeric male mouse, we found XX cells composing fully half of the Sertoli and Leydig cell populations of the testes. Yet these XX cells were endowed with as much H-Y antigen as their neighboring XY cells (Ohno et al., 1978a). If H-Y structural genes are situated on the Y chromosome, the presence of substantial amounts of H-Y antigen on XX gonadal cells of the chimeric mouse (and bovine freemartin) must indicate that both XX and XY gonadal cells possess H-Y antigen receptors. (The essential difference between XX and XY gonadal cells must lie, then, in the ability of the latter to produce their own H-Y antigen.)

Although XY gonadal cells can obviously persuade neighboring XX cells to engage in testicular organogenesis (via disseminated H-Y antigen), XY gonadal cells are themselves sometimes persuaded to function in ovarian organogenesis; hence, the occasional development of ovaries in XX/XY chimeric gonads of the mouse. Yet, purely ovarian differentiation of the XX/XY gonad should be correlated with the absence of H-Y antigen from the XY moiety, for under the slow-rotation culture conditions described by Moscona (1961), dispersed testicular Sertoli cells (XY) that are lysostripped of H-Y antigen reaggregate as though they were ovarian follicular cells (Ohno et al., 1978b; Zenzes et al., 1978), and, as we have already noted, mutational suppression of H-Y antigen synthesis leads to the formation of an ovary by XY cells in the wood lemming.

Viewed from this perspective, the rare development of ovotestes is not merely the consequence of XX/XY chimerism or mosaicism, with XY cells in the testicular portion of the gonad and XX cells in the ovarian portion. To the contrary, the majority of human true hermaphrodites have the 46,XX karyotype, with no indication of mosaicism involving XY cells. It is presence of a local gonadal cell population from which H-Y antigen has been expelled that leads to the formation of an ovotestis. Thus, in our study of one human XX true hermaphrodite, H-Y antigen was found in a population of cells cultured from the testicular portion of a scrotal ovotestis but not in a population of cells cultured from the ovarian portion. What is it that drives testis-inducing H-Y antigen from its anchorage site on the plasma membrane? Is it a corresponding *ovary*-inducing "antigen"?

Since H-Y antigen is periodically disseminated to function as a testis-inducing hormone, it does not appear to exist as an integral part of the plasma membrane in the strict sense. Instead, H-Y antigen must utilize another structure as an anchorage site — a structure that is itself an integral part of the plasma membrane (Fig. 10). The occasional development of an ovary in the XX/XY gonad implies that the corresponding ovary-inducing agent is also disseminated. But then the ovary-inducer does not exist as an integral part of the plasma membrane in the strict sense either, and this implies that the ovary inducer must also utilize a "stable" plasma membrane anchorage site.

These considerations have led to the proposal that mammals avoid the formation of mosaic organs by a strategy of "competitive displacement" (Ohno, 1977b). Displacement of one organogenesis-directing molecule by another is made feasible by assuming presence of an anchorage site on the plasma membrane able to be utilized by both molecules. In the case of XX/XY mosaic or chimeric gonads, the

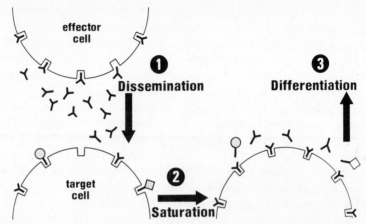

Figure 10.   Hormone-like role of H-Y antigen in embryonic gonad.

1, Dissemination. At a specific stage in development, effector cell is stimulated to secrete H-Y antigen (small Y's). Disseminated H-Y antigen competes with other molecules for nonspecific plasma membrane anchorage sites in the XX/XY mosaic gonad.

2, Saturation. In the presence of excess H-Y antigen, other molecules are driven from anchorage sites and replaced by H-Y antigen. Specific plasma membrane receptor sites (not shown) are also saturated with H-Y antigen.

3, Differentiation. Binding of H-Y antigen induces conformational changes in the plasma membrane that signal differentiation of Sertoli cells, Leydig cells, and spermatogonia, thereby committing XY cells to organize a testis. In mosaic gonads XX cells are also induced to organize a testis.

testis-inducing H-Y antigen of XY cells and the yet-unidentified ovary-inducing "antigen" of XX cells are placed in competitive positions on the plasma membranes of both XY and XX cells. When H-Y antigen succeeds in displacing the ovary-inducer from the plasma membrane of XX gonadal cells, a testis is formed. Conversely, dominance of the ovary-inducer leads to the formation of an ovary, and in the special case of H-Y antigen positive XX gonads, local dominance of the ovary-inducer leads to the formation of an ovotestis (see Figure 10).

THE MAJOR HISTOCOMPATIBILITY COMPLEX (MHC) AND ORGANOGENESIS

The role of general utility anchorage site for organogenesis-directing plasma membrane components such as H-Y antigen has been assigned to β_2-microglobulin–MHC antigen dimers (Ohno, 1977a). Indeed, the MHC of the mouse (H-2) exerts a telling effect on the expression of H-Y antigen; male-incompatible graft rejection by female mice is profoundly influenced by the H-2 type of the *donor*

(Silvers and Billingham, 1967; Wachtel et al., 1973a). Moreover, recent in vitro studies have shown that cytotoxic female T cells behave in the same manner toward H-Y antigen as they behave toward viral antigens so that T cell mediated lysis of H-Y incompatible target cells is just as H-2-restricted as the lysis of virus-infected or transformed target cells (Gordon et al., 1975, 1976; Simpson and Gordon, 1977). As to the cause of this H-2 restriction, direct evidence has now been obtained of a physical association between H-Y antigen and β_2-microglobulin–HLA antigen dimers on the plasma membrane of human male cells. In the mutational absence of β_2-microglobulin–HLA antigen dimers, the level of H-Y antigen in the "Daudi" cultured cell line (human male Burkitt lymphoma) was reduced to only 20 percent of that in control lymphoma cell lines. When male Daudi cells were cultured together with female HeLa D98 cells, β_2-microglobulin supplied by the latter restored expression of Daudi HLA antigens on the plasma membrane of somatic cell hybrids (Daudi × HeLa). The point is that the restoration of HLA antigens caused a ten-fold increase in the level of H-Y antigen in these hybrids, compared with the level in the original Daudi line (Beutler et al., 1978).

It has been suggested that parasitic viruses have profited from the developmental strategy of competitive displacement by mimicking organogenesis-directing antigens with their own viral antigens, thereby competing for a foothold among the anchorage sites of the host cell plasma membrane. Presumably, H-2-restriction in T cell mediated lysis of virus-transformed or virus-infected target cells is due to the physical association of viral antigens and β_2-microglobulin–MHC antigen dimers (Ohno, 1977a). In fact, there is convincing evidence for such physical association: Four different H-2 antigens (H-$2K^b$, H-$2K^d$, H2D^b and H-$2D^d$) form dimers with β_2-microglobulin on the plasma membrane of cells from (BALB.B × BALB/c) F$_1$ hybrid mice. Yet when these F$_1$ mice are infected with Friend leukemia virus, infectious particles that are recovered contain H-$2D^b$ antigen specifically, and this suggests preferential association of Friend leukemia virus with β_2-microglobulin–H-$2D^b$ antigen dimers. Furthermore, it has been shown that killing of Friend leukemia virus–infected (BALB.B × BALB/c) F$_1$ hybrid target cells by T cells is not restricted with regard to the H-2K region but is specifically restricted with regard to the H-$2D^b$ allele (Blank and Lilly, 1977).

Of all the loci in the mammalian genome, the MHC is notable for its extreme diversity of haplotypes. It follows that extensive HLA polymorphism in man may have evolved as a means of avoiding disease susceptibility resulting from affinities of viral components for particular MHC products. The association of certain human diseases with certain HLA haplotypes is becoming increasingly apparent

(McMichael and McDevitt, 1977). From this standpoint, if the binding affinity between a given organogenetic component and a particular MHC haplotype were either too weak or too strong, organogenesis might be disrupted. For this reason it may be worthwhile to look for any correlation between HLA haplotypes and true hermaphroditism in nonmosaic human subjects.

CELL LINEAGE ANTIGENS IN GONADAL DIFFERENTIATION

During the organization of the embryonic mammalian testis, somatic elements within the central blastema must "sort out" before Sertoli cell precursors can aggregate to form the seminiferous cord wall. At the same time, Leydig cell precursors, which are not involved in cord formation, must form islands in the spaces between cords. Inasmuch as the "sorting out" processes of organogenesis depend upon the mutual recognition of cells belonging to the same lineage, it follows that plasma membrane components *other* than ubiquitous H-Y antigen are essential in testicular differentiation.

Indeed, female mice immunized with suspensions of Sertoli cells (from the testes of H-2-compatible *Sxr*, XX sex-reversed males) produce two antibodies; one is directed, predictably, against H-Y antigen, but the other is specifically cytotoxic for Sertoli cells. This latter antibody detects an identical or very similar antigen on ovarian follicular cells — but not on other components of the ovary. Thus, absorption of this antibody with an excess number of ovarian follicular cells abolishes its cytotoxicity for Sertoli cells (Ciccarese and Ohno, 1978).

We have already pointed out that Sertoli cells lysostripped of H-Y antigen behave as though they were ovarian follicular cells. In fact, testicular Sertoli cells and ovarian follicular cells have more in common. Both play a supporting role for their respective germ cells, and both are rich in microsomal aromatase, which converts androstenedione to estrone, and testosterone to estradiol. There is little doubt that both cell types originate from a common primordium. Yet, if they were to lose their common antigen in order to acquire a sex-specific one, the removal of H-Y antigen from the plasma membrane would have little effect on the specific organogenetic function of testicular Sertoli cells. Thus, sex-independent expression of cell lineage-specific (i.e., Sertoli cell) antigen constitutes the foundation upon which ubiquitously expressed but male-specific H-Y antigen plays its critical role in mammalian sex determination.

SUMMARY

Widespread phylogenetic occurrence and heterogametic sex-specific expression of serologically detectable H-Y antigen have led to the proposition that this cell surface component is the primary determinant of vertebrate sex, inducing the indifferent embryonic gonad to differentiate as a testis in male-heterogametic (XY) species such as the human and as an ovary in female-heterogametic (ZW) species such as the chicken.

All experimental evidence supports this hypothesis. In humans, for example, testicular differentiation is invariably correlated with presence of H-Y antigen irrespective of phenotypic sex or apparent karyotype.

There are multiple copies of the H-Y structural gene on the mammalian Y chromosome. In man, these are clustered on the short arm near the Y centromere. However, a long arm locus is not ruled out in at least some individuals.

Abnormal inheritance (e.g., translocation) or loss of H-Y structural genes or suppression of these genes by a regulatory element on the mammalian X chromosome may lead to various modes of sex reversal, examples of which are the XX male syndrome and XX true hermaphroditism of the dog and human and the fertile XY female condition of the wood lemming.

The presence of H-Y antigen on XX gonadal cells of the bovine freemartin and on corresponding cells of the chimeric XX/XY male mouse indicates a hormone-like mechanism in the differentiation of the testis: H-Y antigen, disseminated by XY cells, may be bound by either XY or XX target cells, both of which possess H-Y antigen–receptors (anchorage sites). Once "coated" with H-Y antigen, target cells are induced to engage in testicular organogenesis.

The gonads of XX/XY chimeric mice almost never become ovotestes but may occasionally develop as ovaries. This implies the existence of an ovary-inducing "antigen" that competes with H-Y antigen for plasma membrane anchorage sites on the cells of the indifferent embryonic gonad. Competitive displacement of one antigen by the other promotes testicular or ovarian differentiation, depending on which antigen is displaced.

H-Y antigen expression is profoundly influenced by MHC antigens. In addition, T cell–mediated lysis of H-Y-incompatible target cells is MHC-restricted, as is T cell–mediated lysis of virus-infected target cells. Accordingly, it has been proposed that MHC antigens serve as nonspecific receptors for both H-Y antigen and the ovary-inducing antigen and conceivably for other cell surface components, including viral antigens.

Because H-Y antigen is expressed by all cells of the heterogametic gonad, other cell lineage–specific antigens are required in the cell movements and "sorting out" processes of testicular organogenesis.

Hormone-induced functional sex reversal in fish and amphibians suggests that H-Y loci may not be restricted to the Y(W) chromosome in these animals. Thus, compared with its role in mammals, H-Y antigen may play a less significant role in the sex-determining scheme of nonmammalian vertebrates.

ACKNOWLEDGMENTS: The authors are grateful to Vicki Scher for preparation of the manuscript, and to David Purnell for the illustrations.

References

Akram, H., and J.P. Weniger. 1968. Féminisation, en culture *in vitro* du testicule embryonnaire de poulet par le testicule embryonnaire de veau. Arch. Anat. Microsc. Morphol. Exp. 57:369–378.

Bardin, C.W., L.P. Bullock, R.J. Sherins, I. Moskowitz, and W.R. Blackburn. 1973. Androgen metabolism and mechanism of action of male pseudohermaphroditism: a study of testicular feminization. Recent Prog. Horm. Res. 29:65–105.

Bennett, D., E.A. Boyse, M.F. Lyon, B.J. Mathieson, M. Scheid, and K. Yanagisawa. 1975. Expression of H-Y (male) antigen in phenotypically female *Tfm*/Y mice. Nature 257:236–238.

Bennett, D., B.J. Mathieson, M. Scheid, K. Yanagisawa, E.A. Boyse, S.S. Wachtel, and B.M. Cattanach. 1977. Serological evidence for H-Y antigen in *Sxr*, XX sex-reversed phenotypic males. Nature 265:255–257.

Berger, R., D. Abonyi, A. Nodot, J. Vialatte, and J. Lejeune. 1970. Hermaphrodisme vrai et "garçon XX" dans une fratrie. Rev. Eur. Etud. Clin. Biol. 15:330–333.

Beutler, B., Y. Nagai, S. Ohno, G. Klein, and M. Shapiro. 1978. The HLA dependent expression of testis-organizing H-Y antigen by human male cells. Cell 13:509–513.

Blank, K.J., and F. Lilly. 1977. Evidence for H-27 viral protein complex on the cell surface as the basis of H-2 restriction of cytotoxicity. Nature 269:808–809.

Bunker, M.C. 1966. Y-chromosome loss in transplanted testicular teratomas of mice. Canad. J. Genet. Cytol. 8:312–327.

Cattanach, B.M. 1975. Sex Reversal in the Mouse and Other Mammals. In The Early Development of Mammals, Balls, M., and A. Wild (Eds.), p. 305. New York, Cambridge University Press.

Cattanach, B.M., C.E. Pollard, and S.G. Hawkes. 1971. Sex-reversed mice: XX and XO males. Cytogenetics 10:318–337.

Ciccarese, S., and S. Ohno. 1978. Two plasma membrane antigens of testicular Sertoli cells and H-2 restricted versus unrestricted lysis by female T-cells. 13:643–650.

Cooke, H. 1976. Repeated sequence specific to human males. Nature 262:182–186.

de la Chapelle, A. 1972. Analytic review: nature and origin of males with XX sex chromosomes. Am. J. Hum. Genet. 24:71–105.

de la Chapelle, A., J. Schroder, J. Murros, and G. Tallqvist. 1977. Two XX males in one family and additional observations bearing on the etiology of XX males. Clin. Genet. 11:91–106.

Dosik, H., S.S. Wachtel, F. Khan, G. Spergel, and G.C. Koo. 1976. Evidence for the presence of Y-chromosomal genes in a phenotypic male with a 46, XX karytoype. JAMA 236:2505–2508.

Eichwald, E.J., and C.R. Silmser. 1955. Communication. Transpl. Bull. 2:148–149.

Engelstein, J.M. 1967. Induced expression of the male isoantigen in the skin of female mice. Proc. Soc. Exp. Biol. Med. 126:907–912.

Erickson, R.P. 1977. Androgen-modified expression compared with Y linkage of male specific antigen. Nature 265:59–61.

Espiner, E.A., A.M.O. Veale, V.E. Sands, and P.H. Fitzgerald. 1970. Familial syndrome of streak gonads and normal male karyotype in five phenotypic females. New Eng. J. Med. 283:6–11.

Ferguson-Smith, M.A. 1966. X-Y chromosomal interchange in the aetiology of true hermaphroditism and of XX Klinefelter's syndrome. Lancet 2:475–476.

Fredga, K., A. Gropp, H. Winking, and F. Frank. 1976. Fertile XX- and XY-type females in the wood lemming Myopus schisticolor. Nature 261:225–227.

Fredga, K., A. Gropp, H. Winking, and F. Frank. 1977. A hypothesis explaining the exceptional sex ratio in the wood lemming (Myopus schisticolor). Hereditas 85:101–104.

Gasser, D.L., and W.K. Silvers. 1972. Genetics and immunology of sex-linked antigens. Adv. Immunol. 15:215–247.

Gehring, U., G.M. Tomkins, and S. Ohno. 1971. Effect of the androgen-insensitivity mutation on a cytoplasmic receptor for dihydrotestosterone. Nature–New Biol. 232:106–107.

Gilmour, D.G. 1967. Histocompatibility antigen in the heterogametic sex in the chicken. Transplantation 5:699–706.

Goldberg, E.H., T. Arrington, and S. Tokuda. 1978. Simpler technique for the serological detection of H-Y antigen on human male leukocytes. J. Immunol. Methods 23:203–206.

Goldberg, E.H., E.A. Boyse, D. Bennett, M. Scheid, and E.A. Carswell. 1971. Serological demonstration of H-Y (male) antigen on mouse sperm. Nature 232:478–480.

Gordon, R.D., B.J. Mathieson, L.E. Samelson, E.A. Boyse, and E. Simpson. 1976. The effect of allogenic presensitization on H-Y graft survival and in vitro cell-mediated responses to H-Y antigen. J. Exp. Med. 144 (3):810–820.

Gordon, R.D., E. Simpson, and L.E. Samelson. 1975. In vitro cell-mediated immune responses to the male specific (H-Y) antigen in mice. J. Exp. Med. 142(5):1108–1120.

Hamerton, J.L., J.M. Dickson, C.E. Pollard, S.A. Grieves, and R.V. Short. 1969. Genetic intersexuality in goats. J. Reprod. Fertil. (Suppl.) 7:25–51.

Hare, W.C.D. 1976. Intersexuality in the dog. Canad. Vet. J. 17:7–15.

Hildemann, W.H., M. Morgan, and L. Frautnick. 1970. Immunogenetic components of weaker histoincompatibility systems in mice. Transpl. Proc. 2:24–31.

Jost, A., 1970. Hormonal factors in the sex differentiation of the mammalian foetus. Philos. Trans. R. Soc. Lond. (Biol.)259:119–130.

Kasdan, R., H.R. Nankin, P. Troen, N. Wald, S. Pan, and T. Yanaihara. 1973. Paternal transmission of maleness in XX human beings. New Eng. J. Med. 288:539–545.

Keenan, B.S., W.J. Meyer, III, A.J. Hadjian, H.W. Jones, and C.J. Migeon. 1974. Syndrome of androgen insensitivity in man: absence of 5 α-dihydrotestosterone binding protein in skin fibroblasts. J. Clin. Endocr. Metabol. 38:1143–1146.

Koo, G.C., E.A. Boyse, and S.S. Wachtel. 1977a. Immunogenetic Techniques and Approaches in the Study of Sperm and Testicular Cell Surface Antigens. In Immunobiology of Gametes, Edidin, M., and M.H. Johnson (Eds.), Oxford, Alden Press. p. 73.

Koo, G.C., C.W. Stackpole, E.A. Boyse, U. Hammerling, and M. Lardis. 1973. Topographical location of H-Y antigen on mouse spermatozoa by immunoelectronmicroscopy. Proc. Nat. Acad. Sci. U.S.A. 70:1502–1505.

Koo, G.C., S.S. Wachtel, W.R. Breg, and O.J. Miller. 1976. Mapping the Locus of the H-Y Antigen. In Human Gene Mapping 3, Birth Defects: Original Article Series, Bergsma, D. (Ed.), 12:175–177.

Koo, G.C., S.S. Wachtel, K. Krupen-Brown, L.R. Mittl, W.R. Breg, M. Genel, I.M. Rosenthal, D.S. Borgaonkar, D.A. Miller, R. Tantravahi, R.R. Schreck, B.F. Erlanger, and O.J. Miller. 1977b. Mapping the locus of the *H-Y* gene on the human Y chromosome. Science 198:940–942.

Koo, G.C., S.S. Wachtel, P.S. Saenger, M.I. New, H. Dosik, A.P. Amarose, E. Dorus, and V. Ventruto. 1977c. H-Y antigen: expression in human subjects with the testicular feminization syndrome. Science 196:655–656.

Krco, C.J., and E.H. Goldberg. 1976. Detection of H-Y (male) antigen on 8-cell mouse embryos. Science 193:1134–1135.

Kunkel, L.M., K.D. Smith, S.H. Boyer, D.S. Borgaonkar, S.S. Wachtel, O.J. Miller, W.R. Breg, H.W. Jones, Jr., and J.M. Rary. 1977. Analysis of human Y-chromosome-specific reiterated DNA in chromosome variants. Proc. Nat. Acad. Sci. U.S.A. 74:1245–1249.

Lutz, H., and Y. Lutz-Ostertag. 1958. Etude d'un free-martin chez les oiseaux. Arch. Anat. Microsc. Morphol. Exp. 47:205–210.

Lyon, M.F., and S.G. Hawkes. 1970. X-linked gene for testicular feminization in the mouse. Nature 227:1217–1219.

Madan, K., and S. Walker. 1974. Letter: Possible evidence for Xp^+ in an XX male. Lancet 1:1223.

Manuel, M., K.P. Katayama, and H.W. Jones, Jr. 1976. The age of occurrence of gonadal tumors in intersex patients with a Y chromosome. Am. J. Obstet. Gynec. 124:293–300.

McLaren, A. 1976. Mammalian Chimeras. New York, Cambridge University Press.

McMichael, A., and H. McDevitt. 1977. The Association Between the HLA System and Disease. In Progress in Medical Genetics, Steinberg, A.G. et al. (Eds.), pp. 39–100. Philadelphia, W.B. Saunders Company.

Melvold, R.W., H.I. Kohn, G. Yerganian, and D.W. Fawcett. 1977. Evidence suggesting the existence of two H-Y antigens in the mouse. Immunogenetics 5:33–41.

Mikamo, K., and E. Witschi. 1964. Masculinization and breeding of the WW *Xenopus*. Experientia 20:622–624.

Morris, J.M. 1953. The syndrome of testicular feminization in male pseudohermaphrodites. Am. J. Obstet. Gynec. 65:1192–1211.

Moscona, A. 1961. Rotation-mediated histogenic aggregation of dissociated cells. Exp. Cell Res. 22:455–475.

Mullen, Y., and W.H. Hildemann. 1972. X- and Y-linked transplantation antigens in rats. Transplantation 13:521–529.

Nagai, Y., and S. Ohno. 1977. Testis-determining H-Y antigen in XO males of the mole-vole (Ellobius lutescens). Cell 10:729–732.

Nicolis, G.L., L.Y. Hsu, R. Sabetghadam, N.B. Kardon, D.P. Mathur, H.G. Rose, K. Hirschhorn, and J.L. Gabrilove. 1972. Klinefelter's syndrome in identical twins with the 46, XX chromosome constitution. Am. J. Med. 52:482–491.

Ohno, S. 1967. Sex Chromosomes and Sex-linked Genes. New York, Springer-Verlag New York, Inc.

Ohno, S. 1977a. The original function of MHC antigens as the general plasma membrane anchorage site of organogenesis-directing proteins. Immunol. Rev. 33:59–69.

Ohno, S. 1977b. H-Y antigen: organizer of the testis. City of Hope Quarterly 6:3–9.

Ohno, S., L.C. Christian, S.S. Wachtel, and G.C. Koo. 1976. Hormone-like role of H-Y antigen in bovine freemartin gonad. Nature 261:597–599.

Ohno, S., S. Ciccarese, Y. Nagai, and S.S. Wachtel. 1978a. H-Y antigen in testes of XX (BALB)/XY (C3H) chimaeric male mouse. Arch. Androl. 1:127–133.

Ohno, S., Y. Nagai, and S. Ciccarese. 1978b. Testicular cells lysostripped of H-Y antigen organize ovarian follicle-like aggregates. Cytogenet. Cell Genet. 20:351–364.

Peters, H. 1970. Migration of gonocytes into the mammalian gonad and their differentiation. Philos. Trans R. Soc. Lond. (Biol.) 259:91–101.

Polackova, M. 1969. Attempt at inducing male-specific antigen in female skin. Folia Biol. (Praha) 15:181–187.

Rosenfeld, R., L. Luzzatti, R. Hintz, O.J. Miller, G. Koo, and S.S. Wachtel. 1978.

Studies of H-Y antigen in a 46, XYp— phenotypic female with Turner stigmata and undifferentiated gonads. Abstract No. 560. Pediatric Research 12:457.

Scheid, M., E.A. Boyse, E.A. Carswell, and L.J. Old. 1972. Serologically demonstrable alloantigens of mouse epidermal cells. J. Exp. Med. 135:938–955.

Schellhas, H.F. 1974. Malignant potential of the dysgenetic gonad. I. Obstet. Gynec. 44:298–309.

Selden, J.R., and S.S. Wachtel. 1977. H-Y antigen in the dog. Transplantation 24:298–299.

Selden, J.R., S.S. Wachtel, G.C. Koo, M.E. Haskins, and D.F. Patterson. 1978. Genetic basis of XX male syndrome and XX true hermaphroditism: evidence in the dog. Science 201:644–646.

Short, R.V. 1970. The bovine freemartin: a new look at an old problem. Philos. Trans. R. Soc. Lond. (Biol.) 259:141–147.

Silvers, W.K., and R.E. Billingham. 1967. Genetic background and expressivity of histocompatibility genes. Science 158:118–119.

Silvers, W.K., R.E. Billingham, and B.H. Sanford. 1968. The H-Y transplantation antigen: a Y-linked or sex-influenced factor? Nature 220:401–403.

Silvers, W.K., and S.S. Wachtel. 1977. H-Y antigen: behavior and function. Science 195:956–960.

Silvers, W.K., and S-L. Yang. 1973. Male specific antigen: homology in mice and rats. Science 181:570–572.

Simpson, E., and R.D. Gordon. 1977. Responsiveness to H-Y antigen Ir gene complementation and target cell specificity. Immunol. Rev. 35:59–75.

Simpson, J.L. 1975. Gonadal Dysgenesis and Abnormalities of the Human Sex Chromosomes: Current Status of Phenotypic-Karyotypic Correlations. In Genetic Forms of Hypogonadism, Birth Defects: Original Article Series, Bergsma, D. (Ed.), 11:23–59.

Simpson, J.L. 1976. Disorders of Sexual Differentiation. Etiology and Clinical Delineation, p.225. New York, Academic Press, Inc.

Simpson, J.L. Gonadal Dysgenesis and Sex Chromosome Abnormalities. Phenotypic-Karyotypic Correlations In Genetic Mechanisms of Sexual Development, Albany Birth Defects Conference. 1976. In press.

Singh, L., I.F. Purdom, and H.W. Jones. 1977. Effect of different denaturing agents on the detectability of specific DNA sequences of various base compositions by in situ hybridisation. Chromosoma 60:377–389.

Sternberg, W.H., D.L. Barclay, and W. Kloepfer. 1968. Familial XY gonadal dysgenesis. New Eng. J. Med. 278: 695–700.

Tokuda, S., T. Arrington, E.H. Goldberg, and J. Richey. 1977. Simpler technique for serological detection of H-Y antigen on mouse lymphocytes. Nature 267:433–434.

Wachtel, S.S. 1977. H-Y antigen: genetics and serology. Immunol. Rev. 33:33–58.

Wachtel, S.S., P. Basrur, and G.C. Koo. 1978. Recessive male-determining genes. Cell 15:279–281.

Wachtel, S.S., D.L. Gasser, and W.K. Silvers. 1973a. Male-specific antigen: modification of potency by the H-2 locus in mice. Science 181:862–863.

Wachtel, S.S., E.H. Goldberg, E. Zuckerman, and E.A. Boyse. 1973b. Continued expression of H-Y antigen on male lymphoid cells resident in female (chimaeric) mice. Nature 244:102–103.

Wachtel, S.S., G.C. Koo, W.R. Breg, S. Elias, E.A. Boyse, and O.J. Miller. 1975a. Expression of H-Y antigen in human males with two Y-chromosomes. New Eng. J. Med. 293:1070–1072.

Wachtel, S.S., G.C. Koo, W.R. Breg, T.H. Thaler, G.M. Dillard, I.M. Rosenthal, H. Dosik, P.S. Gerald, P. Saenger, M. New, E. Lieber, and O.J. Miller. 1976a. Serological detection of a Y-linked gene in XX males and XX true hermaphrodites. New Eng. J. Med. 295:750–754.

Wachtel, S.S., G.C. Koo, and E.A. Boyse. 1975b. Evolutionary conservation of H-Y ("male") antigen. Nature 254:270–272.

Wachtel, S.S., G.C. Koo, S. Ohno, A. Gropp, V.G. Dev, R. Tantravahi, D.A. Miller, and O.J. Miller. 1976b. H-Y antigen and the origin of XY female wood lemmings (*Myopus schisticolor*). Nature 264:638–639.

Wachtel, S.S., G.C. Koo, E.E. Zuckerman, U. Hammerling, M.P. Scheid, and E.A. Boyse. 1974. Serological crossreactivity between H-Y (male) antigens of mouse and man. Proc. Nat. Acad. Sci. U.S.A. 71:1215–1218.

Wachtel, S.S., S. Ohno, G.C. Koo, and E.A. Boyse. 1975c. Possible role for H-Y antigen in the primary determination of sex. Nature 257:235–236.

Weissman, I.L. 1973. Failure to demonstrate postnatal testicular dependent expression of the male-specific transplantation antigen in mice. Transplantation 16:122–125.

Welshons, W.J., and L.B. Russell. 1959. The Y-chromosome as the bearer of male-determining factors in the mouse. Proc. Nat. Acad. Sci. U.S.A. 45:560–566.

Yamamoto, T. 1961. Progenies of sex-reversal females mated with sex-reversal males in the medaka, *Oryzias latipes*. J. Exp. Zool. 146:163–180.

Zenzes, M.T., U. Wolf, E. Gunther, and W. Engel. 1978. Studies on the function of H-Y antigen: dissociation and reorganization experiments of rat gonadal cells. Cytogenet. Cell Genet. 20:365–372.

4

Syndromes with Multiple Endocrine Gland Involvement

R. Neil Schimke

Professor of Medicine and Pediatrics; Director, Division of Metabolism, Endocrinology and Genetics; Kansas University Medical School; Kansas City, Kansas 66103

INTRODUCTION

The advent and general availability of radioimmunoassays for various hormones have greatly facilitated the study of endocrine gland dysfunction. Quite frequently, an abnormality in hormone secretion is uncovered during the course of a systematic search for the etiology of problems such as short stature and infertility. At other times, the endocrine aberrancy is detected serendipitously by the increasingly prevalent use of routine screening procedures, or a hormone imbalance is found because the attending clinician is interested in the full delineation of a new syndrome. Whatever the reason for the initiation of the study of the endocrine system, it has become apparent that the simultaneous malfunction of more than one endocrine gland is not so uncommon. This review will attempt to summarize the available information on those genetic syndromes in which multiple endocrine glands are involved. In some of these conditions, the multigland abnormality appears to be a primary pleiotropic effect of the mutant gene. In others, the endocrine disorder may be a secondary phenomenon. All too frequently, the precise reason for hormone hyper- or hyposecretion is unknown. No consideration will be given here to infiltrative or storage disorders, in which multiple endocrine gland involvement is almost certainly secondary, or to congenital anomalies that result in multitropic deficiency of the hypothalamic-pituitary axis. In addition, disorders in which endocrine dysfunction is unclear or is a poorly documented primary effect of the basic genetic lesion, such as that which probably occurs in acute intermittent porphyria (Tschudy et al., 1975), will also be excluded. There is no doubt that a syndrome or two has been overlooked, as new heritable conditions are being described with disquieting regularity. More detailed expositions of many of the clinical, genetic, and hormonal features of these various conditions are available (Rimoin and Schimke, 1971; Schimke, 1978).

SYNDROMES WITH MULTIPLE ENDOCRINE GLAND HYPERFUNCTION OR NEOPLASIA

Multiple Endocrine Neoplasia, Type I (MEN I)

The MEN I syndrome comprises tumors of the parathyroids, the pancreatic islet cells, the anterior pituitary, the adrenal cortex, and the thyroid gland, in decreasing order of frequency (Schimke, 1976). Symptoms are highly variable and depend upon whether one or more of the potentially affected glands is elaborating hormones or, as in the case of pituitary tumors, is causing endocrine hypofunction by virtue of the compression of normal tissue. As is generally true with familial tumors, the lesions are commonly multifocal, even within a single involved gland, and it seems likely that diffuse hyperplasia may precede malignancy by many months. Nearly half the patients with the Zollinger-Ellison (ZE) syndrome probably have MEN I, although it appears that other hypersecretory states less frequently are indicative of MEN I (e.g., perhaps only 10 percent of insulinomas belong in the MEN I diagnostic category [Schimke, 1973a]). Conversely, it is likely that virtually all patients with familial hyperparathyroidism actually have MEN I (Marx et al., 1973).

Symptoms indicative of MEN I may appear at any age but only rarely do they commence primarily before the age of 20 years or past the age of 60 years. The initial signs of the disease may be related to the classic features of excess hormone secretions (acromegaly, nephrolithiasis, or untractable peptic ulceration), and affected individuals may show evidence of simultaneous hyperfunction of more than one gland at a time. Alternatively, many years may elapse between the diagnosis of one adenoma and the appearance of the next. Occasionally, the disease may be heralded by more bizarre presentations. For example, hyperplasia of the pancreatic islet delta cells may result in a condition known as pancreatic cholera, or the Verner-Morrison syndrome, in which the tumor secretes vasoactive intestinal polypeptide (VIP), which initiates profuse watery diarrhea (Verner and Morrison, 1974). Although diarrhea may be a facet of both the ZE syndrome and the Verner-Morrison syndrome, the two conditions can be differentiated on the basis of finding low serum gastrin levels and achlorhydria in the Verner-Morrison syndrome. Excessive levels of tumor-associated prostaglandin E have also been implicated in the etiology of the diarrhea (Jaffe et al., 1977). Glucagonomas may produce an unusual symptom complex, which is characterized by a peculiar skin rash (termed necrotizing migratory erythema), stomatitis, unexplained weight loss, and diabetes mellitus (Mallinson et al., 1974). Whether or not glucagonomas are symptomatic may depend on the amount of the hormone being secreted, as tumors of high molecular weight (> 9000 daltons) tend to have few metabolic effects (Boden and Owen, 1977).

The adrenal glands are involved less frequently, and some workers feel that adrenocortical hyperfunction is invariably secondary to excess pituitary or ectopic adrenocorticotropic hormone (ACTH) — the source of the latter not infrequently being a pancreatic islet cell tumor. Involvement of the thyroid consists of simple adenoma, colloid goiter, thyroiditis, or, more rarely, thyrotoxicosis. Medullary thyroid carcinoma, the tumor type typical of MEN II (see later discussion), is not found in MEN I. In fact, in view of the rather inconsistent clinical picture in reported patients there is some question as to whether involvement of the thyroid gland should be considered a part of the potential spectrum of MEN I.

Other tumors seen in MEN I include carcinoid tumors (usually bronchial or upper intestinal in location), thymomas, schwannomas, and single or multiple cutaneous lipomas (Schimke, 1978).

MEN I is inherited as an autosomal dominant trait, with essentially full penetrance if the individual's entire lifespan is taken into account. For this reason, the spontaneous mutation rate is probably low, and relatives of patients presumed to have sporadic involvement should be considered affected until proven otherwise. Yearly screening studies of at-risk relatives is recommended. The pituitary and parathyroid tumors are only rarely malignant, but the pancreatic tumors frequently are and the adrenal lesions may be. Surgical removal of the relevant gland is the usual treatment offered. However, in some patients with the Zollinger-Ellison syndrome, total gastrectomy has been effective, with disappearance of hepatic metastases having been documented, albeit rarely, by "second-look" procedures (Fox et al., 1974). Cimetidine, a histamine H_2-receptor antagonist, has been useful in controlling the hyperacidity and diarrhea seen with excessive gastrin secretion. The long-term effects of the drug on preventing the spread of the tumor are not known for certain (McCarthy et al., 1977), but it is not likely that it has any intrinsic chemotherapeutic potential.

It has been suggested that the fundamental lesion in MEN I results from faulty differentiation of the neural crest — an embryologic tissue thought by many to be the source of not only the classic endocrine system but perhaps also of other secretory cells, such as those capable of elaborating gastrointestinal hormones (Weichert, 1970). Although it would be attractive to categorize MEN I as a neurocrestopathy, much current evidence is to the contrary, and for the present at least, the basic genetic defect remains obscure (Schimke, 1977).

Multiple Endocrine Neoplasia, Type II (MEN II)

There is much more evidence to support the contention that MEN II is related to a basic aberrancy in neural crest development.

MEN II comprises pheochromocytoma, which is frequently bilateral and even extra-adrenal, and multifocal medullary thyroid carcinoma (MTC), with some patients displaying additional parathyroid hyperplasia (Schimke, 1976). The MTC is derived from the parafollicular cell of the thryoid, which has its phylogenetic origin in the ultimobranchial body — a separate branchial arch–derivative in lower animals. MTC almost invariably elaborates excessive amounts of calcitonin in affected patients. The condition bears the eponymic designation of Sipple's syndrome, since Sipple (1961) was the first to call attention to the association of thyroid carcinoma and pheochromocytoma. However, others independently established that the thyroid lesion was always MTC and that the association was in fact a hereditary entity (Schimke and Hartmann, 1965; Williams, 1965).

Considerable histochemical work has established that neural crest cells are able to take up, store, and decarboxylate precursors of aromatic amines that fluoresce after exposure to formaldehyde. Using this phenomenon as a marker, it is possible to identify a host of cells (including enterochromaffin and argyrophilic cells of the intestine, some pancreatic islet cells, and the thyroid parafollicular cells) as potential derivatives of the neural crest. These cells have collectively been termed the APUD system (Amine Precursor Uptake and Decarboxylation) (Pearse and Polak, 1971). Other embryologic studies had previously established that sensory and sympathetic ganglia, melanocytes, and adrenal chromaffin cells were of neural crest origin. Confirmatory evidence of a relationship between the endocrine system and neural tissue has been provided by a recent report showing that monolayer cultures of both pheochromocytoma and MTC exhibited short duration action potentials when stimulated with microelectrodes (Tischler et al., 1976).

The MTC may be clinically silent and may be undetectable by palpation or radioiodine scanning. In fact, it is likely that C cell hyperplasia precedes frank malignancy by many years. Radioimmunoassay of plasma calcitonin will reveal the presence of the tumor, although other ectopic sites of calcitonin production (breasts, lungs, pancreatic islet cells) must be excluded. On occasion, pentagastrin stimulation or short-term calcium infusion may be necessary to confirm the diagnosis when the levels of the hormone are borderline (Schimke, 1977). The pheochromocytoma may also be asymptomatic and may become evident only by the study of urinary catecholamine metabolites. The MTC may secrete other substances, including ACTH, serotonin, VIP, histaminase, and various prostaglandins, while displaying a confusing array of symptoms. Interestingly, when found in children, excessive VIP secretion is commonly associated with other neural crest derivatives, such as ganglioneuroblas-toma (Jansen-Goemans and Engelhardt, 1977). Whether the parafol-licular cell per se actually elaborates these ectopic substances is not certain, since at least one other cell type with morphologic features reminiscent of the carcinoid cell has been found in the MTC (Ljungberg, 1972). The amyloid deposits regularly seen in MTC are derived from calcitonin, but it is important to recognize that amy-loid per se is not diagnostic of MTC, as it has been seen on occa-sion in other thyroid tumors (Valenta et al., 1977). Perhaps the latter observation accounts for the occasional reports of thyroid hormone–induced regression of MTC, since in reality, the tumor might be a papillary or follicular lesion rather than MTC, and the favorable re-sponse of papillary tumors to thyroid suppression is well known. Alternatively, amyloid may be absent from as many as one quarter of patients with true MTC (Normann et al., 1976).

Parathyroid hyperplasia occurs frequently enough in MEN II to be considered part of the syndrome. Controversy continues over whether or not there is primary involvement of the glands resulting from a gene defect or secondary involvement as a response to calci-tonin excess. Primary parathyroid involvement would seemingly weaken the argument favoring neural crest origin of the syndrome, but it has not been demonstrated conclusively that the parathyroids (or at least the hyperplastic secretory cells) are not derived from the neural crest, although the bulk of evidence favors an epithelial ori-gin.

Other tumors seen in the MEN II syndrome include gliomas, glioblastomas, and meningiomas, all of which might be considered to be central neural crest derivatives. Breast carcinoma and cancer of the pyriform sinuses have also been seen in isolated instances, but it is likely that these tumors are coincidental (Schimke, 1977).

By studying tumor cells from an individual who is heterozygous for two G6PD variants, both the MTC and the pheochromocytoma have been shown to be derived from a clonal event (Baylin et al., 1978). Increased virus-induced transformation has also been seen (Schimke, 1977). All these observations are in keeping with the "two-hit" hypothesis regarding hereditary tumors (Knudson et al., 1973). The C cells of the thyroid gland (as well as the adrenal chro-maffin cells) would presumably harbor the germinal mutation nec-essary for oncogenesis, but a second or somatic event would be nec-essary before frank neoplasia would occur; hence the variable age of patients at the onset of the tumors and the temporal discrepancy often seen between the detection of MTC and the pheochromocy-toma.

Like MEN I, the MEN II syndrome is an autosomal dominant trait. The MTC is invariably malignant, but prolonged survival has been seen. Calcitonin assay can be used to assess the completeness of surgical removal of the tumor and to locate and follow the possible development of future metastases that may be operatively accessible. Radioiodine treatment, x-ray treatment, and chemotherapy have not been noticeably effective in MTC. The pheochromocytomas are usually benign and are also treated surgically. Unresectable malignant adrenal lesions may require alpha and beta blocking agents for the control of symptoms. As in MEN I, MEN II is probably highly penetrant, and it is likely that the spontaneous mutation rate is low.

Multiple Endocrine Neoplasia, Type III (MEN III)

This endocrine neoplasia syndrome also features MTC and pheochromocytoma, but in addition, affected individuals have a rather striking array of physical findings, including neuromas of the conjunctival, labial, and buccal mucosa, the tongue, the larynx, and the gastrointestinal tract; hence the alternate designation of this condition as the mucosal neuroma syndrome (Schimke, et al., 1968). Other features include enlarged corneal nerves, "blubbery" lips, and soft tissue hypertrophy of the chin, along with an elongated habitus as seen in Marfan's syndrome, lax joints, kyphoscoliosis, genu valgum and pes cavus. Hypotonia is often quite striking and has been noted on one occasion to be the first symptom in an affected neonate (Moyes and Alexander, 1977). The patients may show diffuse freckling or café au lait spots and occasional cutaneous neuromas or neurofibromas (Schimke, 1977). Megacolon may be a presenting feature, and bowel problems are not uncommon (Carney et al., 1976).

Some nosologists term this entity MEN II(b), since there is an overlap with MEN II(a) insofar as the malignant changes are concerned. The best current evidence supports the idea that the syndromes are quite distinct. For example, parathyroid hyperplasia is common in MEN II and rare in MEN III (Khairi et al., 1975). Ectopic hormone production has also been described less frequently in MEN III, although this may be an artifact, since the number of cases of MEN III reported are fewer in number. The most compelling evidence has been provided by Williams (1977), who showed that the mean survival of patients with MEN III was 27 years versus 60 years for MEN II, suggesting a more virulent process in

MEN III. Despite advice to the contrary, it seems evident that early surgical removal of the thyroid gland in patients with the other features of MEN III, is mandatory whether calcitonin values are elevated or not (Schimke, 1973b). MTC has been documented in children with MEN III, and C cell hyperplasia has been found at operation in patients as young as 15 months of age (Moyes and Alexander, 1977).

MEN III is also an autosomal dominant disorder, but the degree of penetrance and the range of expressivity are unknown, since only some 50 cases have been reported. It will be necessary to study all first-degree relatives, looking carefully for physical as well as endocrinologic clues to support the diagnosis. Because of the disability engendered by the neurologic aspect of the syndrome and the individual's shortened survival, it may be that reproductive performance is poor, and the spontaneous mutation rate is substantially higher than with either MEN I or MEN II.

McCune-Albright Syndrome

The McCune-Albright syndrome is a most unusual disorder that has long been of interest to pediatricians and endocrinologists alike. It is classically characterized by the triad of polyostotic fibrous dysplasia, café au lait skin pigmentation, and isosexual precocity — the latter occurring predominantly, but not exclusively, in females. In the years since the original characterizations of the disease by Albright et al. (1937), it has become evident that a host of other endocrine disorders may accompany the basic symptoms. For example, Cushing's syndrome and either gigantism or acromegaly have been seen on a number of occasions. The presence of either or both of these endocrinopathies in association with the sexual precocity has prompted the suggestion that the basic lesion in the disorder is hypothalamic in origin (Lightner et al., 1975). Although the discovery of a chromophobe adenoma in such a patient neither confirms nor refutes a hypothalamic etiology (Joishy and Morrow, 1976), some patients have been documented as having Cushing's syndrome on a primary adrenal basis with low plasma ACTH levels (Danon et al., 1975). Other individuals have had hyperthyroidism, usually with nodular goiters (Samuel et al., 1972), and in those few cases studied in recent years, plasma thyroid-stimulating hormone (TSH) levels were also shown to be low (DiGeorge, 1975). Moreover, although the pituitary gonadotropin levels are inappropriately high enough to account for the sexual precocity in some patients, in others the disorder seems to occur on a primary gonadal basis. Bilateral pheochromocytomas have also been seen (Kissel et al., 1975). Current evidence favors multiple primary endocrine gland dysfunction rather than a hypothalamic abnormality.

The bone lesion that is characteristic of the condition resembles that seen in hyperparathyroidism and may even be responsible for pathologic fractures. Parathyroid hyperplasia has been described histologically on a number of occasions, but clear evidence of consistent clinical hyperparathyroidism is lacking (Benedict, 1962).

The various endocrine glands that are responsible for the symptoms generally show adenomatous hyperplasia at operation, but no verified malignancy has been described. The McCune-Albright syndrome has been reported once in monozygotic female twins, one of whom showed the classic findings, whereas the other had only bone lesions (Lemli, 1977). Otherwise, all cases have been sporadic in occurrence. The strongly associated tendency of the patients to have endocrine hyperfunction provides a good rationale for classifying the disease as a multiple endocrine adenoma syndrome. The underlying pathogenetic mechanism responsible for the condition is unknown.

Beckwith-Wiedemann Syndrome

The Beckwith-Wiedemann syndrome is a constellation of abnormalities, which includes fetal and early postnatal gigantism — frequently with hemihypertrophy, omphalocele, macroglossia, visceromegaly, neonatal hypoglycemia, a predilection for malignancy, and a host of other variable anomalies (Reddy et al., 1972). A recent compilation of available cases indicates that one in seven patients with the Beckwith-Weidemann syndrome has hemihypertrophy, and if this facet of the condition is present, the risk of associated malignancy may be as high as 20 percent (Sotelo-Avila and Good, 1976). The most common malignancy is Wilms' tumor, but adrenal cortical carcinoma is also frequent. Islet cell hyperplasia (so-called nesidioblastosis) as well as hyperplastic changes in other endocrine organs such as the gonads and pituitary have also been seen. Relative hyperinsulinism may be present early and probably accounts, at least partially, for the hypoglycemia seen in some cases. It is interesting to note that whereas some patients have interstitial cell hyperplasia of the testes, others have cryptorchidism and evidence of hypogonadism. Affected females may have large ovaries, large uteri and clitoromegaly (Fillipi and McKusick, 1970).

Most reported cases have been in sibs, but two-generation transmission has been seen (Ben-Galim et al., 1977). The syndrome may well be an autosomal dominant trait, with much reduced penetrance and variable expressivity.

Other Potential Syndromes Involving Multiple Endocrine Gland Neoplasia

A number of reports have suggested the existence of additional syndromes of endocrine gland adenomatosis or neoplasia. For the most part, the patients described were isolated examples of the condition in question, and the family history was negative. As an example, Berg et al. (1976) cited a female patient with a chemodectoma, a bronchial carcinoid, a pituitary adenoma, and hyperplasia of the parathyroids and the antral and duodenal gastrin-producing cells. Others have postulated the existence of multiple endocrine adenomatosis syndromes of mixed type, comprising some features of the established syndromes described earlier (Hansen et al., 1976). Hyperparathyroidism occurs with papillary thyroid carcinoma more frequently than would be expected by chance, but no familial examples have been recorded, and the reason for the association remains unclear (LiVolsi and Feind, 1976).

Thyroid cancer, usually papillary or mixed papillary and follicular, has been reported in a number of heritable syndromes in which malignancy is a prominent feature, e.g., Gardner's syndrome, Cowden's syndrome, Werner's syndrome, and what has been termed the *cancer family syndrome*. In the latter condition, the predisposition to malignancy appears to be inherited as an autosomal dominant trait, and affected individuals may suffer from multiple malignancies (Schimke, 1978). There may be a number of these cancer family syndromes, but two seem to be reasonably well delineated. Both feature a high incidence of breast carcinoma, but in the first, the associated lesions are primarily adenocarcinomas of the gastrointestinal and reproductive systems, whereas in the second, the tendency to develop breast cancer is combined with embryonal tumors in children and soft tissue sarcomas in both children and adults. Adrenal cortical and ovarian cancers have also been seen intermittently in family members affected by these malignant syndromes. Adrenal tumors have also been reported in patients with Gardner's syndrome, and it may well be that endocrine tumors are an occasional pleiotropic manifestation of this autosomal dominant gene defect.

A family in which multiple females were affected with thyroid adenomas over four generations has been described, and it is of interest that at least three individuals had arrhenoblastomas (Jensen et al., 1974). The incidence of thyroid adenomas varies widely, depending largely on the zeal of the examining clinician or pathologist, and since ovarian tumors have been recorded over multiple generations on a number of occasions, it is conjectural whether or not this family represents a new endocrine tumor syndrome.

Pheochromocytoma may be a facet of von Recklinghausen's syndrome and the von Hippel-Lindau syndrome as well as of MEN types II and III. A variety of other endocrine lesions have been seen with neurofibromatosis, including hyperparathyroidism, nonspecific goiter, acromegaly, and precocious puberty — the latter two being seen in numbers significant enough to warrant consideration of von Recklinghausen's syndrome in the differential diagnosis of such patients (Saxena, 1970). Recent studies support an embryologic relationship between the adrenal medulla and the paraganglia (carotid and aortic bodies, glomus jugulare, ganglion nodusum, and other related structures), and tumors of both organs have been seen in a familial setting. For example, a father with a glomus jugulare tumor had two daughters with bilateral carotid body tumors, and one of these girls subsequently developed a pheochromocytoma (Pollack, 1973). Interestingly, extra-adrenal pheochromocytomas (paragangliomas) have been reported on at least two occasions in conjunction with the Naegeli type of incontinentia pigmenti. One of the patients had a pituitary adenoma and parathyroid hyperplasia as well (Farhi et al., 1976). A positive family history for the typical skin lesions was present in one instance, but other endocrinopathy was not present in either family. Although it is hazardous to speculate on the basis of one or two cases, the known neural crest origin of both the pheochromocyte and the melanocyte is noteworthy.

SYNDROMES WITH MULTIPLE ENDOCRINE GLAND HYPOFUNCTION

Polyglandular Deficiency Syndrome

The combination of idiopathic hypoadrenalism and lymphocytic thyroiditis was first reported in 1926 by Schmidt, whose name has become eponymously attached to the syndrome (Rimoin and Schimke, 1971). In recent years, it has become evident that the failure of virtually any endocrine organ can occur in this syndrome, even to the point of simulating panhypopituitarism. Coexistent diabetes mellitus, which is often but not invariably insulin-dependent, may complicate the clinical picture (Carpenter et al., 1964). The serologic hallmark of the disease is the presence of one or more endocrine gland autoantibodies. Other autoantibodies such as those directed toward gastric parietal cells may be detected, with or without clinical evidence of pernicious anemia. The clinical spectrum may also include sprue, IgA deficiency, vitiligo, and, not surprisingly, Graves' disease.

The majority of case descriptions of Schmidt's syndrome are of sporadic incidents in predominantly female patients. The early reports of familial instances noted affected sibs with varying manifestations of the syndrome, suggesting recessive inheritance. More recently, two-generation transmission of this polyendocrine syndrome has been documented, occasionally with incomplete penetrance insofar as clinical affliction is concerned (Frey et al., 1973; Van Thiel et al., 1977). However, some presumably unaffected individuals had antiendocrine gland antibodies, and very few others were studied from this point of view. It seems quite likely that this syndrome is indeed inherited — probably as a variably expressed autosomal dominant trait — the heritable factor possibly being a tendency to develop autoimmune endocrine disease, which may or may not become clinically evident, depending upon other, unknown factors. Volpe (1977) has suggested that fundamentally the condition is not an endocrinopathy but an immunopathy, with the basic lesion resulting from abnormal immune surveillance — a function normally mediated by T lymphocytes. The various antibodies formed may cause endocrine hypofunction by blocking hormone-receptor interaction. Alternatively, they may be stimulatory, as in Graves' disease, in which it is the antigen-antibody interaction that apparently produces thyrotoxicosis. This theory does not satisfactorily explain why members of the same family develop different diseases or why some individuals with serologic abnormalities are asymptomatic —if not indefinitely, at least for prolonged periods.

The statistical association of many of these endocrine disorders with specific HLA antigens might provide a clue to their basic etiology. HLA-B8 and DW3 are the two alleles that have been most commonly associated with autoimmune endocrine disease, although other HLA types may be seen in nonwhite populations (Nerup et al., 1974; Thomsen et al., 1975). The reason for this association is not known, but some speculation has centered on the possibility that the HLA region may be closely linked to certain mutant *immune response (Ir)* genes and thereby may serve as a marker for the presence of these genes. The entire topic of HLA-disease association and linkage disequilibrium has been extensively discussed in an earlier volume of this series (McMichael and McDevitt, 1977). If one or more *Ir* genes were abnormal, it is possible that an appropriate immune response could not be generated to combat certain, presumably viral, exogenous agents. If the virus were polytropic, especially with respect to the endocrine system, cellular lysis would occur, resulting in the release of "forbidden" contents in high concentrations. Presumably, the remaining normal immune system would be stimulated, producing autoantibodies and perhaps cytolytic cellular autoimmunity, thereby perpetuating the destructive process. Whether or not a given individual developed clinical disease might then depend upon appropriate contact with the virus in sufficient titer to initiate infection, or the possession of a quite independent immune capability for dealing with that virus or a host of other possibilities. Seen in this light, the basic lesion in Schmidt's syndrome might reside in an *Ir* gene. Thus, in certain families in which HLA–B8 is segregating, for example, individuals might also possess the mutant *Ir* gene and be at risk for autoimmune endocrine disease. If the gene is closely linked or even contiguous to the HLA locus, one might predict that 50 percent of the first-degree relatives of a patient with HLA–B8 and endocrinopathy would be at risk for autoimmune endocrine disease as well. In its minimal manifestation, this condition might appear merely as antiendocrine tissue antibodies, whereas in its maximal expression polyglandular failure would result. Thus, the offspring of patients with juvenile diabetes and an HLA–B8 haplotype might have far less than a mendelian risk for developing diabetes, but the risk for failure of any endocrine gland within their lifetime may well approach 50 percent. Obviously, such a hypothesis requires that families of patients with autoimmune endocrine disease be studied extensively, not only with regard to overt endocrine dysfunction but also seeking evidence of abnormal immune responses. Longitudinal studies are essential, since the presence of autoimmunity may be an age-related phenomenon. It is also quite conceivable that the etiology of the polyglandular deficiency syndrome is heterogeneous, so that the abnormal suppressor T-cell theory and the defective *Ir* gene hypothesis might each account for a subgroup of such patients. Alternatively, the two postulates may be reconciled if the preliminary studies showing that *Ir* genes are expressed on T (suppressor) cells can be verified (Mozes, 1975).

Schmidt's syndrome has features in common with the candidiasis-endocrinopathy syndrome — another disorder in which autoimmune endocrine disease is associated with demonstrably defective cellular immunity (see later discussion). However, the latter syndrome appears in early childhood, whereas Schmidt's syndrome more commonly becomes evident in later life, although it may develop in adolescence. Diabetes mellitus is a fairly consistent feature of Schmidt's syndrome but not of the candidiasis-endocrinopathy complex whereas the converse is true with hypoparathyroidism. No HLA association has been shown for the candidiasis-endocrinopathy syndrome, and current evidence favors an autosomal recessive mode of inheritance.

At present, the pathogenesis of various disorders involving autoimmune endocrine failure remains enigmatic. Yet, rapid advances in fractional and specific immunologic testing may well uncover the basic gene defect or defects in the not-too-distant future.

Candidiasis-Endocrinopathy Syndrome

Whitaker et al. (1956) and Spinner et al. (1968) have reported a number of families, occasionally consanguineous, in which more then one sibling exhibited mucocutaneous candidiasis in conjunction with hypoparathyroidism or adrenal insufficiency, or both. Organ-specific antibodies have been detected in these patients — not only against the parathyroid glands and the adrenal glands but also against the thyroid gland and the gastric parietal cells. In addition, some affected patients have concomitant thyroiditis and pernicious anemia. Other individuals have a sprue-like illness, and premature primary ovarian failure has been seen (Lucky et al., 1977). Defective cellular immunity to *Candida albicans* has been demonstrated in affected patients, and some have more generalized anergy (Kirkpatrick et al., 1970). The fungal infection becomes evident in the first years of life. No cause and effect relationship has been shown between the endocrinopathy and the candidiasis; i.e., neither has been convincingly implicated in the etiology of the other. Because of the circulating antibodies, an autoimmune basis for the disease has been invoked, but this explanation begs the question. It has been postulated that the candidiasis results from a deficit in the release of cellular factors mediating delayed hypersensitivity (Kirkpatrick et al., 1976). Although a mechanistically similar releasing defect might account for the endocrine hypofunction, it does not explain the presence of the autoantibodies. Other workers have postulated that the syndrome is due to a primary T cell deficiency with resultant B cell dysfunction, the latter being responsible for the endocrine gland autoantibodies (Cahill et al. 1974).

The fungal infection is refractory to conventional antibiotics alone, but at least partial remission has been achieved by administration of antifungal agents coupled with transfer factor (Kirkpatrick et al., 1976). Successful treatment of the candidiasis does not ameliorate the endocrinopathy, and appropriate replacement therapy is required. Interestingly, at least one patient required excessively large doses of 1,25-dihydroxyvitamin D_3 to normalize serum calcium levels (Chesney et al., 1977). Although it is hazardous to speculate on the basis of one case, this relative refractoriness to conventional therapy may also be related to some immune process involving vitamin D–receptors.

The available evidence suggests that the candidiasis-endocrinopathy complex is inherited as an autosomal recessive defect. Possible genetic heterogeneity is indicated by a report of a family in which the adrenal deficiency was felt to be secondary to low pituitary ACTH reserve (Castells et al., 1971). It is conceivable that, like the parathyroid glands or the adrenal glands, the anterior pituitary gland or at least some of its secretory cells might be primarily involved in the syndrome on occasion. Both idiopathic Addison's disease and hypoparathyroidism have been reported separately in familial aggregates (Rimoin and Schimke, 1971), and they may occur together in Schmidt's syndrome. Fungal infection is not evident in any of these conditions; the age of onset of the endocrine failure is generally in adulthood, and although endocrine gland autoantibodies have occasionally been found in asymptomatic family members, a definitive mode of inheritance has not been established. However, as mentioned previously, autosomal dominant inheritance of Schmidt's syndrome is likely. The fact that severe *Candida* infection may complicate a number of heritable phagocytic disorders confuses the differential diagnosis further (McKusick, 1975). Wells et al. (1972) have described familial candidiasis without endocrinopathy, which is also apparently inherited as a recessive trait. Candidiasis of later onset and of a seemingly sporadic nature may herald the presence of lymphoreticular malignancy — particularly thymoma (Kirkpatrick, 1976).

Ataxia-Telangiectasia

Ataxia-telangiectasia (AT) is a complex multisystem autosomal recessive disorder that features childhood onset of cerebellar ataxia, oculocutaneous telangiectasia, and a variety of immunologic abnormalities, which include an absent or dysplastic thymus, disorganized or poorly formed lymphoid tissue, with deficient numbers of both T and B cells, impaired cellular immunity, and, classically, absent or markedly reduced serum levels of IgA and IgE (McFarlin et al., 1972). Recurrent sinopulmonary infections are quite common. Perhaps less well known are the endocrine disturbances in AT. Sexual infantilism with growth retardation, absent or dysgenetic ovaries, adrenal hypoplasia, carbohydrate intolerance, and nonspecific cytomegalic changes in the anterior pituitary gland have been seen in various patients (Gershanik and James, 1971). Undoubtedly, the chronic infections suffered by these patients contribute to the growth failure and perhaps the overall decreased endocrinologic reserve, although in some patients infections are not strikingly frequent. Pituitary gland function has been normal in most patients tested, despite the histologic changes. In particular, growth hormone responses to insulin and glucose have generally been adequate (Ammann et al., 1970; Gershanik and James, 1971), although exceptions have been noted (Severi et al., 1976). The reason for the growth failure is not clear but may be related to a pleiotropic effect of the gene or to other as yet unspecified factors.

Gonadal dysgenesis, particularly noteworthy in the ovary, has been a relatively consistent feature of AT (Miller and Chatten, 1967). In older surviving individuals, these dysgenetic ovaries may undergo malignant degeneration into gonadoblastomas and dysgerminomas (Goldsmith and Hart, 1975; Buyse et al., 1976). The latter may be part of the general propensity of patients with AT to develop neoplasia, particularly of the reticuloendothelial system but also of other organs such as stomach and skin (Schimke, 1978). Interestingly, neonatal thymectomy in mice induces ovarian but not testicular dysgenesis (Nishizuka and Sakakura, 1971). Cytomegalic changes in the anterior pituitary gland have also been seen after this procedure in mice (Biachi et al., 1971). In addition to hairlessness, mice homozygous for the autosomal recessive *nude mutation* have thymic and ovarian dysgenesis, hypothyroidism, and persistence of the fetal adrenal gland (Besedowsky and Sorkin, 1974). The immunologic and reproductive defects in these mice can be overcome by grafts of thymus or thymic epithelium, although the hairlessness persists (Wortis, 1975). If the parallel is appropriate, one might conclude that the ovarian and possibly the other endocrine maldevelopment in AT is a secondary consequence of the immunologic defect, perhaps originating in a destructive intrauterine infectious process or some kind of autoimmune oophoritis. It is of interest that the IgA deficiency in some patients with AT apparently results from anti-IgA antibodies (McFarlin et al., 1972). Despite the virtual absence of a thymus gland, *nude* mice also develop autoantibodies. An alternative explanation for the findings in both AT and the murine *nude* mutation might be an absence of suppressor T cells, allowing for the expression of autoimmune phenomenon. This interpretation might also be applied to the glucose intolerance commonly noted in AT. Affected individuals frequently show marked hyperglycemia, resistance to ketosis, relatively little glucosuria, and elevated insulin levels (Schalch et al., 1970). The blood glucose response to exogenous insulin is also blunted. Although other interpretations are possible, these findings are compatible with an abnormal interaction between insulin and its cellular receptors, perhaps engendered by antireceptor antibodies, such as has been seen in acquired forms of lipodystrophy.*

Patients with AT also show biochemical evidence of hepatic dysfunction, although it is probably not severe enough to account for the carbohydrate abnormalities seen in this condition. Waldman and McIntire (1972) found elevated serum alpha-fetoprotein levels in all 30 patients with AT studied and have suggested that the continued production of this hepatic fetal protein is indicative of functional immaturity of the liver and perhaps of other organs as well. They offered the hypothesis that the primary gene defect in AT is an abnormality in the interaction between endodermal and mesodermal cell lines, resulting in incomplete differentiation of several organs derived from visceral epithelium, including the thymus gland and the liver. A more generalized and perhaps less specific developmental defect would have to be postulated to include the central nervous system, the ovary, and perhaps a certain proportion of other endocrine tissues. At present, the fundamental genetic lesion in this complex disorder remains unknown.

Congenital Lipodystrophy

This condition, variously referred to as lipodystrophic (or lipoatrophic) diabetes or the Seip-Bernardinelli syndrome, is often noticed at birth or in early childhood. The major features of the disease include an almost total absence of subcutaneous fat, muscular hypertrophy, large hands and feet, visceromegaly with a protu-

---

*A recent report implicates a defect in affinity of insulin receptors. Bar, R. S., W. R. Levis, M. M. Rechler, L. C. Harrison, C. Siebert, J. Podskalny, J. Roth, and M. Mugges. 1978. Extreme insulin resistance in ataxia-telangiectasia. New Eng. J. Med. 298:1164–1170.

berant abdomen, clitoral enlargement, hirsutism, hyperpigmenta-
tion, and acanthosis nigricans (Seip, 1971). Affected children usually exhibit an increased growth rate prior to puberty, but ultimate
adult height is normal. Mental deficiency is occasionally present, as
are various anomalies of the heart, bones, and kidneys. Although
glucose intolerance is not always evident early, the majority of individuals ultimately develop frank diabetes; in all patients studied in
detail, serum insulin levels were markedly elevated, even in the
face of a normal glucose tolerance test. The diabetes is not accompanied by ketosis, but hyperlipidemia is common, and patients may
succumb to the usual vascular complications of diabetes (Arky and
McCully, 1975). The hepatomegaly results from fatty infiltration and
may eventuate in frank cirrhosis with varices or hepatic failure, or
both.

It has been suggested that the diabetes in this condition is due
to an abnormal insulin-receptor (Kahn et al., 1976), but this finding
is seemingly insufficient to explain the whole clinical picture. Elevated growth hormone levels have been found in some but not all
affected individuals (Tzagournis et al., 1973), and both urinary and
plasma steroid levels have been raised in a few (Seip and Trygstad,
1963). A number of affected young women have had oligomenorrhea, with polycystic ovaries having been suggested as the cause
(Givens et al., 1974). A basic hypothalamic defect has been postulated without much evidence (Seip, 1971). Whatever the fundamental
lesion, the syndrome is almost assuredly genetic. Affected male and
female sibs have been reported — frequently within consanguineous families. Both findings strongly support autosomal recessive
inheritance. However, not all such early-onset cases need be heritable, as the condition may apparently be mimicked by the dien-
cephalic syndrome or by a variety of congenital and acquired lesions of the hypothalamus.

An association between acanthosis nigricans and endocrinopathy has long been noted, e.g., pituitary adenomas (with or without acromegaly), the Stein-Leventhal syndrome, Addison's disease,
and diabetes mellitus (Winkelman et al., 1960; Brown et al., 1966).
In the majority of cases, the skin-endocrine disease complex appears in later life, and treatment of the hormone dysfunction may
ameliorate the pigmentary disturbance (Givens et al., 1974). The
pathogenesis of the skin lesion is unknown, although an abnormal
pituitary peptide has been etiologically incriminated (Nordlund and
Lerner, 1975).

It is assumed that both the cutaneous and endocrine lesions are
acquired. In fact, some patients with adult-onset insulin-resistant di-

abetes and acanthosis have been found to have circulating antibodies against the insulin-receptor, as well as other immunologic abnormalities (Kahn et al., 1976). It is possible that heterogeneity exists. A few patients have been described in whom many of the features of the congenital form of the disease have appeared at or near adolescence. However, in these adolescents, the face is full rather than lipodystrophic, early growth is usually not excessive, retardation is not a feature, and other anomalies are absent. Those patients, chiefly female, who have been studied thus far, show the same primary insulin-receptor defect as has been found in the congenital variety of the condition (Kahn et al., 1976). This adolescent-onset disease is usually sporadic, but dominant transmission over four generations has been seen (Dunnigan et al., 1974). Since affected individuals are almost invariably female, differentiation of an autosomal disorder from an X-linked dominant disorder is impossible at present.

Pseudohypoparathyroidism

Pseudohypoparathyroidism (PHP) was first described by Albright et al. in 1942. The clinical features are quite variable from patient to patient and include hypocalcemia, hyperphosphatemia, subcutaneous and basal ganglia calcification, tetany, short stature, short metacarpals and metatarsals, rounded facies with tooth aplasia, mild to moderate mental retardation, cataracts, and bone lesions that may be a peculiar mixture of osteitis fibrosa cystica and osteosclerosis. Patients with the usual clinical features but with normocalcemia have been designated as having pseudo-pseudohypoparathyroidism (PPHP); however, both normo- and hypocalcemia have been seen in the same family, and indeed, from time to time in the same individual. The more inclusive term *Albright's hereditary osteodystrophy* has been suggested for the condition, but in view of the fact that the bones are only radiographically abnormal about 25 percent of the time, perhaps PHP is the better term.

Classically, PHP shows end-organ resistance to parathyroid hormone; i.e., plasma levels of the hormone are high, and there is no hypercalcemic response to exogenous hormone, hyperphosphaturia does not occur, and urinary cyclic-AMP does not increase (Chase et al., 1969). However, in vitro study of the renal cortex of a single affected patient showed that both the parathyroid hormone–receptor and adenyl cyclase (the enzyme catalyzing the conversion of ATP to cyclic-AMP) appeared to be intact (Marcus et al., 1971). The nonresponding form of PHP is designated as type I, since a type II variety has been described in which urinary cyclic AMP generation is normal, although phosphaturia does not occur (Drezner et al., 1973). To make the situation more confusing, either calcium infusion or vitamin D treatment will normalize the hypercalcemic and phosphaturic response to exogenous parathyroid hormone — in some cases with the expected rise in urinary cyclic AMP (Rodriguez et al., 1974). However, in other patients, no corresponding increase in this compound occurs (Stögman and Fischer, 1975). In other words, PHP, type I might be construed as a defect in the generation of cyclic AMP, whereas PHP, type II might be a failure to respond to the cyclic AMP signal. The presence or absence of bone lesions probably should not be used to differentiate one type of PHP from another, since osteitis fibrosa is a gross manifestation of parathyroid hormone excess and its presence may depend upon the ability of a given patient to metabolize vitamin D to more polar metabolites (Parfitt, 1976). Vitamin D is normally converted to 25-hydroxycholecalciferol in the liver and to 1,25-dihydroxycholecalciferol in the kidney, the latter step, at least, being parathyroid hormone–dependent (Werder et al., 1976). Whatever the exact mechanism, the 1 α–hydroxylation step seems to share in the parathyroid hormone–resistance of PHP, since small doses of 1,25-dihydroxycholecalciferol are effective in normalizing calcium balance and healing the bone lesions, whereas large doses of the parent vitamin (500,000 to 1,500,000 units) are often required (Lambert and Johanson, 1977).

X-linked dominant inheritance was initially postulated for the PHP-PPHP complex, since the majority of published pedigrees showed 2 to 1 female preponderance and only questionable male-to-male transmission. However, males are not usually more severely affected than heterozygous females — unlike the usual situation with X-linked disorders — raising the possibility of sex-limited autosomal dominant inheritance. In support of this latter contention, male-to-male transmission has now been seen in a number of pedigrees, which appear to be valid (Spranger, 1969). In view of the aforementioned variability in urinary cyclic AMP response to exogenous parathyroid hormone, it is likely that genetic heterogeneity exists — a contention further supported by a recent report showing that bone and kidney responsiveness (or resistance) may be separable (Metz et al., 1977).

A number of reports suggest that the condition has more profound implications than merely parathyroid hormone resistance. For example, patients have been described as having PHP and concomitant hypothyroidism, which in some cases was due to inadequate thyrotropin (the level of plasma thyrotropin was immunologically normal in the one case studied) and in other cases was due to primary thyroid deficiency (Marx et al., 1971). Diabetes mellitus and primary amenorrhea have been seen (Rimoin and Schimke, 1971), and prolactin deficiency has been documented in some cases (Carlson et al., 1977). Defective ACTH and growth hormone action have been suggested but not proven. In fact, at least one study showed both normal growth hormone and sulfation factor (somatomedin) activity (Urdanivia et al., 1975). Unfortunately, few of these reports record the family history, and there is no evidence indicating that one PHP type is more prone to additional endocrinopathy than the other. Interestingly, some patients with PHP (type unknown) have been shown to have Turner's syndrome, or at least mosaicism involving a monosomy-X cell line, in such numbers as to seem more than coincidental (Gardner, 1970). This phenomenon is easily explicable if PHP is truly an X-linked disorder. The reasons are less clear if PHP is actually an autosomal dominant condition. Unfortunately, relevant family history has not been available in these cases.

Needless to say, the entire PHP symptom complex is poorly delineated at present and may consist of a number of subtypes. Some of these may show other endocrine dysfunction, perhaps as a consequence of a more generalized inadequate production of or decreased responsiveness to the "hormonal trigger,'" cyclic AMP.

Diabetes Mellitus, Diabetes Insipidus, and Optic Atrophy

This clinical triad has been reported in sibs on a number of occasions and probably constitutes a distinct genetic entity that is inherited as an autosomal recessive defect. Nerve deafness, which is most often mild, may complicate some cases. The diabetes mellitus is of the insulin-requiring, juvenile-onset type, and the diabetes insipidus is of neurohypophyseal origin, usually developing prior to 20 years of age. The frequency of the syndrome has reportedly been as high as 1 in 150 juvenile diabetics (Gunn et al., 1976). Furthermore, it has been suggested that heterozygotes for the gene have an increased probability of developing juvenile mellitus (Fraser and Gunn, 1977). Neither of these latter contentions has been statistically verified. There seems to be a disquieting number of families in which affected sibs do not manifest the entire spectrum of the disease. This observation is not typical of recessively inherited disorders, perhaps indicating that the syndrome is not uniform. HLA testing would be of interest in such families. The basic gene lesion or lesions is not known.

Myotonic Dystrophy

The presenting symptom of this condition is usually weakness or instability, although close questioning of the patient will frequently reveal that myotonia has been present for many years. Although the muscular abnormality dominates the clinical picture, the condition has many nonmuscular symptoms. Cataracts, premature frontal balding in males (and sometimes in females), cardiac conduction defects, pulmonary hypoventilation that is often out of proportion to the muscular disability, mild to moderate mental retardation, and occasionally dementia may all be seen. Affected individuals are prone to recurrent pneumonia in the later stages of the disease, which probably results from a combination of factors, including hypoventilation and an excessive catabolism of immunoglobulins that also seems to be peculiar to the condition.

Hypogonadism is the most prominent endocrinologic feature of this multisystem autosomal dominant disorder, particularly in males. The gonadal failure is progressive and is generally considered to be primary, with seminiferous tubule degeneration being the most striking histologic finding. Early in the course of the disease, plasma levels of testosterone and gonadotropins may be normal, and affected males can reproduce. However, stimulation of gonadotropins with luteinizing hormone–releasing hormone often yields an excessive response without a corresponding rise in basal testosterone levels (Sagel et al., 1975; Takeda and Ueda, 1977).

The ovarian function of affected women is usually better preserved, but oligomenorrhea, spontaneous abortion, and early menopause are not uncommon. Febres et al. (1975) have suggested that in some patients the hypogonadism is at least in part secondary to hypothalamic dysfunction. Indirect support for this contention comes from the observation that there is an absence of sleep-related growth hormone elevation in myotonic dystrophy (Culebras et al., 1977). This phenomenon has been interpreted as deriving from a failure of subcortical integration of the slow-wave phase of sleep with the hypothalamic-pituitary mechanism of growth hormone secretion. Cytoplasmic inclusion bodies have been found in thalamic neurons of affected individuals at necropsy, and it is conceivable that more generalized thalamic malfunction could be responsible in part for hypersomnia, central hypoventilation, occasional endocrine abnormalities, and so forth. Reports of growth hormone responses to insulin-induced hypoglycemia have been conflicting, probably because some patients manifest a certain degree of insulin resistance (Tevaarwerk and Hudson, 1977). Exaggerated responses have been seen, however, and acromegaly has been recorded (Caughey and Koochek, 1974). An apparently nonfunctioning pituitary adenoma has also been seen (Banna et al., 1973). Interestingly, patients with myotonic dystrophy seem to respond normally to exogenous growth hormone, as measured by a net positive retention of sodium, potassium, and nitrogen (Chyatte et al., 1974).

Serum insulin levels are generally increased in individuals with myotonic dystrophy — often in the face of glucose tolerance curves of diabetic configuration. The pancreatic β cells seem to be hyperresponsive to a variety of stimuli (e.g., leucine, arginine, glucagon, tolbutamide) in roughly half the affected patients (Paffenbarger et al., 1976). An abnormal insulin-receptor interaction, akin to that seen in lipodystrophic diabetes (vide infra), has been postulated but no receptor antibodies have been detected in those few patients studied (Kahn et al., 1976), and in at least one group of patients, the insulin-receptor was found to be normal (Kobayashi et al., 1977). Moreover, the glucose response to exogenous insulin is normal, the insulin response to glucose may vary in individual patients, and nearly half the individuals tested will have normal carbohydrate tolerance and insulin responses (Huff and Lebovitz, 1968). The carbohydrate abnormality evidently is not related to the duration or severity of the disease (Cudworth and Walker, 1975), but there are no definitive longitudinal studies. Once diabetes develops, the incidence of microangiopathic complications in myotonic dystrophy appears to be no different than in the usual diabetic patient. Although an abnormal insulin molecule has been incriminated in the pathogenesis of the disease (Huff and Lebovitz, 1968), supportive evidence is lacking, and the serum insulin-proinsulin ratio is not appreciably different from that in controls (Paffenbarger et al., 1976). Patients with progressive muscular dystrophies, such as X-linked Duchenne's disease, also show carbohydrate intolerance but without abnormal insulin secretion — a finding that has been attributed to the absence of muscle bulk that normally would assimilate glucose (Zierler, 1964).

A mild degree of hypothyroidism may be seen in individuals with myotonic dystrophy, but profound myxedema appears to be uncommon (Brumlik and Maier, 1972). No other endocrine abnormalities have been demonstrated consistently.

Obesity-Hypogonadism Syndromes

There are a number of disorders that have obesity and hypogonadism in common, along with a varying series of other congenital anomalies. For the sake of convenience, it might be best to consider them all under the blanket heading of obesity-hypogonadism syndromes. The best known among them is the Biedl-Bardet syndrome, which is an autosomal recessive disorder classically characterized by retinitis pigmentosa, postaxial polydactyly, obesity, mental retardation, and hypogonadotropic hypogonadism. Many authors use the term *Lawrence-Moon-Biedl-Bardet syndrome,* but it is not certain that the patients described by Lawrence and Moon and those reported separately by Biedl and Bardet suffered from the same disorder (Ammann, 1970). Hypogonadism, when present in these syndromes, is more common (or at least more commonly diagnosed) in affected males than in affected females, and it is associated with small genitalia, a reduction in secondary sex characteristics, and occasionally gynecomastia. Diabetes mellitus has been described in some patients (Klein and Ammann, 1969); however, it is unclear whether the carbohydrate intolerance is truly a feature of the disease (perhaps being unmasked when significant obesity develops) or whether such cases actually suffered from the Alström-Hallgren syndrome. The latter condition, which is inherited as an autosomal recessive trait, comprises retinitis pigmentosa, nerve deafness, obesity, hypogonadism, and diabetes mellitus (Goldstein and Fialkow, 1973). In addition to deafness, the differential features include the absence of digital anomalies or significant mental retardation and primary rather than secondary gonadal failure. Like the Biedl-Bardet syndrome, hypogonadism is also more frequently reported.

Another similar condition is Biemond's syndrome, which resembles the Biedl-Bardet syndrome in that it features hypogonadotropic hypogonadism, obesity, and postaxial polydactyly, but it shows other findings as well, such as coloboma of the iris, rather than pigmented retinopathy and more severe retardation (Biemond, 1934). Patients with the Prader-Willi syndrome (obesity, hypogonadism, hypotonia, mental retardation) also have mild carbohydrate intolerance that begins at maturity (Hall and Smith, 1972). The genetics have not been established in either Biemond's syndrome or the Prader-Willi syndrome.

These various conditions have considerable phenotypic overlap, and it is quite likely that additional heterogeneity exists (Edwards et al., 1976). No other endocrine dysfunction has been convincingly demonstrated in this confusing array of syndromes.

Noonan's Syndrome

Individuals with Noonan's syndrome have many features of Turner's syndrome, including short stature, hypogonadism, webbed neck, and ptosis. However, the karotype in Noonan's syndrome is normal, the cardiovascular lesion is that of pulmonary valvar obstruction rather than aortic coarctation, both males and females may be affected, and whereas heterogeneity cannot be totally excluded, autosomal dominant transmission of the condition has been documented (Bolton et al., 1974). The gonadal deficiency appears to be relatively more severe in males and it is usually primary and associated with cryptorchidism. However, hypothalamic dysfunction may be seen either concomitantly or independently, and, in fact, patients with varying types and degress of gonadal hypofunction have been described in the same family. Autoimmune thyroiditis has also been found in a number of individuals affected with this condition (Vesterhus and Aarskog, 1973). The short stature component of the syndrome is probably primary, as no hormonal basis for the growth deficiency has been elucidated.

Werner's Syndrome

This condition is characterized by premature aging, growth retardation, cataracts, scleroderma-like skin changes, diabetes mellitus, and hypogonadism. The diabetes is mild, ketosis is rare, and vascular complications are uncommon. Insulin response to glucose may be exaggerated, and there is relative resistance to exogenous insulin similar to that seen in lipodystrophic diabetes. The gonadal failure is relative and may be progressive, since affected individuals have reproduced. The external genitalia in both males and females are small and atrophic, and secondary sex characteristics are frequently lacking or poorly developed. No other consistent endocrine abnormalities have been described in this rare autosomal recessive disorder.

Fanconi's Syndrome

Chronic pancytopenia with bone marrow hypoplasia, pigmentary disturbances, upper limb malformations, growth retardation, and small genitalia characterize Fanconi's syndrome. There is also an increased susceptibitiy to chromosome breakage and a high incidence of malignancy, particularly leukemia. Panhypopituitarism (Cussen, 1965), isolated growth hormone deficiency (Pochedly, et al., 1971), and adrenal and testicular atrophy (Cowdell et al., 1955) have been seen in a few patients with small pituitary glands having been found at autopsy. These few reports do not permit a decision as to whether or not endocrine dysfunction is a consistent feature of the syndrome. It is important to remember that patients with anemia, on whatever basis, who have been multiply transfused may develop hemosiderosis to such an extent that endocrine gland failure occurs (Steel et al., 1972). Although diabetes mellitus has not been reported in Fanconi's syndrome, an increased prevalence of diabetes has been noted in heterozygotes for this autosomal recessive disorder (Swift et al., 1972).

ENDOCRINE DYSFUNCTION AND CHROMOSOME ANEUPLOIDY

Despite the fact that patients with chromosome aberrations are encountered relatively frequently in referral hospitals and clinics, little metabolic or endocrinologic data is available. This may be due in part to the poor survival potential of aneuploidy for the larger autosomes, with consequent reluctance on the part of the attending physician to undertake extensive testing. The complex chromosome syndromes are frequently characterized by urogenital malformations accompanied by gonadal absence or maldevelopment. Growth hormone deficiency was suggested in the etiology of short stature in a patient with trisomy D (Ruvalcaba et al., 1972) and a patient with a short arm deletion of chromosome 18 (Leisti et al., 1973). Another patient with an interstitial deletion of chromosome 1 was found to have primary hypothyroidism and growth hormone deficiency in addition to other malformations (Koivisto et al., 1976). In general, however, even the partial deletion or trisomy syndromes are not well delineated, at least not from an endocrinologic point of view.

The best known chromosomal syndrome is probably trisomy 21. Hypogonadism is perhaps universal in males, and menstrual irregularities and early menopause are common in females, although at least a few have been fertile. Some researchers think that there is an increased prevalence of diabetes mellitus in Down's syndrome, although most studies have not been well controlled (Farquhar, 1969). Diabetes mellitus does seem unduly frequent in the parents of patients with Down's syndrome, and this disease has been advocated as a possible cause of nondisjunction (Neilsen, 1972). Similarly, primary hypothyroidism has been reputed to be more frequent in this disorder than in the general population, and this may be true in older affected individuals (Murdock et al., 1976).

Glucose intolerance occurs regularly enought in both Turner's syndrome and Klinefelter's syndrome to warrant its inclusion as a facet of these primary hypogonadal disorders. In Turner's syndrome, the prevalence of abnormal glucose tolerance increases with age (Rimoin et al., 1970). Autoimmune thyroiditis may also complicate Turner's syndrome, particularly in females with an isochromosome X. Engel et al. (1969) suggest that the combination of diabetes mellitus and thyroiditis occurs almost exclusively in individuals with isochromosome X constitutions. Although Graves' disease is considered to be immunologically related to Hashimoto's thyroiditis, very few patients with Turner's syndrome and thyrotoxicosis have been reported (Brooks et al., 1977). Abnormal thyroid function does not seem to be an integral feature of Klinefelter's syndrome.

Occasionally both growth hormone and somatomedin levels have been reported to be high in patients with Turner's syndrome, and an end-organ resistance phenomenon has been invoked to reconcile this observation with the short stature that is characteristic of gonadal dysgenesis (Saenger et al., 1976). However, such patients are not totally resistant to exogenous growth hormone with respect to linear growth, so more complex explanations for the growth failure must be sought.

Other endocrine abnormalities have not been found with unusual frequency in either Turner's syndrome or Klinefelter's syndrome or indeed in any of the other sex chromosome aneuploidy syndromes.

References

Albright, F., C. H. Burnett, P. H. Smith, and W. Parsons. 1942. Pseudohypoparathyroidism, an example of "Seabright-Bantam Syndrome." Endocrinology 30:922–932.

Albright, F., A. M. Butler, A. O. Hampton, and P. Smith. 1937. Syndrome characterized by osteitis fibrosa disseminata, areas of pigmentation and endocrine dysfunction with precocious puberty in females. New Eng. J. Med. 216:727–746.

Ammann, A. J., R. J. Duquesnoy, and R. A. Good. 1970. Endocrinological studies in ataxia telangiectasia and other immunological deficiency diseases. Clin. Exp. Immunol. 6:587–595.

Ammann, F. 1970. Investigations cliniques et genetiques sur le syndrome de Bardet-Biedl en Suisse. J. Genet. Hum. 18 (Suppl):1–310.

Arky, R. A., and K. S. McCully. 1975. Lipoatrophic diabetes in a young woman. New Eng. J. Med. 292:35–41.

Banna, M., W. G. Bradley, and G. W. Pearce. 1973. Massive pituitary adenoma in a patient with dystropica myotonica. J. Neurol. Sci. 20:1–6.

Barbosa, J., F. Q. Nuttall, W. Kennedy, and F. Goetz. 1974. Plasma insulin in patients with myotonic dystrophy and their relatives. Medicine 58:307–323.

Baylin, S. B., H. S. Hsu, D. S. Gann, R. C. Smallridge, and S. A. Wells, Jr. 1978. Inherited medullary thyroid carcinoma: a final monoclonal mutation in one of multiple clones of susceptible cells. Science 199:429–431.

Benedict, P. H. 1962. Endocrine features in Albright's syndrome (fibrous dysplasia of bone). Metabolism 11:30–45.

Ben-Galim, E., M. N. Gross-Kieselstein, and A. Abrahamov. 1977. Beckwith-Wiedemann syndrome in a mother and son. Am. J. Dis. Child. 131:801–803.

Berg, B., A. Biörklund, L. Grimelius, S. Ingemansson, L. Larsson, U. Stenram, and M. Akerman. 1976. A new pattern of multiple endocrine adenomatosis. Acta Med. Scand. 200:321–326.

Besedowsky, H. O., and E. Sorkin. 1974. Thymus involvement in female sexual maturation. Nature 249:356–358.

Biachi, E., W. Pierpaoli, and E. Sorkin. 1971. Cytological changes in the mouse anterior
pituitary after neonatal thymectomy: a light and electron microscope study. J.
Endocr. 51:1–6.

Biemond, A. 1934. Het syndrome van Lawrence-Moon en een aanverwant, nieuw
syndrome. Ned. Tijdschr. Geneeskd. 78:1423–1426.

Boden, G., and O. E. Owen. 1977. Familial glucagonemia — an autosomal dominant
disorder. New Eng. J. Med. 296:534–538.

Bolton, M. R., D. M. Pugh, L. F. Mattioli, M. I. Dunn, and R. N. Schimke. 1974. The
Noonan syndrome: a family study. Ann. Intern. Med. 80:626–629.

Brooks, W. H., J. C. Meek, and R. N. Schimke. 1977. Gonadal dysgenesis with Graves'
disease. J. Med. Genet. 14:128–129.

Brown, J., R. K. Winkelmann, and R. V. Randall. 1966. Acanthosis nigricans and pituitary
tumors. J A M A 198:619–623.

Brumlik, J., and R. J. Maier. 1972. Myxedema and myotonic dystrophy. Arch. Intern.
Med. 129:120–122.

Buyse, M., C. T. Hartmann, and M. G. Wilson. 1976. Gonadoblastoma and Dysgerminoma with Ataxia-telangiectasia. In Birth Defects: Original Article Series, Bergsma, D.
(Ed.), Vol. 12, pp. 165–169. White Plains, The National Foundation.

Cahill, L. T., E. Ainbender, and P. E. Glade. 1974. Chronic mucocutaneous candidiasis.
T cell deficiency associated with B cell dysfunction in man. Cell. Immunol. 14:215–
225.

Carlson, H. E., A. S. Brickman, and G. F. Bottazo. 1977. Prolactin deficiency in pseudohypoparathyroidism. New Eng. J. Med. 296:140–144.

Carney, J. A., V. L. Go, G. W. Sizemore, and A. B. Hayles. 1976. Alimentary tract
ganglioneuromatosis. New Eng. J. Med. 295:1287–1291.

Carpenter, C. C., N. Solomon, S. G. Silverberg, T. Bledsoe, R. C. Northcutt, J. R.
Klinenberg, I. L. Bennett, and A. M. Harvey. 1964. Schmidt's syndrome (thyroid and
adrenal insufficiency). Medicine 43:153–180.

Castells, S., S. Fikrig, S. Inamdar, and E. Orli. 1971. Familial moniliasis, defective
delayed hypersensitivity and adrenocorticotropic hormone deficiency. J. Pediat.
79:72–79.

Caughey, J. E., and M. H. Koochek. 1974. Growth hormone in dystrophica myotonia. NZ
Med. J. 70:685–687.

Chase, L. R., G. L. Melson, and E. D. Aurbach. 1969. Pseudohypoparathyroidism:
defective excretion of 3', 5'-AMP in response to parathyroid hormone. J. Clin. Invest.
48:1832–1844.

Chesney, R. W., S. D. Horowitz, B. E. Kream, J. A. Eisman, R. Hong, and H. F. DeLuca.
1977. Failure of conventional doses of 1α, 25-dihydroxycholecalciferol to correct
hypocalcemia in a girl with idopathic hypoparathyroidism. New Eng. J. Med.
297:1272–1297.

Chyatte, S. B., D. Rudman, J. H. Patterson, P. Ahmann, and A. Jordan. 1974. Human
growth hormone in myopathy: myotonic dystrophy, Duchenne muscular dystrophy
and limb-girdle muscular dystrophy. Southern Med. J. 67:170–172.

Cowdell, R. H., P. J. Phizacherly, and D. A. Pyke. 1955. Constitutional anemia (Fanconi's
syndrome) and leukemia in two brothers. Blood 10:788–801.

Cudworth, A. G., and B. A. Walker. 1975. Carbohydrate metabolism in dystrophica
myotonia. J. Med. Genet. 12:127–161.

Culebras, A., S. Podolsky, and N. A. Leopold. 1977. Absence of sleep-related growth
hormone in myotonic dystrophy. Neurology 27:165–167.

Cussen, L. J. 1965. Primary hypopituitary dwarfism with Fanconi's hypoplastic anemia
syndrome, renal hypertension and phycomycosis: report of a case. Med. J. Aust.
2:367–370.

Danon, M., S. J. Robboy, S. Kim, R. Scully, and J. D. Crawford. 1975. Cushing syndrome,
sexual precocity, and polyostotic fibrous dysplasia (Albright syndrome) in infancy. J.
Pediat. 87:917–921.

DiGeorge, A. M. 1975. Editorial: Albright syndrome: is it coming of age? J. Pediat. 87:1018–1020.

Drezner, M., F. A. Neelon, and H. E. Lebovitz. 1973. Pseudohypoparathyroidism type II: a possible defect in the reception of the cyclic AMP signal. New Eng. J. Med. 289:1056–1060.

Dunnigan, M. E., M. A. Cochrane, A. Kelly, and J. W. Scott. 1974. Familial lipoatrophic diabetes with dominant transmission. Q. J. Med. 43:33–48.

Edwards, J. A., P. K. Sethi, A. J. Scoma, R. M. Bannerman, and L. A. Frohman. 1976. A new familial syndrome characterized by pigmentary retinopathy, hypogonadism, mental retardation, nerve deafness and glucose intolerance. Am. J. Med. 60:23–32.

Engel, E., R. C. Northcutt, and K. W. Bunting. 1969. Diabetes and hypothyroidism with thyroid autoantibodies in a patient with a long arm X-isochromosome. J. Clin. Endocr. Metabol. 29:130–132.

Epstein, C. J., G. M. Martin, A. L. Schulz, and A. G. Motulsky. 1966. Werner's syndrome. Medicine 45:177–221.

Farhi, F., S. H. Dikeman, W. Lawson, R. H. Cobin, and F. G. Zak. 1976. Paragangliomatosis associated with multiple endocrine adenomas. Arch. Pathol. Lab. Med. 100:495–498.

Farquhar, J. W. 1969. Early-onset diabetes in the general and the Down's syndrome population. Lancet 2:323–324.

Febres, F., H. Scaglia, R. Lisker, J. Espinosa, T. Morato, M. Shkurovich, and G. Perez-Palacios. 1975. Hypothalamic-pituitary-gonadal function in patients with myotonic dystrophy. J. Clin. Endocr. Metabol. 41:833–840.

Fillipi, G., and V. A. McKusick. 1970. The Beckwith-Wiedemann syndrome. Medicine 49:279–298.

Fox, P. S., J. W. Hofmann, J. J. Decosse, and S. D. Wilson. 1974. The influence of total gastrectomy on survival in malignant Zollinger-Ellison tumors. Ann. Surg. 180:558–566.

Fraser, F. C., and T. Gunn. 1977. Diabetes mellitus, diabetes insipidus and optic atrophy. J. Med. Genet. 14:190–193.

Frey, H. M., J. A. Vogt, and J. Nerup. 1973. Familial poly-endocrinopathy. Acta Endocr. 72:401–414.

Gardner, L. I. 1970. Pseudo-pseudohypoparathyroidism due to unequal crossing-over? Lancet 2:879–880.

Gershanik, J. J., and V. James. 1971. Ataxia telangiectasia and growth failure. Am. J. Dis. Child. 122:538–546.

Givens, J. R., I. J. Kerber, W. L. Wiser, R. N. Anderson, S. A. Coleman, and S. A. Fish. 1974. Remission of acanthosis nigricans associated with polycystic ovary disease and stromal luteoma. J. Clin. Endocr. Metabol. 38:347–355.

Goldsmith, C. I., and W. R. Hart. 1975. Ataxia telangiectasia with ovarian gonadoblastoma and contralateral dysgerminoma. Cancer 35:1338–1342.

Goldstein, J. L., and P. J. Fialkow. 1973. The Alström syndrome. Medicine 52:53–71.

Gunn, T., R. Bertolussi, J. M. Little, F. Andermann, F. C. Fraser and M. Belmonte. 1976. Juvenile diabetes mellitus, optic atrophy, sensory nerve deafness and diabetes insipidus — a syndrome. J. Pediat. 89:565–570.

Hall, B. D., and D. W. Smith. 1972. Prader-Willi syndrome. J. Pediat. 81:286–293.

Hansen, O. P., M. Hansen, H. H. Hansen, and B. Rose. 1976. Multiple endocrine adenomatosis of mixed type. Acta Med. Scand. 200:327–333.

Huff, T. A., and H. E. Lebovitz. 1968. Dynamics of insulin secretion in myotonic dystrophy. J. Clin. Endocr. Metabol. 28:992–998.

Jaffe, B. M., D. F. Kopen, K. DeSchryver-Kecskemati, R. L. Gingerich, and M. Greider. 1977. Indomethacin-responsive pancreatic cholera. New Eng. J. Med. 297:817–821.

Jansen-Goemans, A. and J. Engelhardt. 1977. Intractable diarrhea in a boy with vasoactive intestinal peptide-producing ganglioneuroblastoma. Pediatrics 59:710–716.

Jensen, R. D., H. J. Norris, and J. F. Fraumeni, Jr. 1974. Familial arrhenoblastoma and thyroid adenoma. Cancer 33:218–223.

Joishy, S. K., and L. B. Morrow. 1976. McCune-Albright syndrome associated with a functioning pituitary chromophobe adenoma. J. Pediat. 89:73–75.

Kahn, C. R., R. S. Bar, J. S. Flier, and P. Gordon. 1976. Annotation. New Eng. J. Med. 295:107.

Kahn, C. R., J. S. Flier, R. S. Bar, J. A. Archer, P. Gordon, M. M. Martin, and J. P. Roth. 1976. The syndromes of insulin resistance and acanthosis nigricans. New Eng. J. Med. 294:739–745.

Khairi, M. R., R. N. Dexter, N. J. Burzynski, and C. C. Johnston, Jr. 1975. Mucosal neuroma, pheochromocytoma and medullary thyroid carcinoma: multiple endocrine neoplasia type 3. Medicine 54(2):89–112.

Kirkpatrick, C. H. 1976. Cancer and Immunodeficiency Diseases. In Birth Defects: Original Article Series, Brigsma, D. (Ed.), Vol. 12, pp. 61–78. White Plains, The National Foundation.

Kirkpatrick, C. H., J. W. Chandler, and R. N. Schimke. 1970. Chronic mucocutaneous moniliasis with impaired delayed hypersensitivity. Clin. Exp. Immunol. 6:375–385.

Kirkpatrick, C. H., E. A. Ottenson, T. K. Smith, S. A. Wells, and J. F. Burdick. 1976. Reconstitution of defective cellular unity with foetal thymus and dialysable transfer factor. Clin. Exp. Immunol. 23:414–428.

Kissel, P., J. Floquet, J. M. Andre, M. Fery, and M. Barlier. 1975. Tumeur surrénalienne mixte bilaterale. J. Genet. Hum. 23:207–214.

Klein, D., and F. Ammann. 1969. The syndrome of Lawrence-Moon-Bardet-Biedle and allied diseases in Switzerland. J. Neurol. Sci. 9:479–513.

Knudson, A. G., L. C. Strong, and D. E. Anderson. 1973. Heredity and cancer in man. Prog. Med. Genet. 9:113–158.

Kobayashi, M., J. C. Meek, and E. Streib. 1977. The insulin receptor in myotonic dystrophy. J. Clin. Endocr. Metabol. 45:821–824.

Koivisto, M., H. K. Åkerblom, M. Remes, and A. De la Chapelle. 1976. Primary hypothyroidism, growth hormone deficiency and congenital malformation in a child with the karotype 46, XY, del(1) (q25q32). Acta Paediatr. Scand. 65(4):513–518.

Lambert, L. D., and A. J. Johanson. 1977. Treatment of pseudohypoparathyroidism with oral vitamin D biweekly. J. Pediat. 90:654–656.

Leisti, J., S. Leisti, J. Perkeentupa, E. Savilahti, and P. Aula. 1973. Absence of IgA and growth hormone deficiency associated with short arm deletion of chromosome 18. Arch. Dis. Child. 48:320–322.

Lemli, L. 1977. Fibrous dysplasia of bone. J. Pediat. 91:947–949.

Lightner, E. S., R. Penny, and S. D. Frasier. 1975. Growth hormone excess and sexual precocity in polyostotic fibrous dysplasia (McCune-Albright syndrome): evidence for abnormal hypothalamic function. J. Pediat. 87:922–927.

LiVolsi, V. A., and C. R. Feind. 1976. Parathyroid adenoma and nonmedulary thyroid carcinoma. Cancer 38(3):1391–1393.

Ljungberg, O. 1972. Argentaffin cells in human thyroid and parathyroid and their relationship to C-cells and medullary thyroid carcinoma. Acta Pathol. Microbiol. Scand. (A) 80:589–599.

Lucky, A. W., R. S. Rebar, R. M. Blizzard, and E. M. Goren. 1977. Pubertal progression in the presence of elevated serum prolactins in girls with multiple endocrine deficiencies. J. Clin. Endocr. Metabol. 45:673–678.

Mallinson, C. N., S. R. Bloom, A. P. Warin, P. R. Salmon, and B. Cox. 1974. A glucagonoma syndrome. Lancet 2:1–5.

Marcus, R., J. F. Wilber, and G. D. Aurbach, 1971. Parathyroid hormone–sensitive adenyl cyclase from the renal cortex of a patient with pseudohypoparathyroidism. J. Clin. Endocr. Metabol. 33:537–541.

Marx, S. J., J. M. Hershman, and G. D. Aurbach, 1971. Thyroid dysfunction in pseudohypoparathyroidism. J. Clin. Endocr. Metabol. 33:822–828.

Marx, S. J., D. Powell, P. M. Schimkin, S. A. Wells, A. S. Ketchum, J. E. McGuire, J. P. Bilezikian, and G. D. Aurbach. 1973. Familial hyperparathyroidism. Ann. Intern. Med. 78:371–377.

McCarthy, D. M., E. J. Olinger, R. J. May, B. W. Long, and J. D. Gardner. 1977. H_2-histamine receptor blocking agents in the Zollinger-Ellison syndrome. Ann. Intern. Med. 87:668–675.

McFarlin, D. C., W. Strober, and T. A. Waldmann. 1972. Ataxia-telangiectasia. Medicine 51:231–314.

McKusick, V. A. 1975. Mendelian Inheritance in Man, 4th Ed. Baltimore, Johns Hopkins University Press.

McMichael, A., and H. McDevitt. 1977. The Association Between the HLA System and Disease. In Progress in Medical Genetics, Vol. 2, Steinberg, A. G. et al. (Eds.), pp. 39–150. Philadelphia, W. B. Saunders Company.

Metz, S. A., D. J. Baylink, M. R. Hughes, M. R. Haussler, and R. P. Robertson. 1977. Selective deficiency of 1,25-dihydroxycholecalciferol. New Eng. J. Med. 297:1084–1090.

Miller, M. E., and J. Chatten. 1967. Ovarian changes in ataxia-telangiectasia. Acta Paediatr. Scand. 56:559–561.

Moyes, C. D., and F. W. Alexander. 1977. Mucosal neuroma syndrome presenting in a neonate. Dev. Med. Child Neurol. 19:518–534.

Mozes, E. 1975. Expression of immune response (Ir) genes in T and B cells. Immunogenetics 2:397–410.

Murdock, J. C., W. A. Ratcliffe, D. G. McLarty, J. C. Rodger, and J. G. Ratcliff. 1976. Down syndrome and thyroid function. Lancet 1:36.

Neilsen, J. 1972. Diabetes mellitus in patients with aneuploid chromosome aberrations and in their parents. Humangenetik 16:165–170.

Nerup, J., P. Platz, O. O. Anderson, M. Christy, and J. Lyngsoe. 1974. HL-A antigens and diabetes mellitus. Lancet 2:864–866.

Nishizuka, Y., and T. Sakakura. 1971. Ovarian dysgenesis induced by neonatal thymectomy in the mouse. Endcrinology 59:886–893.

Nordlund, J. J., and A. B. Lerner. 1975. Letter: Cause of acanthosis nigricans. New Eng. J. Med. 293(4):200.

Normann, T., J. V. Johannessew, K. M. Gantvik, B. R. Olsen, and I. O. Brennhovd. 1976. Medullary carcinoma of the thyroid. Cancer 38:366–377.

Paffenbarger, P. L., T. Pozefsky, and J. S. Soeldner. 1976. The dual relationship of proinsulin-insulin hypersecretion to basal serum levels of cholesterol and triglyceride in myotonic dystrophy. J. Lab. Clin. Med. 87:384–396.

Parfitt, A. M. 1976. The actions of parathyroid hormone on bone: relation of bone remodeling and turnover, calcium homeostasis and metabolic bone disease. Metabolism 25:1157–1188.

Pearse, A. G. E., and J. M. Polak. 1971. Neural crest origin of the endocrine polypeptide (APUD) cells of the gastrointestinal tract and pancreas. Gut 12:783–788.

Pochedly, C., P. J. Collipp, S. R. Wolman, S. Suwansirikul, and J. Regvani. 1971. Fanconi's anemia with growth hormone deficiency. J. Pediat. 79:93–96.

Pollack, R. S. 1973. Carotid body tumors — idiosyncracies. Oncology 27:81–91.

Reddy, J. K., R. N. Schimke, C. H. Chang, D. J. Svoboda, J. Slaven, and L. Therou. 1972. Beckwith-Wiedemann syndrome. Arch. Pathol. 94:523–532.

Rimoin, D. L., E. Harder, B. Whitehead, S. Packman, G. T. Peake, and W. S. Sly. 1970. Abnormal glucose tolerance in patients with gonadal dysgenesis and their parents. Clin. Res. 18:395.

Rimoin, D. L., and R. N. Schimke. 1971. Genetic Disorders of the Endocrine Glands. St. Louis, C. V. Mosby Company.

Rodriguez, H. J., H. Villarred, Jr., S. Klahr, and E. Slatopolsky. 1974. Pseudohypoparathyroidism type II: restoration of normal renal responsiveness to parathyroid hormone by calcium administration. J. Clin. Endocr. Metabol. 39(4):693–701.

Ruvalcaba, R. H., H. C. Thuline, and V. C. Kelley. 1972. Plasma growth hormone patients with chromosome anomalies. Arch. Dis. Child. 47:307–309.

Saenger, P., E. Schwartz, E. Wiedemann, L. S. Levine, M. Tsai, and M. I. New. 1976. The interaction of growth hormone, somatomedin and oestrogen in patients with Turner's syndrome. Acta Endocr. (Kbh.) 81(1):9–18.

Sagel, J., L. A. Distiller, J. E. Morley, and H. Issacs. 1975. Myotonia dystrophica: Studies on gonadal function using leuteinizing hormone-releasing hormone (LRH). J. Clin. Endocr. Metabol. 40(6):1110–1113.

Samuel, S., S. Gelman, H. S. Maurer, and I. M. Rosenthal. 1972. Hyperthyroidism in an infant with McCune-Albright syndrome: report of a case with myeloid metaplasia. J. Pediat. 80:275–278.

Saxena, K. M. 1970. Endocrine manifestations of neurofibromatosis in children. Am. J. Dis. Child. 120:265–271.

Schalch, D. S., E. D. McFarlin, and M. H. Barlow. 1970. An unusual form of diabetes mellitus in ataxia telangiectasia. New Eng. J. Med. 282:1396–1402.

Schimke, R. N. 1973a. Genetics of hormone-secreting tumors. Clin. Gastroenterol. 2:661–673.

Schimke, R. N. 1973b. Phenotype of malignancy: the mucosal neuroma syndrome. Pediatrics 52:283–284.

Schimke, R. N. 1976. Multiple endocrine adenomatosis syndromes. Adv. Intern. Med. 21:249–265.

Schimke, R. N. 1977. Tumors of the Neural Crest System. In Genetics of Human Cancer, Mulvihill, J. J., R. W. Muller, and J. F. Fraumeri, Jr. (Ed). New York, Raven Press.

Schimke, R. N. 1978. Genetics and Cancer in Man. Edinburgh, Churchill-Livingston.

Schimke, R. N. and W. H. Hartmann. 1965. Familial amyloid-producing medullary thyroid carcinoma and pheochromocytoma. Ann. Intern. Med. 63:1027–1039.

Schimke, R. N., W. H. Hartmann, T. E. Prout, and D. L. Rimoin. 1968. Syndrome of bilateral pheochromocytoma, medullary thyroid carcinoma and multiple neuromas. New Eng. J. Med. 279:1–7.

Seip, M. 1971. Generalized lipodystrophy. Erg. Inn. Med. Kinderheil. 31:59–95.

Seip, M., and O. Trygstad. 1963. Generalized lipodystrophy. Arch. Dis. Child. 38:447–453.

Severi, F., A. G. Ugazio, V. Magrini, E. Biachi, E. Pedroni, and V. L. Burgio. 1976. Unusual combination of immune and endocrine deficiences. Helv. Pediat. Acta 31:395–405.

Sipple, J. H. 1961. The association of pheochromocytoma with carcinoma of the thyroid gland. Am. J. Med. 31:163–166.

Sotelo-Avila, C., and W. M. Good, III. 1976. Neoplasms associated with the Beckwith-Wiedemann syndrome. Perspect. Pediat. Pathol. 3:255–272.

Spinner, M. W., R. M. Blizzard, and B. Childs. 1968. Clinical and genetic heterogeneity in idiopathic Addison's disease and hypoparathyroidism. J. Clin. Endocr. Metabol. 28:795–804.

Spranger, J. S. 1969. Skeletal Dysplasias and the eye: Albright's Hereditary Osteodystrophy. In Birth Defect: Original Article Series, Bergsma, D. (Ed.), Vol. 5, pp. 122–128. White Plains, The National Foundation.

Steel, C. M., S. T. G. Butterworth, and A. J. Keay. 1972. Endocrine studies in a case of congenital (erythroid) hypoplastic anemia. Acta Haematol. 47:109–117.

Stögmann, W., and J. A. Fischer. 1975. Pseudohypoparathyroidism. Am. J. Med. 59:140–143.

Swift, M., L. Sholman, and D. Gilmour. 1972. Diabetes mellitus and the gene for Fanconi's anemia. Science 178:300–310.

Takeda, R., and M. Ueda. 1977. Pituitary-gonadal function in male patients with myotonic dystrophy–serum luteinizing hormone, follicle stimulating hormone and testosterone levels and histological damage of the testes. Acta Endocr. 84:382–389.

Tevaarwerk, G. J., and J. A. Hudson. 1977. Carbohydrate metabolism and insulin resistance in myotonia dystrophica. J. Clin. Endocr. Metabol. 44:491–498.

Thomsen, M., P. Platz, O. O. Anderson, M. Christry, J. Lyngsoe, N. Nerup, N. Rasmussen, L. P. Ryder, L. S. Nielsen, and A. Sveggaard. 1975. MCL typing in juvenile diabetes mellitus and idiopathic Addison's disease. Transpl. Rev. 22:125–147.

Tischler, A. S., M. A. Dichter, B. Biales, R. A. DeLellis, and H. Wolfe. 1976. Neural properties of cultured human endocrine tumor cells of proposed neural crest origin. Science 192:902–904.

Tschudy, D. P., M. Valsamis, and C. R. Magnussen. 1975. Acute intermittent porphyria: clinical and selected research aspects. Ann. Intern. Med. 83:851–864.

Tzagournis, M., J. George, and J. Herrold. 1973. Increased growth hormone in partial and total lipoatrophy. Diabetes 22:388–396.

Urdanivia, E., A. Mataverle, and M. P. Cohen. 1975. Growth hormone secretion and sulfation factor activity in pseudohypoparathyroidism. J. Lab. Clin. Med. 86:772–776.

Valenta, L. J., M. Michel-Bechet, J. C. Mattson, and F. R. Singer. 1977. Microfollicular thyroid carcinoma with amyloid-rich stroma, resembling the medullary carcinoma of the thyroid. Cancer 39:1573–1586.

Van Thiel, D. H., W. I. Smith, Jr., B. S. Robin, S. E. Fisher, and R. Lester. 1977. A syndrome of immunoglobulin A deficiency, diabetes mellitus, malabsorption, and a common HLA haplotype. Ann. Intern. Med. 86:10–19.

Verner, J. V., and A. B. Morrison. 1974. Endocrine pancreatic islet disease with diarrhea. Arch. Intern. Med. 133:492–500.

Vesterhus, P., and D. Aarskog. 1973. Noonan's syndrome and autoimmune thyroiditis. J. Pediat. 83:237–240.

Volpe, R. 1977. The role of autoimmunity in hypoendocrine and hyperendocrine function. Ann. Intern. Med. 87:86–99.

Waldmann, T. A., and K. R. McIntire. 1972. Serum-alpha-fetoprotein levels in patients with ataxia-telangiectasia. Lancet 2:1112–1115.

Weichert, R. F. 1970. The neural ectodermal origin of the peptide-secreting endocrine glands. Am. J. Med. 49:232–241.

Wells, R. S., J. M. Higgs, A. McDonald, H. Valdimarsson, and P. J. Holt. 1972. Familial chronic muco-cutaneous candidiasis. J. Med. Genet. 9:302–310.

Werder, E. A., H. P. Kurd, F. Egert, J. A. Fischer, and A. Prader. 1976. Effective long term treatment of pseudohypoparathyroidism with oral 1-α-hydroxy and 1,25-dihydroxycholecalciferol. J. Pediat. 89:246–248.

Whitaker, J. A., B. H. Landing, V. M. Esselborn, and R. R. Williams. 1956. Syndrome of familial juvenile hypoadrenocorticism, hypoparathyroidism and superficial moniliasis. J. Clin. Endocr. Metabol. 16:1374–1387.

Williams, E. D. 1965. A review of 17 cases of carcinoma of the thyroid and pheochromocytoma. J. Clin. Pathol. 18:288–292.

Williams, E. D. 1977. Thyroidectomy for genetically determined medullary thyroid carcinoma. Lancet 1:1309–1310.

Winkelmann, R. K., S. R. Scheen, Jr., and L. O. Underdahl. 1960. Acanthosis nigricans and endocrine disease. J A M A 174:1145–1152.

Wortis, H. H. 1975. Pleiotropic Effects of the Nude Mutation. In Birth Defects: Original Article Series, Bergsma, D. (Ed.), Vol. 11, pp. 523–530. White Plains, The National Foundation.

Zierler, K. L. 1964. Diseases of Muscle. In Biochemical Disorders in Human Disease, 2nd Ed., Thompson, R. H. and E. J. King (Eds.). New York, Academic Press, Inc.

5

Inherited Immunodeficiency Diseases: Relationship to Lymphocyte Metabolic Dysfunction*

ELOISE R. GIBLETT

Puget Sound Blood Center and University of Washington School of Medicine, Seattle, Washington

STEPHEN H. POLMAR

Department of Pediatrics, Case Western Reserve University School of Medicine and Rainbow Babies' and Children's Hospital, Cleveland, Ohio

INTRODUCTION
    Complement Components
    Granulocytes
    Lymphocytes
    The Nucleic Acid Cycle, Including Purine Salvage
ADENOSINE DEAMINASE DEFICIENCY
    General Properties of ADA and Heterogeneity in Tissues

*This work was supported in part by U.S. Public Health Service Grants HL-17265, HL-06009, and 5M01RR000 80 and a grant from the National Foundation–March of Dimes (1–424).

INTRODUCTION

The immunodeficiency diseases are a diverse group of disorders characterized by defects in one or more components of the immune system, which result in an increased susceptibility to bacterial, viral, and fungal infection, alone or in combination. Normal cellular and humoral immune responses consist of complex series of biologic events, including diverse activities such as antigen recognition, phagocytosis and processing, interaction of T and B lymphocytes, proliferation, differentiation, and antibody secretion, and antigen-antibody reactions augmented by a variety of intermediating substances such as the complement components. Theoretically, any inherited defect in the cells or the soluble substances that take part in these steps could disrupt a part or all of the normal immune response and consequently could result in an immunodeficiency disease.

Complement Components

In relatively few instances is the molecular basis for a particular immunity defect known. For example, although inherited deficiencies of most of the complement components have been described (the most common of which is C2 deficiency), the accompanying syndrome in this anomaly, when present, is variable. Several affected individuals have had some form of collagen-type disease, but they have not been unusually susceptible to infection, even though their serum had little or no bactericidal or immune adherence activity.

The mode of inheritance for C2 deficiency and nearly all other complement defects (except C1 esterase inhibitor deficiency) is autosomal recessive. The loci for C2, C4, and properdin factor B are on chromosome 6 and are closely linked to the HLA histocompatibility complex. Those rare individuals with defects in complement components other than C2 have variable degrees of susceptibility to infection and, in some instances, a tendency to develop systemic lupus erythematosus or similar diseases.

The deficiency of C1 esterase inhibitor is a special case. It is inherited as an autosomal dominant trait and is associated with episodes of angioedema, which accompany an excess of activated C1. (For detailed descriptions of the inherited complement defects, see Rosen et al., 1971; Rosen, 1975; Alper and Rosen, 1976; and Petersen et al., 1976.)

Granulocytes

A few of the inherited defects in granulocyte function have been traced to deficiencies of specific enzymes required for normal cell function. For example, in those rare individuals with hereditary absence of neutrophil myeloperoxidase, susceptibility to infection seems to be greater than normal, but infections usually are not severe or life-threatening. Myeloperoxidase deficiency is inherited as an autosomal recessive disease (Lehrer and Cline, 1969; Lehrer et al., Salmon et al., 1970; Cheson et al., 1977).

The situation is quite different in chronic granulomatous disease (CGD). This commonly fatal syndrome has an obviously heterogeneous background, its inheritance being either X-linked or autosomal recessive. In very rare instances, a severe deficiency of glucose-6-phosphate dehydrogenase (G6PD) has been implicated (Cooper et al., 1972; Gray et al., 1973). Although the deficiency of a respiratory enzyme, NADPH-dependent oxidase, seems to be the preferred candidate for the cause of most cases of X-linked CGD, the precise enzymatic defect remains a matter of controversy (Patriarca et al., 1971; Hohn and Lehrer, 1975; Iverson et al., 1977). Evidence of more genetic heterogeneity is provided by the fact that in some but not all patients with X-linked CGD, the autosomally controlled Kell blood group system alloantigens are very weakly expressed on red blood cells (Giblett et al., 1971). Moreover, the red blood cells of these patients, as well as the granulocytes of these and nearly all the remaining X-linked cases, lack another antigen called Kx. This antigen, which is present on both granulocytes and red blood cells of normal subjects, is controlled by a locus on the X chromosome (Marsh et al., 1975b). Thus, the molecule bearing the Kx antigenic determinant appears to be a precursor of the Kell system antigens (Marsh et al., 1975a, 1976). This molecule could conceivably be an X-linked enzyme, such as the previously mentioned NADPH-dependent oxidase.

Lymphocytes

In several inherited conditions, lymphocyte dysfunction is associated with varying degrees of immunodeficiency. Determining the molecular bases for these dysfunctions has proven to be very difficult. The present classification of these disorders is based largely upon which lymphocyte subpopulations, T cells or B cells, are primarily involved (Belohradsky et al., 1974; Gatti, 1974; Gelfand et al., 1974; Rosen, 1974, 1975, 1976). Although such a classification is useful, it has definite limitations, particularly since T- and B-cell interaction is required for many immune responses. For example, it is not always possible to determine whether a given syndrome is due to a primary defect in one cell type with a secondary effect on the other.

In some patients, such as those with X-linked hypogammaglobulinemia, there is clear-cut B cell dysfunction. In this disorder, B cells, bearing surface immunoglobulins, are absent (Geha et al., 1973), but pre-B cells are present in the bone marrow (Pearl et al., 1978). Thus, there appears to be a defect in the differentiation of B cell precursors into mature B cells; however, the molecular basis of this defect is not known.

Several partial deficiencies of immunoglobulins have a genetic background, such as the X-linked immunodeficiency with excessive levels of IgM but reduced or absent levels of IgG and IgA (Stiehm and Fudenberg, 1966; Rosen, 1974). Selective deficiency of IgA is the most common immunodeficiency state. This deficiency is genetically heterogenous, having both autosomal recessive and dominant inheritance (Huntley and Stephenson, 1968; Nell et al., 1972). Defects in later stages of B cell and plasma cell differentiation are probably responsible, but the precise causes have not been elucidated.

Inherited dysfunctions of T cells have also eluded definite characterization. For example, the immune defects that accompany ataxia-telangiectasia (an autosomal recessive disease) and the Wiskott-Aldrich syndrome (an X-linked disease) are thought to be associated in some way with thymus dysfunction (Boder, 1975; Rosen, 1975). Whether the resultant T cell effects are primary or secondary and how they are related to the other findings in these syndromes are unresolved questions.

In patients with severe combined immunodeficiency disease (SCID), which was previously termed Swiss-type agammaglobulinemia or thymic alymphoplasia, both B and T cell functions are defective. However, evidence of T cell failure sometimes precedes that of B cell failure by several months, suggesting that T cells may be primarily involved in at least a portion of cases. In addition, the inheritance of SCID is X-linked in some families and autosomal recessive in others, so major differences in the underlying mechanism must exist, even though the end results are often clinically indistinguishable. These patients have an increased susceptibility to infection with a broad spectrum of bacteria, viruses, and fungi. If immunologic reconstitution is not achieved, death usually occurs before the age of 3 years. It has been thought that SCID results from the absence of lymphoid stem cells, however, it now appears that in many SCID patients, stem cells are present but are unable to differentiate into more mature lymphoid cells (Polmar et al., 1975; Pyke et al., 1975; Buckley et al., 1976).

It has recently become evident that although some of the inherited lymphocyte disorders may be due to faulty development or differentiation of an essential structural component, others are clearly due to the absence or the low levels of certain enzymes. So far, such defective enzymes have been related directly or indirectly to the metabolism of purines, pyrimidines, and nucleic acid. A discussion of these enzyme defects, their laboratory and clinical manifestations, and their treatment composes the remainder of this chapter.

The Nucleic Acid Cycle, Including Purine Salvage

The synthesis of purine and pyrimidine nucleotides, which provide the source of cellular genetic information, is maintained by interaction of the de novo and salvage pathways (Fig. 1). The de novo pathways begin with fairly simple compounds and, after undergoing a complex series of metabolic steps, produce the purine nucleotide inosine monophosphate (IMP) and the pyrimidine nucleotide uridine monophosphate (UMP). The deoxyribonucleotides are then formed by the action of one or more reductase enzymes. Although the de novo pathways exist in most mammalian cells, they are apparently incomplete in cells produced by the bone marrow (Murray, 1971), with the exception of lymphocytes after blastogenic stimulation (Schwarzmeier, 1974).

DNA and RNA are constantly being metabolized, and in general their catabolic products are retained for recycling through the salvage pathways, although some cells catabolize the purine bases to uric acid, which is ultimately excreted. The final steps in the salvage pathways involve phosphoribosylation of purine and pyrimidine bases into their respective ribo- and deoxyribonucleotides, with subsequent reincorporation into nucleic acid.

Figure 2 shows the reactions involved in purine metabolism, with enzyme-controlled breakdown of adenosine monophosphate (AMP), IMP, and guanine monophosphate (GMP) to their respective nucleosides — adenosine, inosine, and guanosine. Through the action of nucleoside phosphorylase, inosine and guanosine are converted to their respective bases — hypoxanthine and guanine. Adenosine is a very poor substrate for nucleoside phosphorylase, so it

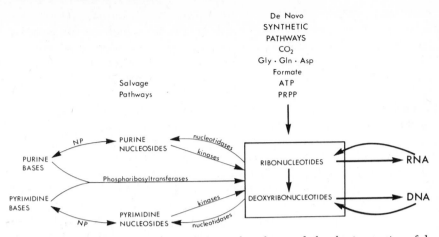

Figure 1. Diagram of the metabolism of nucleic acids by the interaction of de novo and salvage pathways of purines and pyrimidines.

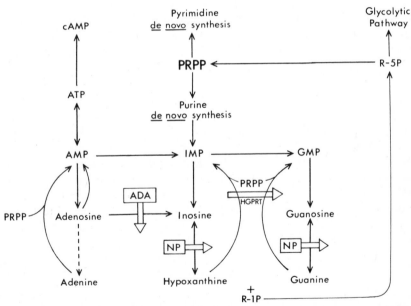

Figure 2. Diagram of purine metabolism, showing the phosphoribosylation steps of the purine bases to their respective nucleotides, the metabolic blocks imposed by three enzyme deficiencies, adenosine deaminase (ADA), nucleoside phosphorylase (NP), and hypoxanthine-guanine phosphoribosyl transferase (HGPRT), as well as the central role of 5-phosphoribosyl-1-pyrophosphate (PRPP) in both purine and pyrimidine de novo synthesis. Deoxy forms of the bases, nucleosides, and nucleotides are not shown.

must be converted to inosine by adenosine deaminase before its subsequent phosphoribosylation. An alternative pathway for adenosine is phosphorylation by a specific enzyme, adenosine kinase. Since the two enzymes have quite different Michaelis constants (K_m), the pathway taken by adenosine is dependent on its concentration (Snyder et al., 1976).

Cells produced by the bone marrow do not contain xanthine oxidase, so the purine bases are not converted to uric acid in these cells. Therefore, the only available next step is phosphoribosylation: hypoxanthine and guanosine to IMP and GMP by hypoxanthine guanine phosphoribosyl transferase (HGPRT); adenine to AMP by adenine phosphoribosyl transferase (APRT).

The importance of the HGPRT-catalyzed step for human homeostasis was first appreciated when Seegmiller et al., (1967) found that deficiency of this enzyme was responsible for the Lesch-Nyhan syndrome. In this disease, failure of HGPRT results in the diversion of purine bases to abnormally large amounts of uric acid. The basis for the associated neurologic dysfunction is unknown. These patients appear to have normal red blood cell and white blood cell metabolism because the bone marrow–produced cells do not produce xanthine oxidase. However, the inherited absence of two other purine salvage enzymes — adenosine deaminase and nucleoside phosphorylase — have profound effects on lymphocyte function.

The fact that disturbances in purine and pyrimidine metabolism interfere with normal function in lymphocytes is well known and forms the basis for the use of many antimetabolites as immunosuppressive drugs (reviewed by Berenbaum, 1975). These drugs primarily inhibit DNA synthesis and cellular proliferation — essential components of virtually all immunologic responses. For example, methotrexate, a long-used antimetabolite, blocks the formation of tetrahydrofolic acid and N^5,N^{10}-methylene tetrahydrofolic acid. The latter compound is required as a methyl donor for the synthesis of thymidine monophosphate from deoxyuridine monophosphate. The conversion of deoxyuridine monophosphate to thymidine monophosphate is also inhibited by 5-fluorouracil and 5-fluoro-2′-deoxyuridine. The purine antimetabolite 6-mercaptopurine and its congener azathioprine inhibit purine metabolism by interfering with the synthesis of inosinic acid to IMP as well as the subsequent conversion of IMP to adenylosuccinic acid and the synthesis of adenylic acid to AMP. These drugs also inhibit xanthylic acid and guanylic acid (GMP) synthesis. Thus, it is not unexpected that many defects in purine and pyrimidine metabolism, resulting either from enzyme deficiency or enzyme inhibition, would adversely affect lymphocyte function.

ADENOSINE DEAMINASE (ADA) DEFICIENCY

General Properties of ADA and Heterogeneity in Tissues

Adenosine deaminase (adenosine aminohydrolase E.C. 3.5.4.4) catalyzes the irreversible deamination and hydrolysis of the purine nucleoside adenosine (as well as of its reduced form, deoxyadenosine). The products of this reaction are inosine (or deoxyinosine) and ammonia (Conway and Cooke, 1939). Most body tissues contain some ADA activity, but particularly high levels are found in the thymus, spleen, other lymphoid tissues, and the intestine (Brady and O'Donovan, 1965; Hirschhorn et al., 1978). In human peripheral blood, ADA is concentrated mainly in lymphocytes and red blood cells, although small amounts are also found in serum. This is also true of certain other animal species, such as the calf. Consequently, the medium of human cell cultures prepared for ADA study should be prepared with horse serum, since it does not contain ADA.

The human adenosine deaminase molecule purified from red blood cells is a monomer with a molecular weight of about 35,000 (Osborne and Spencer, 1973; Agarwal et al., 1975b; Siegenbeek van Heukelom et al., 1976a; Daddona and Kelley, 1977). ADA exists as several different tissue-specific isoenzymes (Ressler, 1969; Akedo et al., 1970; Wüst, 1971; Nishihara et al., 1973), suggesting initially that the human genome contains at least four or five structural gene loci for ADA (Edwards et al., 1971a). However, Hirschhorn and her colleagues (1975) showed that none of the ADA isoenzymes was demonstrable in the tissues of a child with inherited deficiency of ADA. Also, Nishihara et al. (1973) demonstrated an ADA "conversion factor" in human lung, whereas Hirschhorn (1975a) showed that the low molecular weight ADA from normal red blood cells could be converted to the higher weight isoenzymes that are characteristic of other tissues by incubation with tissue extracts obtained from an ADA-deficient child. In another study (Hirschhorn et al., 1976), small amounts of ADA found in the fibroblasts of four ADA-deficient patients had slightly different migration rates when compared with the ADA in normal fibroblasts, suggesting that the abnormal enzyme was produced by a mutant gene at a single ADA structural gene locus. Similar findings were reported by van der Weyden et al. (1974). The various forms of tissue ADA are glycoproteins that differ in their accessible sugar residues, suggesting that the ADA conversion factor could be a single glycoprotein with a heterogeneous carbohydrate content (Swallow et al., 1977).

ADA Genetics

Genetic polymorphism of ADA was first reported by Spencer et al. (1968). Using starch gel electrophoresis, these authors described three inherited electrophoretic phenotypes, ADA 1, ADA 2, and ADA 2-1, representing the homozygous and heterozygous states of two alleles: ADA^1 and ADA^2. The ADA^2 gene frequency in most western European populations is about 0.05, so the ADA 2 phenotype is not very common. Additional ADA phenotypes — all having low frequencies — have subsequently been described (Hopkinson et al., 1969; Dissing and Knudsen, 1969; Detter et al., 1970; Harris et al., 1974; Radam et al., 1974, 1975). Evidence based on mouse-human somatic cell hybrid studies indicate that the structural gene locus for ADA is on chromosome 20 (Creagan et al., 1973b; Tischfield et al., 1974).

Even though the ADA in red blood cells represents the smallest and simplest molecular form of the enzyme, each of the three common phenotypes that are seen after electrophoresis of red blood cell lysates has a three-banded pattern (Spencer et al., 1968). For each phenotype (Fig. 3), the slowest-moving band is the actual gene product. Since the molecule is a monomer, the heterozygous pattern does not contain an isoenzyme with mobility intermediate between

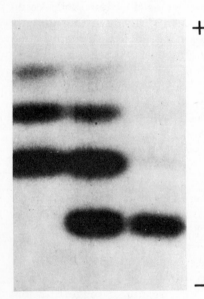

Figure 3. Photograph of starch gel electrophoresis of the three usual phenotypes of adenosine deaminase. (From Meuwissen, H. J. et al. 1975. Impairment of Adenosine Deaminase Activity in Combined Immunological Deficiency Disease. In Combined Immunodeficiency Disease and Adenosine Deaminase Deficiency: A Molecular Defect, Meuwissen, H. J. et al. (Eds.), pp. 73–83. New York, Academic Press, Inc.; and Giblett, E. R. 1975. The Emily Cooley Lecture: Genetic Markers, Enzyme Phenotypes, and Immune Deficiencies. In A Seminar on Polymorphisms in Human Blood, American Association of Blood Banks.)

the ADA^1 and ADA^2 gene products as would be characteristic of a dimeric protein. Lysates of lymphocytes contain the characteristic red blood cell ADA as well as a slower-moving "converted" form of the enzyme (Edwards et al., 1971a; Wüst, 1971). In cultured lymphocytes, this slower-moving (high molecular weight) zone tends to disappear after mitogenic stimulation (Hirschhorn and Levytska, 1974).

Inactive Alleles at the ADA Locus. In 1972, Drs. Hilaire Meuwissen and Bernard Pollara sent a blood specimen to Seattle from a child with severe combined immunodeficiency disease. They requested a study of her blood genetic markers in preparation for a bone marrow transplant. Although none of the other polymorphic enzymes in her red blood cells appeared abnormal, there was complete absence of ADA activity, as shown in Figure 4. A second blood specimen gave the same results, and furthermore, the electrophoretic patterns of her closely related parents had weaker isoenzyme bands than normal subjects of the common ADA 1 phenotype (Fig. 4).

Soon thereafter, blood specimens from another child with SCID

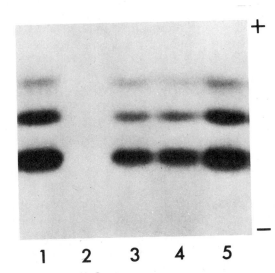

1 2 3 4 5

Figure 4. Photograph of starch gel electrophoresis of five red cell lysates stained for ADA activity. Channels 1 and 5 are from normal controls, channel 2 is from the ADA-deficient child, and channels 3 and 4 are from her consanguineous parents. (From Giblett, E. R., et al. 1972. Adenosine deaminase deficiency in two patients with severely impaired cellular immunity. Lancet 2:1067–1069, Meuwissen, H. J. et al. 1975 Impairment of Adenosine Deaminase Activity in Combined Immunological Deficiency Disease. In Combined Immunodeficiency Disease and Adenosine Deaminase Deficiency: A Molecular Defect, Meuwissen, H. J. et al. (Eds.), pp. 73–83. New York, Academic Press, Inc.; and Giblett, E. R. 1975. The Emily Cooley Lecture: Genetic Markers, Enzyme Phenotypes, and Immune Deficiencies. In A Seminar of Polymorphisms in Human Blood, American Association of Blood Banks.)

and from her parents was received from Dr. Flossie Cohen in De-
troit. The patient also had no demonstrable red blood cell ADA,
and the electrophoretic patterns of her parents' ADA closely resem-
bled those of the parents in the previous family. Spectrophotometric
measurements of ADA activity confirmed that the four parents had
levels that were considerably lower than the normal mean. These
results strongly suggested that the parents were heterozygotes and
their affected children were homozygotes or compound heterozygotes for one or more "silent" alleles at the ADA structural gene
locus. (At that time, there had been a report that the ADA and HLA
loci might be genetically linked on chromosome 6, thus introducing
the possibility that the true genetic lesion was a partial deletion
involving both the ADA locus and some immune response gene.
However, the ADA locus was later assigned to chromosome 20.
Also, some of the ADA-deficient patients were found to have small
amounts of residual enzyme. Thus, the deletion hypothesis became
untenable.)

Descriptions of the first two cases were published near the end
of 1972 (Giblett et al., 1972). A few weeks later, Dissing and Knudsen (1972) reported a similar case from Denmark, and a fourth patient was soon found in Seattle (Ochs et al., 1973). In October 1973,
a symposium on SCID was held in Albany and was subsequently
published (Meuwissen et al., 1975b). Fifty-five cases of SCID were
discussed — of these, 22 had red blood cell ADA measurements and
12 were ADA deficient. The clinical details of these and other cases
are discussed in a later section of this chapter.

In studying the electrophoretic phenotypes of families having
one or more ADA-deficient members, five families were found in
which both ADA^1 and ADA^2 alleles were segregating. In all instances,
there appeared to be abnormal inheritance of ADA types attributable to segregation of a "silent" ADA^0 allele (Chen et al., 1974;
Hirschhorn, 1977b). For example, in the most recently reported
family (Chen et al., 1977b), the parents had ADA 1 and ADA 2
phenotypes but produced four children who had ADA 1, ADA 2,
ADA 2–1, and "ADA 0" phenotypes, respectively. This anomaly,
shown in Figure 5, could readily be explained by assuming that
both parents were carriers of a "silent" gene that was transmitted to
two of their children as an allele of ADA^1 and ADA^2 and to their
affected child in the homozygous state.

At the time of the Albany conference, there was some preliminary information about a young healthy !Kung boy in Botswana
with red blood cell ADA activity that was about 2 percent of normal. It was later reported that his white blood cell activity was

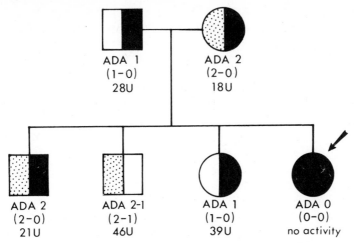

Figure 5. Part of a pedigree showing apparent aberrant inheritance of ADA phenotypes due to presence of a "silent" ADA allele. The presumed genotypes are in parentheses and the amounts of ADA catalytic activity are shown under each symbol. (Adapted from Chen S.-H. et al. 1977. Adenosine deaminase deficiency: another family with a "silent" ADA allele and normal ADA activity in two heterozygotes. Am. J Hum. Genet. 29:642–644.)

about 10 percent of normal and in cultured fibroblasts was up to 30 per cent of normal (Jenkins et al., 1976b). Further studies revealed a second case with similar findings. Tests of 78 healthy !Kung individuals showed a trimodal distribution of ADA levels consistent with the presence of a mutant allele called ADA^8, associated with decreased ADA activity, and having a frequency in that population of about 0.16. The two subjects with very low ADA levels were considered to be homozygous for the ADA^8 allele (Jenkins et al., 1976a).

Quantitative Variation in Red Blood Cell ADA. According to several reports, red blood cell ADA measurements have varied rather widely within any population of normal subjects, and in at least three families, the enzyme level in one or more of the obligate carriers of an ADA^0 allele fell within the normal range of activity (Trotta et al., 1976; Hirschhorn, 1977b; Chen et al., 1977b). These findings are consistent with either genetic heterogeneity or the presence of additional factors influencing the quantitative expression of ADA^1 and ADA^2 alleles. In some patients with inherited T- and B cell dysfunction due to unknown causes, the red blood cells but not the white blood cells or fibroblasts have had ADA levels that were significantly higher (> 3SD [standard deviation]) than the normal mean (Chen et al., 1976). Valentine and his colleagues

(1977) described a large kindred in which 12 members had a dominantly inherited disorder characterized by ADA levels in red blood cells (but not in other tested tissues) that were from 45 to 70 times normal. These patients had hemolytic anemia associated with low adenosine triphosphate (ATP) levels, which were probably due to failure of the cellular adenosine kinase to compete with adenosine deaminase for their common substrate, adenosine. When isolated from the red blood cells of patients with both forms of elevated ADA activity, the enzyme has the same physicochemical and kinetic properties as normal ADA (Osborne, 1977). Thus, the mechanism underlying the increased activity, which is presumably restricted to the red blood cells, is entirely obscure. There is one intriguing report (Siciliano et al., 1978) that fusion of normal mouse fibroblasts with human choriocarcinoma cells that are deficient in ADA produced hybrid clones in which the human ADA became expressed. This finding suggests that in human cells, the production of ADA may be subject to some kind of genetic regulatory mechanism. However, it is important to re-emphasize that the gene responsible for the ADA deficiency in SCID is inherited as an allele of ADA^1 and ADA^2. A suppressor gene could only show this inheritance pattern if its locus were very closely linked to the ADA locus.

The possibility of prenatal diagnosis of ADA deficiency has been tested on several occasions (Chen et al., 1975; Hirschhorn et al., 1975; Hirschhorn, 1977a). In at least four cases, the birth of a normal child was correctly predicted on the basis of ADA levels in cultured cells obtained at amniocentesis. In one other case, the ADA activity of amniotic fluid cells was only 1 percent of normal, and the prediction of an ADA-deficient child was confirmed at birth (Hirschhorn et al., 1975).

Immunologic and Clinical Findings in ADA Deficiency

The deficiency of ADA in man is associated with the clinical picture of SCID or a variant of this disorder termed *Nezelof's syndrome* (Meuwissen et al., 1975c). ADA deficiency has not been detected in any other group of immunodeficient patients (Meuwissen et al., 1975a). Patients with SCID characteristically manifest profound lymphopenia, a marked reduction or absence of both T- and B lymphocytes, the absence of cutaneous delayed hypersensitivity, and the inability of lymphocytes to proliferate when exposed to phytohemagglutinin (PHA), Concanavalin A, pokeweed mitogen, allogeneic cells, and other antigens. These patients are usually agammaglobulinemic or hypogammaglobulinemic and are incapable of synthesizing specific antibodies. Recurrent episodes of infection begin within the first few months of life and involve bacteria, fungi, and viruses. *Pneumocystis carinii* pneumonitis is frequent in SCID patients as are giant cell pneumonia and heptatitis resulting from infection with chicken pox or measles. Progressive and fatal diseases frequently follow immunization with vaccinia (or bacille Calmette Guérin) (BCG) (Fulginiti et al., 1968; Matsaniotis and Economou-Mavrou, 1968). Failure to gain weight, chronic diarrhea, and dermatitis are also common in these patients.

Heterogeneity in the immunologic manifestations of the immunodeficiency associated with ADA deficiency was apparent in the first three cases reported (Giblett et al., 1972; Dissing and Knudsen, 1972). Two patients had marked lymphopenia, depressed cutaneous hypersensitivity, and diminished or absent in vitro lymphocyte responses to mitogens, but serum immunoglobulin levels were in the normal range for age, although specific antibody production was defective (Giblett et al., 1972). These patients might be classified as having Nezelof's syndrome — an autosomal recessive disease with lymphopenia, cell-mediated immunodeficiency, and normal immunoglobulin levels (Nezelof et al., 1964). However, Nezelof's syndrome appears to be a form of SCID, since children with Nezelof's syndrome have been reported in families in which other children have had classic SCID (Hirschhorn et al., 1975). The patient described by Dissing and Knudsen (1972) had both agammaglobulinemia and absent cell-mediated immunity. Immunologic studies of 12 ADA-deficient patients have been reviewed by Wara and Ammann (1975). In eight of these patients, immunoglobulin and antibody production was absent, as were in vitro lymphocyte responses to mitogens and T lymphocytes. Of the remaining four patients, three had normal amounts of serum immunoglobulins, and some antibody synthesis was demonstrated in the other. Three patients had some demonstrable T lymphocytes, and in vitro lymphocyte responses to mitogens was reduced but not absent. Variations in the severity of immunologic defects have also been observed in SCID patients with normal ADA activity (Wara and Ammann, 1975).

In many patients with ADA-deficient SCID, the immunologic defects become more severe with increasing age. This progression may explain, in part, the variability in immunologic findings described in these patients. In three patients, normal or only slightly reduced serum immunoglobulin levels were found during infancy, but severe hypogammaglobulinemia developed subsequently (Wara and Ammann, 1975). One patient, who was diagnosed prenatally as having ADA deficiency, had normal lymphocyte counts, normal T- and B lymphocyte counts, and approximately 25 percent of normal in vitro lymphocyte responses to mitogens shortly after birth but became markedly lymphopenic and unresponsive to mitogens by 6 weeks of age (Polmar et al., 1975). Progressive development of immunodeficiency was observed in another child whose presumed ADA deficiency was based on later family studies (Hitzig et al., 1971; Ackeret et al., 1976). Further evidence of immunologic involution comes from studies of the thymuses of ADA-deficient SCID patients. In five such patients, differentiated central epithelium and Hassall's corpuscles were found, as well as numerous large blood vessels. These findings suggest that at least some degree of thymic differentiation had occurred but that it was followed by an involutionary phase. In contrast, the thymus in SCID patients with normal ADA activity usually shows little or no evidence of differentiation (Huber and Kersey, 1975).

The degree of ADA deficiency required for the development of SCID has not been established. All patients with ADA-deficient SCID lack detectable enzyme activity in their erythrocytes but may have up to 10 percent of normal activity in their lymphocytes. A child who was diagnosed at birth as being ADA deficient had erythrocyte ADA levels similar to other ADA-deficient SCID patients, but the residual activity in his mononuclear cells was 18 percent of normal (Hirschhorn et al., 1978). This patient, who is now 1½ years old, has maintained normal lymphocyte counts and normal responses to mitogens in vitro. His serum immunoglobulin levels are normal for age, and he has made antibodies in response to polio, diphtheria, and tetanus toxoid immunizations. Individuals in the !Kung tribe who are homozygous for the ADA^8 allele (see page 191) have only 2 to 3 percent of normal catalytic activity in their erythrocytes and 10 percent of normal or greater activity in their white blood cells and are immunologically competent (Jenkins et al., 1976a,b). It remains to be determined whether the amount of enzyme activity or perhaps other properties of the mutant enzyme (e.g., substrate specificity) are more important in protection against immunodeficiency.

Adenosine deaminase is present in most body tissues and, therefore, ADA deficiency might be expected to cause abnormalities in tissues other than the thymus and lymphocytes. Pronounced bone abnormalities have been described in some ADA-deficient patients (Wolfson and Cross, 1975; Cedarbaum et al., 1976), including concavity and prominent cupping of the anterior ends of the ribs, "squaring off" of the ilia, platyspondylysis of the thoracic and lumbar vertebrae, shortened extremities, and irregular metaphyses. Although these findings superficially resemble those in cartilage-hair hypoplasia, the bone histopathology is distinctly different from any other chondrodysplasia (Cedarbaum et al., 1976). The natural history of these bone abnormalities is not known, since few untreated patients survive for more than 2 years. The resolution of bone abnormalities has been observed in patients treated by enzyme replacement therapy and bone marrow transplantation. However, interpretation of this observation is difficult without knowledge of the natural course of the bone dysplasia (Yulish et al., 1978).

Adenine nucleotides play an important role in platelet aggregation, therefore, a disturbance in adenosine metabolism might be expected to alter platelet aggregation phenomena. Platelets from an ADA-deficient SCID patient were indeed found to have markedly diminished aggregation responses to adenosine diphosphate (ADP) and collagen (Schwartz et al., 1978). However, clinically significant bleeding problems have not been recorded in association with ADA deficiency.

Biochemical Bases of the Immune Defect in ADA Deficiency

The existence of a causal relationship between ADA deficiency and severe combined immunodeficiency disease was suggested by the exclusive association of ADA deficiency with SCID and no other disease entity (Giblett et al., 1972; Meuwissen et al., 1975c). The concept of a causal relationship between enzyme defect and immunodeficiency was further strengthened by the observation that the addition of ADA to lymphocyte cultures from ADA-deficient SCID patients restored the ability of those cells to proliferate when stimulated with PHA or Concanavalin A (Polmar et al., 1975; Schmalstieg et al., 1977). Furthermore, the infusion of normal red blood cells in an ADA-deficient SCID patient resulted in rapid restoration of in vitro lymphocytes as well as in the appearance of normal numbers of T- and B cells, increases in serum immunoglobulins, and the development of a thymus shadow on chest roentgenogram (Polmar et al., 1976).

The precise metabolic mechanism or mechanisms by which ADA deficiency interferes with lymphocyte function or development is poorly understood. A limited number of studies have been performed on lymphocytes, erythrocytes, and fibroblasts from ADA-deficient patients. A larger number of studies have employed lymphoid cell lines or normal lymphocytes in which ADA activity has been inhibited by agents such as erythro-9-(2 hydroxyl-3-nonyl) adenine (EHNA) or coformycin. In many instances, the results of these studies and their interpretations are at variance, and it is not now possible to resolve all these disparities. It is our opinion that observations of ADA-deficient SCID patients or their cells are more likely to be correct than those of enzyme-inhibited model systems that are thought to mimic the true disease state. In this discussion, data obtained by studies of patient material will be emphasized.

In most human cells, adenosine is either deaminated to inosine by ADA or phosphorylated to adenine nucleotides by adenosine kinase. In ADA deficiency, one would expect adenosine to be metabolized exclusively to adenine nucleotides. Agarwal et al. (1976) found that red blood cells from ADA-deficient SCID patients that were incubated with adenosine accumulated ATP and to a lesser extent ADP, whereas normal erythrocytes (i.e., those containing ADA) converted adenosine to inosine monophosphate. Elevated erythrocyte ATP concentrations have been observed in ADA-deficient patients, but the levels of ADP, AMP, and pyrimidine nucleotide were normal (Mills et al., 1976). The lymphocytes from ADA-deficient patients also have marked elevations of ATP (Polmar et al., 1976; Schmalstieg et al., 1977) and a two- to three-fold increase of normal intralymphocyte cyclic AMP levels (Schmalstieg et al., 1977).

ATP is converted to cyclic AMP (cAMP) by the action of adenylate cyclase. Cyclic AMP has marked inhibitory or suppressive effects upon lymphocyte function (Bourne et al., 1974). Elevated intracellular levels of cAMP are associated with suppression of (1) lymphocyte proliferation and blast transformation (Hirschhorn et al., 1970; DeRubertis et al., 1974), (2) "E" rosette formation by T lymphocytes (Chisari and Edgington, 1974), (3) cellular cytotoxicity (Henney and Lichtenstein, 1971), (4) antibody-dependent lymphocyte mediated cytotoxicity (Garovoy et al., 1975), and (5) in vitro antibody synthesis (Watson et al., 1973). A possible immunosuppressive role for cAMP in ADA deficiency was suggested by the observations that agents that increased intracellular cAMP (norepinephrine and prostaglandin E_1 and E_2) inhibited the proliferation of ADA-deficient lymphocytes (from an enzyme-treated patient) to a far greater extent than they inhibited normal lymphocytes (Polmar et al., 1977). Conversely, lithium chloride, an agent that inhibits adenylate cyclase activity, was found to differentially enhance the proliferation of ADA-deficient lymphocytes (Polmar et al., 1977).

The sensitivity of ADA-deficient cells to agents that stimulate adenylate cyclase activity may be due to the high intracellular concentration of ATP available for conversion to cAMP. The degree to which this mechanism contributes to the immunodeficiency of ADA-deficient SCID is not clear.

Theoretically, ATP itself may interfere with lymphocyte function either by inhibiting de novo pyrimidine synthesis or by inhibiting glycolysis. Green and Chan (1973) found that adenosine inhibited the proliferation of lymphoblastoid cell lines and caused pyrimidine starvation, possibly due to the inhibition of 5-phosphoribosyl-1-pyrophosphate (PRPP) synthetase, which is subject to strong allosteric inhibition by ATP. PRPP is an important intermediate in de novo synthesis of pyrimidines. The toxic effect of adenosine on these cell lines could be reversed by supplementation with uridine as a source of pyrimidine nucleosides. However, lymphocytes from one ADA-deficient patient were found to have normal pyrimidine concentrations (Schmalstieg et al., 1977). Also, there is no evidence of PRPP deficiency in these cells (Raivio et al., 1976), and addition of uridine to ADA-deficient lymphocytes in culture does not restore their ability to proliferate (Parkman et al., 1975; Polmar et al., 1975). It is also unlikely that glycolysis of the ADA-deficient lymphocyte is significantly inhibited by ATP. In ADA-deficient SCID patients, the enzyme deficiency is more extreme in erythrocytes than in lymphocytes (Hirschhorn et al., 1975; Parkman et al., 1975). Erythrocytes in which the glycolytic pathway is inhibited have shortened half-lives, usually associated with a hemolytic anemia (reviewed by Piomelli and Corash, 1976). A syndrome such as this has not been observed in ADA deficiency; therefore, there is little evidence to support a direct role for ATP in the causation of the immunodeficiency of ADA deficiency.

Deoxyadenosine (as well as adenosine) is a substrate for adenosine deaminase and adenosine kinase, thus, in the absence of ADA, deoxyadenosine nucleotides would be expected to accumulate. Recently, elevated levels of deoxyadenosine triphosphate (dATP) have been found in the urine and erythrocytes of several immunodeficient, ADA-deficient SCID patients (Coleman et al., 1977; Cohen et al., 1978b; Simmonds et al., 1978). ADA replacement therapy resulted in the rapid disappearance of dATP, without significantly affecting the concentrations of ATP (Cohen et al., 1978b). One child with ADA deficiency who has remained immunocompetent does not have elevated dATP levels (Cohen et al., 1978b). The finding that ADA-deficient lymphocytes (either from an enzyme-treated ADA-deficient SCID patient or from an EHNA-inhibited normal lymphocyte) are

1000 times more sensitive to inhibition by deoxyadenosine than by adenosine itself is supporting evidence that deoxyadenosine plays a more important role than adenosine in these patients (Polmar et al., 1978b; Carson et al., 1977; Simmonds et al., 1978).

Deoxyadenosine triphosphate can serve as a substrate for adenylate cyclase, producing a 2'-deoxy analogue of cAMP (Barr and Hechter, 1969; Burke, 1970). The finding that agents that increase intracellular cAMP differentially inhibit ADA-deficient lymphocytes also applies to the 2'-deoxy analogue of cAMP. In addition, dATP is a potent inhibitor of the ribonucleotide reductase responsible for the reduction of purine and pyrimidine ribonucleotides to their respective 2'-deoxyribonucleotides, which are necessary precursors for DNA synthesis. The deoxyadenosine-induced inhibition of ADA-deficient lymphocytes can be completely reversed in vitro by supplementation with deoxycytidine and thymidine but not with deoxyuridine, uridine, cytidine, or any of the purine ribonucleosides or deoxyribonucleosides (Polmar et al., 1978b). Carson et al. (1978) found that deoxyadenosine toxicity of EHNA-inhibited normal lymphocytes could be reversed by deoxycytidine but not by uridine. These findings are consistent with the hypothesis that ADA deficiency produces an accumulation of dATP, which then inhibits the production of pyrimidine deoxyribonucleotides, and consequently interferes with DNA synthesis, lymphocyte proliferation, and immune responses. The reversal of this inhibition with deoxycytidine and thymidine, as well as the previously described enhancement of ADA-deficient lymphocyte function by inhibition of adenylate cyclase activity, suggests that pharmacologic approach to the therapy of ADA deficiency may be possible in the near future.

Still another mechanism that is potentially capable of causing immune dysfunction in ADA deficiency has recently been proposed by Kredich and Martin (1977) and Hershfield and Kredich (1978). These investigators studied the effects of adenosine and homocysteine on normal and mutant lymphoblasts lacking adenosine kinase, both of which were treated with EHNA to suppress ADA catalytic activity. Under these conditions, the addition of 100 μm homocysteine was associated with growth inhibition and a marked rise in S-adenosylhomocysteine. The latter substance is an inhibitor of S-adenosylmethionine-dependent methylases. Its accumulation in the treated cells was accompanied by decreased methylation of DNA. Unfortunately, there is no information currently available to us concerning any measurements of S-adenosylhomocysteine in the homocysteine-treated cells of ADA-deficient patients.

Therapy of ADA-Deficient Severe Combined Immunodeficiency Disease

Histocompatible bone marrow transplantation is the therapy of choice for patients with severe combined immunodeficiency disease. Immunologic reconstitution has been achieved in ADA-deficient SCID patients with bone marrow transplantation (Parkman et al., 1975; Trotta et al., 1976; Dischino, 1976; Hong and Horowitz, 1977). One patient required seven transplants before reconstitution was achieved; another required four (Trotta et al., 1976). However, other patients have required only a single marrow infusion to achieve immunologic competence (Parkman et al., 1975; Hong and Horowitz, 1977). In the transplanted cases, the grafted lymphocytes have normal ADA activity, but the patient's erythrocytes and other cells remain ADA deficient. These data suggest that, in the presence of normal lymphocyte ADA activity, the buildup in other tissues of adenosine and deoxyadenosine and their phosphorylated products is not sufficient to cause significant alterations in lymphocyte function.

Bone marrow transplantation for therapy of SCID is severely limited by the need for histocompatible donors; thus, for the majority of patients, a suitable donor is not available. Two patients with ADA-deficient SCID received fetal liver transplants and achieved at least partial restoration of lymphocyte function for up to 1½ years, but both patients subsequently died (Keightley et al., 1975; Ackeret et al., 1976; Hirschhorn, 1975b).

Since deficiency of ADA is causally related to the immunodeficiency in ADA-deficient SCID, enzyme replacement therapy is an additional therapeutic possibility. Polmar et al. (1975) showed that the addition of ADA to cultures of ADA-deficient lymphocytes restored their ability to respond to mitogens in vitro. Irradiated human erythrocytes, which were frozen and then thawed and were free of viable lymphocytes, served as a convenient and safe source of encapsulated ADA. The infusion of these erythrocytes into an ADA–deficient patient restored his in vitro lymphocyte responses to mitogens and allogeneic cells, accompanied by lymphocytosis with normal proportions of T- and B lymphocytes appearing in the peripheral blood (Polmar et al., 1976). Within 2 weeks of the initiation of therapy, a thymic shadow could be identified on chest roentgenogram and within 1 month thymic hormone levels rose into the normal range (Lewis et al., 1978). Serum immunoglobulin levels became normal within 5 months of treatment. This patient has remained free of significant infection for more than 2½ years on a regimen of monthly transfusions of frozen irradiated red blood cells. Seven additional ADA-deficient SCID patients have been treated with red blood cells, but therapy and immunologic evaluation of these patients has not been standardized, thus making it difficult to analyze even the small amount of available data. Two of these patients experienced restoration or improvement of immunologic function as well as improvement in general clinical status (Wolf et al., 1976; Daoud et al., 1977). Two other patients showed marked improvement in clinical condition but no restoration of immunologic competence (Hong and Horowitz, 1977), whereas the other three patients showed no improvement in their clinical or immunologic status (Schmalstieg et al., 1977; Gelfand, 1978; Ziegler et al., 1978). It is unclear why some patients respond to enzyme replacement therapy and others do not. In those patients who do respond, there are marked changes in the lymphocyte levels of adenine nucleotide (Polmar et al., 1976). However, some patients who do not show restoration of immunologic competence (Cohen et al., 1977) have similar biochemical changes. Since the immunodeficiency of ADA-deficient SCID appears to be progressive, at some point it may become irreversible. Such an event might occur if toxic metabolites severely damaged the thymus or if lymphoid stem cells were completely depleted. In such instances, correction of metabolic defects would not be expected to restore immunologic competence. However, a combination of enzyme replacement therapy with thymic epithelium transplantation (Hong et al., 1976) might be effective.

Pharmacologic or dietary approaches to the therapy of ADA-deficient SCID may also be feasible. These approaches require a clear understanding of the metabolic consequences of ADA deficiency and the biochemical basis of the immunodeficiency in this disorder.

NUCLEOSIDE PHOSPHORYLASE (NP) DEFICIENCY

General Properties of NP and Tissue Distribution

Purine nucleoside phosphorylase (NP, E.C. 2.4.2.1) catalyzes the reversible conversion of inosine to hypoxanthine and of guanosine to guanine, as shown in Figure 2. However, it has little if any capability of converting adenosine to adenine, thus emphasizing the importance of adenosine deaminase in the metabolism of adenosine. NP is present in most body tissues, with a particularly high

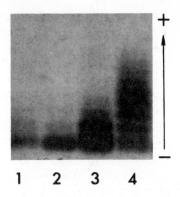

Figure 6. Starch gel electrophoretic nucleo-side phosphorylase (NP) patterns of extracts from (1) fibroblasts, (2) hair follicles, (3) lymphocytes, and (4) red cells of the same individual.

concentration in red blood cells (Huennekins et al., 1956). The NP molecule weighs about 84,000 daltons (Kim et al., 1968a,b) and has at least three binding sites for hypoxanthine (Agarwal and Parks, 1969). This finding is consistent with the hypothesis that the NP molecule is a trimer with identical subunits, each having a molecular weight of about 28,000. This postulate was substantiated by the work of Edwards et al. (1971b, 1973). Extensive descriptions of the physicochemical and kinetic properties of NP have been provided by Kim et al. (1968a,b), Sheen et al. (1968), Agarwal and Parks (1969, 1971), Agarwal et al. (1975a), and Krenitsky et al. (1968).

The starch gel electrophoretic patterns of NP obtained from various human tissues consist of a variable number of isoenzymes (Edwards et al., 1971b). Red blood cell hemolysates contain seven NP bands, with the electrophoretically slowest-moving component being predominant in young red blod cells and the intensity of the faster-moving components increasing with cell age. Extracts of fibroblasts and lymphocytes essentially have a single, slow-moving zone of NP activity, and the additional zones observed in red blood cells reflect the effects of ageing (Fig. 6). The kinetic behavior of the separate electrophoretic components has been studied by Turner et al. (1971) and Agarwal et al (1975a).

NP Genetics

Studies of somatic cell hybrids and of the inheritance of NP in families with autosomal abnormalities have shown that the NP structural gene locus is on chromosome 14 (Creagan et al., 1973a) on the long arm in the region 14q11 to 14q21 (Francke et al., 1976; George and Francke, 1976). Edwards et al. (1971b) developed a staining technique for NP based on oxidation of hypoxanthine (formed at the site of NP activity) by xanthine oxidase coupled with the reduction of a tetrazolium salt, MTT. Electrophoresis of red blood cell hemolysates and tissue extracts revealed the isoenzyme patterns described in the previous section. Although the enzyme was not found to be genetically polymorphic, three rare phenotypic variants were identified, called 2-1, 3-1, and 4-1. Family studies showed that these were the heterozygous states of the common NP^1 gene and three unusual mutant NP alleles associated with isoenzymes having faster or slower migration rates than those usually observed in NP. Because the NP patterns of red blood cell lysates are so complex, white cells, hair follicles, and fibroblasts from two of the individuals with heterozygous types were examined. Their electrophoretic patterns contained four isoenzyme bands rather than the usual single band, which is consistent with the fact that the NP molecule is a trimer (i.e., the four isoenzymes consisted of two homotrimers and two heterotrimers, respectively).

Inactive NP Alleles. Since half the children diagnosed as having SCID have normal or even elevated levels of adenosine deaminase, it seemed reasonable that deficiencies of other enzymes in the purine and pyrimidine metabolic pathways might also be associated with immunodeficiency diseases. Accordingly, qualitative (and in some instances, quantitative) assays were set up in Seattle to test the red blood cells of patients having inherited immune defects for purine nucleoside phosphorylase, adenylate guanylate kinase, adenine phosphoribosyltransferase, PRPP synthetase, pyrimidine 5' nucleotidase, uridine monophosphate kinase, uridine diphosphate kinase, and (for white blood cells, when available) cytidine deaminase. Descriptions of the methods used are found in Giblett et al. (1974), Teng et al. (1975), Anderson et al. (1975), and Harris and Hopkinson (1976).

The First Family (San Francisco). In January 1975, Dr. Arthur Ammann sent a blood specimen from San Francisco to Seattle from a 5-year-old girl who had a history of lymphopenia, recurrent infections, and an anemia that had previously been severe but was no longer evident. Unlike children with the SCID syndrome, this patient had no clinical or laboratory signs of a B cell defect, but tests for T cell function were markedly abnormal (see later section on clinical findings).

Her red blood cells contained a normal level of ADA activity, but the starch gel stained for NP activity was completely blank (Fig. 7). The red blood cell NP electrophoretic patterns of her parents (who are second cousins) were distinctly abnormal, having three

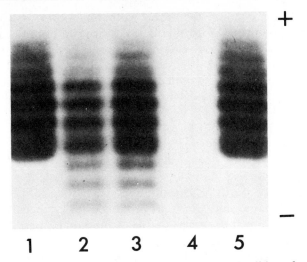

Figure 7. Starch gel electrophoretic patterns of five red cell hemolysates stained for NP activity. Channels 1 and 5 were from normal controls, channel 4 was from the NP-deficient patient, and channels 2 and 3 were from her consangineous parents. (From Giblett, E. R. et al. 1975. Nucleoside phosphorylase deficiency in a child with severely defective T-cell immunity and normal B-cell immunity. Lancet 1:1010–1013; and Giblett, E. R. 1975. The Emily Cooley Lecture: Genetic Markers, Enzyme Phenotypes, and Immune Deficiencies. In A Seminar on Polymorphisms in Human Blood, American Association of Blood Banks.)

more slow-moving zones than those of normal controls. Furthermore, the NP activity of their red blood cells, which was measured spectrophotometrically, was considerably less than half of the normal mean. The NP level and electrophoretic pattern in their one normal child were not remarkable. These findings suggested that the parents were heterozygous and their affected child was homozygous for a rare "silent" allele at the NP structural gene locus. The additional isoenzyme bands of the parents' NP strongly suggested that the abnormal *NP* gene product, although having no catalytic activity, was to form heteromers with the normal NP^1 allele product. It was also anticipated that if the abnormal protein could be isolated, it would have a very slow electrophoretic migration rate if stained for protein (Giblett et al., 1975).

Because of the complex pattern of NP obtained from red blood cell lysates, it was impossible to determine if the three additional slow-moving isoenzymes in the parents' electrophoretic pattern represented altered forms of a trimer consisting of one normal and two abnormal subunits as well as one abnormal and two normal subunits. Accordingly, the electrophoretic patterns of NP in the red blood cells and lymphocytes of the patient's mother were compared with those of a normal control (Fig. 8). Since the lymphocytes of the mother contained slow-moving components not seen in her red blood cells, we concluded that they probably represented the trimer containing two of the catalytically inactive subunits produced by the mutant allele combined with a normal subunit (Berglund et al., 1975).

The extreme instability of the abnormal gene product was shown by the work of Osborne et al. (1977). They were unable to find any evidence of a precipitin arc when the lysate of this first patient (LM) with NP deficiency was tested with an antibody prepared against NP purified from human red blood cells. Thus, it appears that this abnormal *NP* gene product is very unstable as a homotrimer but becomes more stable when combined in trimeric forms with the normal gene product.

THE SECOND FAMILY (THE NETHERLANDS). The next patient with NP was a female infant seen by Siegenbeek van Heukelom et al. (1976b) and Stoop et al. (1977). They retrospectively diagnosed the same syndrome in two of the patient's deceased sisters, whose course had been described by Stoop et al. (1976). As was seen in

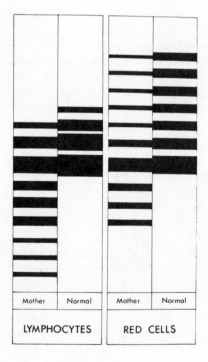

Figure 8. Diagram of NP electrophoretic patterns of lymphocyte and red cell extracts from the NP-deficient patient's mother compared with those of a normal control. After prolonged incubation, the maternal lymphocytes showed more slow-moving components than those of her red cells.

the San Francisco child, these three children had no evidence of B cell dysfunction, but T-cell function was grossly abnormal. The single remaining affected child had no measurable NP activity, whereas red blood cell ADA activity was somewhat elevated. The parents were not known to be consanguineous, but their red blood cell NP activity and that of their one normal child was about half of normal. On starch gel electrophoresis, the parental patterns could not be distinguished from normal patterns except by the decreased intensity of the isoenzyme bands. Small differences in Michaelis constants, heat stability, and pH optimum were reported when the parental red blood cell NP was compared with that of normal controls (Siegenbeek van Heukelom et al., 1976b). These apparent abnormalities are difficult to reconcile with the normal electrophoretic patterns of both parents, since one would anticipate any catalytic abnormalities in heterozygotes to be secondary to the interaction of the normal gene product with that of the "silent" allele. Such interaction would not, of course, be observed in the electrophoretic pattern if the normal and mutant gene products had the same migration rates.

THE THIRD FAMILY (FRANCE). Virelizier et al. (1978) have recently described a 19-month-old boy who died of progressive vaccinia and during hospitalization was found to have no red blood cell NP activity. As in the previous cases, humoral immunity appeared unimpaired, but tests for cellular immunity were markedly abnormal. The parents, who apparently were not consanguineous, had levels of NP that were approximately half of normal. Electrophoretic patterns were not reported.

THE FOURTH FAMILY (EASTERN CANADA). Two brothers, aged 10 and 12 years, were the subjects of recent papers by Fox et al. (1977), Osborne et al. (1977), Biggar et al. (1978), Edwards et al. (1978), and Gelfand et al. (1978).

In this family, the red blood cell NP levels of the nonrelated parents were about half of normal, whereas those of their two affected sons were less than 1 percent. The electrophoretic pattern of the mother had the same isoenzyme bands as the common phenotype, but the father's pattern contained some additional fast-moving components. Thus, although both parents were heterozygous for the common NP^1 allele, they did not have the same abnormal NP allele on the homologous chromosome. As a result, instead of being homozygous for an aberrant NP "silent" allele, these two brothers were compound heterozygotes. Their electrophoretic patterns, which were identical, could be visualized after prolonged staining. As shown in Figure 9, the pattern had isoenzymes that were different

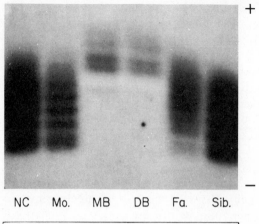

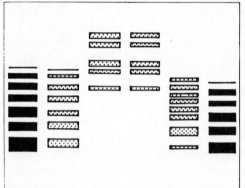

Figure 9. Photograph and diagram of the starch gel electrophoretic pattern of six red cell lysates stained for NP activity. The patterns of the two Canadian boys with NP deficiency are shown in the middle (MB and DB). Those of their parents (Mo. and Fa.) are on each side, a normal sibling is on the extreme right, and a normal control is on the extreme left. The patterns of the two (unrelated) parents are not the same.

from those of both parents, consisting of five fast-moving components. Fox et al. (1977) have shown that their abnormal NP had a K_m approximately ten times that of the normal enzyme.

Osborne et al. (1977) demonstrated that the red blood cells of these two brothers contained a protein that cross-reacts immunologically with normal NP when tested with an antiserum prepared by injecting purified human NP into rabbits. In the father's cells, the catalytic activity of NP was half of normal, but the amount of protein that reacted with anti-NP was at least as high as that of normal cells. The mother had very little or no evidence of cross-reactive material (i.e., she lacked CRM-positive, catalytically inactive NP protein). Therefore, it is virtually certain that the father's abnormal *NP* allele was the source of most or all of his sons' cross-reactive protein.

Immunologic and Clinical Findings in NP Deficiency

Two more unrelated patients with NP deficiency have·recently been found (Rich, 1977; Carapella-De Luca et al., 1978), but full details are not yet available for an expanded description here.

In the nine children with NP deficiency from six families that have been reported so far, the most consistent immunologic finding is apparently intact humoral immunity (including normal immunoglobulin levels–except terminally in one or two cases), normal isohemagglutinin titers, normal numbers of C3-receptor B cells, and the ability to produce circulating antibodies to injected vaccines. Indeed, one patient with NP deficiency who died of vaccinia produced antibodies with specificity for vaccinia virus (Virelizier et al., 1978). In addition, all patients showed distinct signs of T cell dysfunction, including variable lymphopenia, reduced numbers of "E"-rosetting cells, failure of lymphocytes to respond to mitogens or allogeneic cells, and poor to absent responses to skin tests for delayed hypersensitivity to streptokinase-streptodornase, PPD, mumps, and *Candida*. The two Canadian boys were studied for the ability to generate plaque-forming cell response to in vitro antigen sensitization. The results indicated that these patients at least had some T helper and T regulator cell function (Gelfand et al., 1978).

Skeletal x-rays have not shown any of the abnormalities described in some children with ADA deficiency. Furthermore, although there was transient anemia in two cases, there has not been a consistent involvement of erythroid cells, except for a case of autoimmune hemolytic anemia associated with cytomegalovirus infection (Carapella-De Luca et al., 1978). In the Dutch family, two of the affected children were said to have slight spastic tetraparesis with motor function retardation. However, neurologic dysfunction does not appear to be a common accompaniment of NP deficiency, in contrast to children with hypoxanthine-guanine phosphoribosyltransferase deficiency (Lesch-Nyhan syndrome).

The children who lack NP generally have a milder course than those with ADA deficiency, but there is considerable variability. The age of onset (i.e., when definite symptoms first become apparent) has ranged from 2 months to 6 years, but in eight of the nine children, definite abnormalities were noted before the age of 2 years. In some instances, T cell function appeared to be normal soon after birth. For example, the lymphocytes of the second and third affected siblings in the Dutch family had a normal response to phytohemagglutinin initially, but the response declined during the ensuing year (Stoop et al., 1976, 1977). The same observation was made in the French child, suggesting that, at least in some cases, the need for lymphocyte nucleoside phosphorylase is minimal in infancy unless there is a severe challenge to the immune system, such as overwhelming infection.

The San Francisco child had repeated blood transfusions during the first 3 years of life with no obvious ill effects. However, the second child in the Dutch family had a fatal graft-versus-host reaction — presumably the result of a blood transfusion (Stoop et al., 1976). In the Canadian family, both boys were given smallpox vaccinations when they were 1 year of age with no apparent complications. However, one of the Dutch children nearly died of vaccinia when given a vaccination at the age of 8 months, and the French patient expired from that cause when vaccinated at 19 months of age. Similarly, varicella was the cause of death in the San Francisco child and was associated with the onset of recurrent infections in one of the Canadian boys who had been in good health until that time (age 6 years).

In at least five of the nine cases, lymph nodes were obtained either by biopsy or autopsy. In all five instances known to us, there was a paucity of lymphocytes in the deep cortical regions. Germinal centers were variable in appearance — from absent to well developed. Plasma cells were unusually abundant. The thymus in one of the Dutch cases was very small, with no Hassall's corpuscles. In the French case, the thymus was hypoplastic, but Hassall's corpuscles were visible.

Of the four patients who we know have expired, death was due to overwhelming vaccinia, varicella, lymphosarcoma, and graft-versus-host disease, respectively.

Biochemical Effects of Purine Nucleoside Phosphorylase Deficiency

As mentioned previously, Figure 2 shows the metabolic pathway leading to purine salvage in which adenosine deaminase and nucleoside phosphorylase play sequential roles. A blockade in the activity of NP should result in a rise in inosine and guanosine levels, and in patients whose plasma and urine were studied, these nucleosides, as well as their respective 2′-deoxyribonucleosides, were present in large quantities (Cohen et al., 1976, 1978a; Siegenbeek van Heukelom et al., 1976b; Osborne et al., 1977). Inosine and deoxyinosine were the major abnormal metabolites in plasma and red blood cells. In the San Francisco and Dutch patients, hypouricemia and hypouricosuria were also pronounced. The red blood cells were said to contain an increased concentration of phosphoribosylpyrophosphate, but this was not true of the cultured fibroblasts.

The two Canadian patients reportedly do not have hypouricemia (Edwards et al., 1978), and they seem to be pursuing a somewhat milder course than the children in other families. According to Gelfand et al. (1978), the fact that their metabolic block is incomplete may account for the less severe symptomatology and the somewhat less impaired immune dysfunction as indicated by laboratory tests. Cohen et al. (1977) have recently reported that the urine of both the San Francisco child and one of the Dutch patients tested contained amounts of orotic acid that were considerably higher than those measured in five normal subjects. Furthermore, treatment of one patient with oral uridine was accompanied by a fall in urinary orotic acid.

Cohen et al. (1977) postulated that in patients with NP deficiency, some (unspecified) cell types may be depleted of PRPP. This compound is necessary for the phosphoribosylation step in both the de novo synthetic pathways of purines and pyrimidines and in the salvage of adenine by adeninephosphoribosyltransferase and of hypoxanthine and guanine by HGPRT. Theoretically, then, orotic acid could accumulate in the pyrimidine de novo pathway if there was insufficient intracellular PRPP to permit the conversion of orotic acid to orotidine monophosphate.

Cohen et al. (1977) pointed out that Skaper et al. (1976) had demonstrated a dependency on exogenous inosine for maintaining PRPP levels when cultured human fibroblasts were deprived of glutamine. The only known way for inosine to increase PRPP is through its phosphorolysis to ribose-1-phosphate, which, when converted to ribose-5-phosphate, is the immediate precursor of PRPP. Therefore, in the absence of nucleoside phosphorylase, the accumulated inosine could not be converted to PRPP. If T cells were to require inosine as a critical source of PRPP, a deficiency of NP might result in T cell dysfunction.

However, as discussed in an earlier section on ADA biochemistry, one of the first mechanisms postulated to explain the effect of ADA deficiency was "pyrimidine starvation" based on the studies of Green and Chan (1973). In their experimental model, a buildup of orotic acid occurred in cells treated with adenosine, and this lesion was reversed upon the addition of uridine. Arguments against a pyrimidine de novo pathway blockade in ADA deficiency were presented previously in this discussion.

Another postulated mechanism by which NP deficiency causes immune dysfunction was suggested by Ullman et al (1976). According to this theory, the intracellular buildup of inosine causes product inhibition of the ADA reaction, thus causing adenosine accumulation and cell damage similar to that observed in ADA deficiency. However, recent studies have shown that human ADA shows no definable product inhibition (Osborne et al., 1978). In addition, Ochs et al. (1977) found that inosine concentrations as high as 4 mM have no depressing effect on lymphocyte transformation as measured by the incorporation of tritiated thymidine.

Another way in which NP deficiency might cause T lymphocyte dysfunction is through the accumulation of guanosine or deoxyguanosine. Ochs et al. (1977) found that normal lymphocyte transformation was definitely inhibited by 0.25 mM guanosine and that this effect could not be reversed by adding uridine. According to Ito and Uchino (1976), both guanine and guanosine inhibit induction of enzymes catalyzing the first step in both purine and pyrimidine de novo synthesis (i.e., several steps before orotic acid formation) in mitogen-treated lymphocytes. If this were the actual underlying mechanism in NP deficiency, one would not expect to see oroticaciduria, such as has been reported.

Urine of patients with NP deficiency contains high concentrations of deoxyinosine and deoxyguanosine as well as inosine and guanosine (Cohen et al., 1976, 1978a). Although nucleosides readily diffuse into and out of cells, nucleotides do not. Therefore, phosphorylation of nucleosides by their respective kinases represents intracellular trapping mechanisms, leading to accumulation of nucleotides. Carson et al. (1977) failed to detect inosine or guanosine kinase in tissues of normal human newborns. In contrast, deoxyinosine and deoxyguanosine kinases are found primarily in thymus, tonsil, and peripheral blood lymphocytes, thus permitting selective accumulation of these deoxyribonucleotides. Both deoxyguanosine and deoxyinosine inhibit phytohemagglutinin-induced lymphocyte proliferation. However, the biochemical basis of this inhibition is not clear (Carson et al., 1977). Deoxyguanosine triphosphate does not inhibit ribonucleotide reductase in bacterial cells but does inhibit mammalian ribonucleotide reductase (Moore and Hurlbert, 1966) and could cause lymphocyte dysfunction by inhibiting formation of deoxypyrimidine nucleotide in a manner similar to that proposed for ADA deficiency (Cohen et al., 1978a).

Therapy of NP Deficiency

The first child in whom NP deficiency was diagnosed had a long regimen of treatment — first to alleviate her anemia (which subsequently disappeared for unexplained reasons) and then to treat her T cell deficiency (Giblett et al., 1975). The transfusion of red blood cells failed to reverse the immune lesion (Sandman et al., 1977). After she developed asthmatic symptoms on thymosin therapy, she was begun on a course of oral uridine (100 mg per kg per day) of several months' duration. This treatment resulted in the reduction of her orotic aciduria (Cohen et al., 1977), but the patient subsequently died of overwhelming varicella (Ammann, 1978).

In the Dutch family with three NP-deficient members, the metabolic basis for the disease in the first two affected children was determined postmortem from abnormal serum inosine levels (Stoop et al., 1976). The first of these children had been treated with several thymus transplants and injections of transfer factor. This therapy resulted in resolution of the severe vaccinia lesions and transient, partial restoration of T cell function. However, none of these maneuvers prevented the development of fatal lymphosarcoma. The second child in this family had little time for treatment, since she succumbed early to graft-versus-host reaction after blood transfusion. The third affected child was treated with oral uridine, which resulted in an increase in the percentage of "E"-rosetting cells, but the patient remained lymphopenic and unresponsive to PHA (Zegers et al., 1978). Enzyme replacement therapy was then attempted with frozen irradiated red blood cells as described by Polmar et al. (1976) for ADA deficiency. This treatment was associated with an increase in lymphocytes from 400 to 1000/mm³, and the percentage of E-rosettes increased from 20 to 60 percent. After eight transfusions, responsiveness to PHA rose to 50 percent of normal control values. The numbers of T cells and PHA responses tend to decrease approximately 2 weeks after each transfusion, but there has been prolonged maintenance of E-rosetting cells and PHA responsiveness. In addition, granulocytopenia (1600/mm³) disappeared after enzyme replacement therapy was begun. These improvements in immunologic function occurred even though the addition of purified NP and red blood cells containing NP to cultures of NP-deficient lymphocytes did not improve their responses to PHA (Zegers et al., 1978).

The NP-deficient French child had already developed severe progressive vaccinia before being seen by Virelizier et al. (1978) and had little opportunity to respond to treatment, which included antibiotics, transfer factor, irradiated red blood cells, and a thymus graft.

In vitro experiments (Gelfand et al., 1978) with the two Canadian boys showed that addition of uridine and hypoxanthine, alone or in combination, did not improve the mitogenic response of their NP-deficient mononuclear cells, whereas hypoxanthine consistently increased the response of normal cells. They also found that the addition of NP itself or of human red blood cells (rich in NP) failed to influence the proliferative response of the NP-deficient cells. Indeed, neither red blood cell nor uridine treatment has had any demonstrable effect in vivo.

None of the patients known to have NP deficiency has yet received a bone marrow graft or thymic epithelium. Since the former treatment has been effective in some cases of ADA deficiency, it may be the treatment of choice until some less drastic procedure or medication is proven to be effective.

References

Ackeret, C., H. J. Pluss, and W. H. Hitzig. 1976. Hereditary severe combined immunodeficiency and adenosine deaminase deficiency. Pediat. Res. 10:67–70.

Agarwal, K. C., R. P. Agarwal, J. D. Stoeckler, and R. E. Parks. 1975a. Purine nucleoside phosphorylase. Microheterogeneity and comparison of kinetic behavior of the enzyme from several tissues and species. Biochemistry 14:79–84.

Agarwal, R. P., G. W. Crabtree, R. E. Parks, J. A. Nelson, R. Keightley, R. Parkman, F. S. Rosen, R. C. Stern, and S. H. Polmar. 1976. Purine nucleoside metabolism in the erythrocytes of patients with adenosine deaminase deficiency and severe combined immunodeficiency. J. Clin. Invest. 57:1025–1035.

Agarwal, R. P., and R. E. Parks. 1969. Purine nucleoside phosphorylase from human erythrocytes. IV. Crystallization and some properties. J. Biol. Chem. 244:644–647.

Agarwal, R. P., and R. E. Parks. 1971. Purine nucleoside phosphorylase from human erythrocytes. V. Content and behavior of sulfhydryl group. J. Biol. Chem. 246:3763–3768.

Agarwal, R. P., S. M. Sagar, and R. E. Parks. 1975b. Adenosine deaminase from human erythrocytes: purification and effects of adenosine analogs. Biochem. Pharmacol. 24(6):693–701.

Akedo, H., H. Nishihara, K. Shinkai, and K. Komatsu. 1970. Adenosine deaminase of two molecular sizes in human tissues. Biochim. Biophys. Acta 212:189–191.

Allison, A. C., R. W. E. Watts, T. Hovi, and A. D. B. Webster. 1975. Immunological observations on patients with Lesch-Nyhan syndrome, and on the role of de novo purine synthesis in lymphocyte transformation. Lancet 2:1179–1180.

Alper, C. A. 1976. Inherited structural polymorphism in human C2: evidence for genetic linkage between C2 and Bf. J. Exp. Med. 144(4):1111–1115.

Alper, C. A., and F. S. Rosen. 1976. Genetics of the complement system. Adv. Hum. Genet. 7:141–188.

Ammann, A. J. 1978. Personal communication.

Ammann, A. J., and R. Hong. 1971. Selective IgA deficiency: presentation of 30 cases and a review of the literature. Medicine (Baltimore) 50:223–236.

Anderson, J. E., Y.-S. Teng, and E. R. Giblett. 1974. Stains for Six Enzymes Potentially Applicable to Chromosomal Assignment by Cell Hybridization. In Human Gene Mapping 2, Cytogenetics and Cell Genetics Series, Bergsma, D. (Ed.), Vol. 14, pp. 295–299, Basel, S. Karger.

Barr, H.-P., and O. Hechter. 1969. Substrate specificity of adenyl cyclase from rat fat cell ghosts. Biochim. Biophys. Acta 192:141–144.

Belohradsky, B. H., J. Finstad, H. H. Fudenberg, R. A. Good, H. G. Kunkel, and F. S. Rosen. 1974. Meeting Report of the Second International Workshop on Primary Immunodeficiency Diseases in Man. Clin. Immunol. Immunopathol. 2:281–295.

Berenbaum, M. D. 1975. The Clinical Pharmacology of Immunosuppressive Agents. In Clinical Aspects of Immunology. Gell, P. G. H., R. R. A. Coombs, and P. J. Lachman (Eds.), pp. 689–758. Oxford, Blackwell Scientific.

Berglund, C., A. J. Ammann, and E. R. Giblett. 1975. Characteristics of nucleoside phosphorylase in the parents of a child with deficiency of the enzyme. (Abstr.) Am. J. Hum. Genet. 27:17A.

Biggar, W. D., E. R. Giblett, R. L. Ozere, and B. D. Grover. 1978. A new form of nucleoside phosphorylase deficiency in two brothers with defective T-cell function. J. Pediat. 92:354–357.

Boder, E. 1975. Ataxia-telangiectasia: Some Historic, Clinical and Pathologic Observations. In Immunodeficiency in Man and Animals. Bergsma, D., R. A. Good, J. Finstad, and N. W. Paul (Eds.), pp. 255–270. Sunderland, Sinauer Associates, Inc.

Borgers, M., H. Verhaegen, M. DeBrabander, F. Thoné, J. van Reempts, and G. Geuens. 1977. Purine nucleoside phosphorylase, a possible histochemical marker for T cells in man. J. Immunol. Methods 16:101–110.

Bourne, H. R., L. M. Lichtenstein, K. L. Melmon, C. S. Henney, Y. Weinstein, and G. M. Shearer. 1974. Modulation of inflammation and immunity by cyclic AMP. Science 184:19–28.

Brady, T. G., and C. I. O'Donovan. 1965. A study of tissue distribution of adenosine deaminase in six mammalian species. Comp. Biochem. Physiol. 14:101–120.

Buckley, R. H., R. B. Gilbertsen, R. I. Schiff, E. Ferreira, S. O. Sanal, and T. A. Waldmann. 1976. Heterogeneity of lymphocyte subpopulations in severe combined immunodeficiency: Evidence against a stem cell defect. J. Clin. Invest. 58:130–136.

Burke, G. 1970. Substrate specificity of thyroid adenyl cyclase. Life Sci. 9:789–795.

Burke, W. G., S.-H. Chen, C. R. Scott, and A. J. Ammann. 1977. Incorporation of purine nucleosides in cultured fibroblasts from a patient with purine nucleoside phosphorylase deficiency and associated T-cell immunodeficiency. J. Cell Physiol. 92:109–114.

Carapella-De Luca, E., F. Aiuti, P. Lucarelli, M. C. Tozzi, P. Vignetti, L. Bruni, D. Roos, R. M. Corbo, and C. Imperato. 1978. Nucleoside phosphorylase deficiency, autoimmune haemolytic anaemia and selective T-cell deficiency. (Abstr.) Pediat. Res. 12:64.

Carson, D. A., J. Kaye, and J. E. Seegmiller. 1977. Lymphospecific toxicity in adenosine deaminase deficiency and purine nucleoside phosphorylase deficiency: possible role of nucleoside kinase(s). Proc. Nat. Acad. Sci. U.S.A. 74:5677–5681.

Carson, D. A., J. Kaye, and J. E. Seegmiller. 1978. Biochemical Mechanisms in Human Immunodeficiency Disease. In Inborn Errors of Immunity and Phagocytosis. Wamberg, E., and F. Güttler (Eds.), Lancaster, MTP Press. In press.

Cassidy, J. T., A. Burt, R. Petty, and D. Sullivan. 1968. Selective IgA deficiency in connective tissue diseases. New Eng. J. Med. 280:275.

Cedarbaum, S. D., I. Kaitila, D. L. Rimoin, and E. R. Stiehm. 1976. The chondro-osseous dysplasia of adenosine deaminase deficiency with severe combined immunodeficiency. J. Pediat. 89:737–742.

Chen, S.-H., W. G. Burke, C. R. Scott, E. R. Giblett, W. D. Biggar, E. W. Gelfand, and A. J. Ammann. 1977a. Purine nucleoside metabolism in cultured skin fibroblasts from three patients with purine nucleoside phosphorylase (NP) deficiency. (Abstr.) Am. J. Hum. Genet. 29:30A.

Chen, S.-H., H. Ochs, and C. R. Scott. 1976. Elevated adenosine deaminase in erythrocytes from patients with inherited immunodeficiency diseases. (Abstr. 57) Mexico City, 5th Int. Congr. Hum. Genet.

Chen, S.-H., C. R. Scott, and E. R. Giblett. 1974. Adenosine deaminase: demonstration of a "silent" gene associated with combined immunodeficiency disease. Am. J. Hum. Genet. 26:103–107.

Chen, S.-H., C. R. Scott, E. R. Giblett, and A. S. Levin. 1977b. Adenosine deaminase deficiency: another family with a "silent" ADA allele and normal ADA activity in two heterozygotes. Am. J. Hum. Genet. 29:642–644.

Chen, S.-H., C. R. Scott, and K. R. Swedberg. 1975. Heterogeneity for adenosine deaminase deficiency: Expression of the enzyme in cultured skin fibroblasts and amniotic fluid cells. Am. J. Hum. Genet. 27(1):46–52.

Cheson, B. D., J. T. Curnutte, and B. M. Babior. 1977. The oxidative killing mechanisms of the neutrophile. Prog. Clin. Immunol. 3:1–65.

Chisari, F. V., and T. A. Edgington. 1974. Human T-lymphocyte "E" rosette function. I. A process modulated by intracellular cyclic AMP. J. Exp. Med. 140(4):1122–1126.

Cohen, A., D. Doyle, D. W. Martin, and A. J. Ammann. 1976. Abnormal purine metabolism and purine overproduction in a patient deficient in purine nucleoside phosphorylase. New Eng. J. Med. 295:1449–1454.

Cohen, A., L. J. Gudas, A. J. Ammann, G. E. J. Staal, and D. W. Martin, Jr. 1978a. Deoxyguanosine triphosphate as a possible toxic metabolite in purine nucleoside phosphorylase deficiency. J. Clin. Invest. 61:1405–1409.

Cohen, A., R. Hirschhorn, S. D. Horowitz, A. Rubenstein, S. H. Polmar, R. Hong, and D. W. Martin, Jr. 1978b. Deoxyadenosine triphosphate as a toxic metabolite in adenosine deaminase deficiency. Proc. Nat. Acad. Sci. U.S.A. 75:472–476.

Cohen, A., G. E. J. Staal, A. J. Ammann, and D. W. Martin. 1977. Orotic aciduria in two unrelated patients with inherited deficiencies of purine nucleoside phosphorylase. J. Clin. Invest. 60:491–494.

Coleman, M. S., J. Donofrio, J. J. Hutton, A. Daoud, B. Lampkin, and J. Dyminski. 1977. Abnormal concentrations of deoxynucleotides in adenosine deaminase (ADA) deficiency and severe combined immunodeficiency. (Abstr.) Blood 50 (Suppl):292.

Conway, E. J., and R. Cooke. 1939. The deaminases of adenosine and adenylic acid in blood and tissues. Biochem. J. 33:479–492.

Cooper, M. R., L. R. DeChatelet, C. E. McCall, M. F. La Via, C. L. Spurr, and R. L. Baehner. 1972. Complete deficiency of leukocyte glucose-6-phosphate dehydrogenase with defective bactericidal activity. J. Clin. Invest. 51:769–778.

Creagan, R. P., Y. H. Tan, S. Chen, J. A. Tischfield, and F. H. Ruddle. 1973a. Mouse/Human Somatic Cell Hybrids Utilizing Human Parental Cells Containing a (14:22) Translocation: Assignment of the Gene for Nucleoside Phosphorylase to Chromosome 14. In Human Gene Mapping. Bergsma, D. (Ed.), pp. 83–85. White Plains, The National Foundation.

Creagan, R. P., J. A. Tischfield, E. A. Nichols, and F. H. Ruddle. 1973b. Letter: Autosomal assignment of the gene for the form of adenosine deaminase which is deficient in patients with combined immunodeficiency syndrome. Lancet 2:1449.

Daddona, P. E., and W. N. Kelley. 1977. Human adenosine deaminase. Purification and subunit structure. J. Biol. Chem. 252:110–115.

Daoud, A., B. Lampkin, J. Dyminski, M. S. Coleman, J. Donofrio, and J. J. Hutton. 1977. Response to adenosine deaminase (ADA) replacement therapy in a child with severe combined immunodeficiency (SCID) and ADA deficiency. (Abstr.) Blood 50 (Suppl):168.

DeRubertis, F. R., T. V. Zenser, W. H. Adler, and T. Hudson. 1974. Role of cyclic adenosine 3', 5'-monophosphate in lymphocyte mitogenesis. J. Immunol. 113:151–161.

Detter, J. C., G. Stamatoyannopoulos, E. R. Giblett, and A. G. Motulsky. 1970. Adenosine deaminase: racial distribution and report of a new phenotype. J. Med. Genet. 7:356–357.

Dischino, M. 1976. Déficit immunitaire combiné sévère avec déficit en adénosine déaminase. Doctoral thesis. Lyon, Claude Bernard University.

Dissing, J., and J. B. Knudsen. 1969. A new red cell adenosine deaminase phenotype in man. Hum. Hered. 19:375–377.

Dissing, J., and J. B. Knudsen. 1972. Adenosine-deaminase deficiency and combined immunodeficiency syndrome. Lancet 2:1316.

Edwards, N. L., E. W. Gelfand, W. D. Biggar, and I. H. Fox. 1978. Partial deficiency of purine nucleoside phosphorylase: studies of purine and pyrimidine metabolism. J. Lab. Clin. Med. 91:736–749.

Edwards, Y. H., P. A. Edwards, and D. A. Hopkinson. 1973. A trimeric structure for mammalian purine nucleoside phosphorylase. FEBS Let. 32:235–237.

Edwards, Y. H., D. A. Hopkinson, and H. Harris, 1971a. Adenosine deaminase isozymes in human tissues. Ann. Hum. Genet. 35:207–219.

Edwards, Y. H., D. A. Hopkinson, and H. Harris. 1971b. Inherited variants of human nucleoside phosphorylase. Ann. Hum. Genet. 34:395–408.

Fox, I. H., C. M. Andres, E. W. Gelfand, and W. D. Biggar. 1977. Purine nucleoside phosphorylase deficiency: altered kinetic properties of a mutant enzyme. Science 197(4308):1084–1086.

Francke, U., N. Busby, D. Shaw, S. Hansen, and M. G. Brown. 1976. Intrachromosomal gene mapping in man: assignment of nucleoside phosphorylase to region 14cen leads to 14q21 by interspecific hybridization of cells with a t(X;14) (p22:q21) translocation. Somat. Cell Genet. 2(1):27–40.

Friedrichson, U., K. Reichel, H. Ritter, and J. Schmitt. 1975. Genetic variation of red cell nucleoside phosphorylase in primates. Humangenetik 28:253–254.

Fulginiti, V. A., C. H. Kempe, W. E. Hathaway, D. S. Pearlman, O. F. Sieber, J. J. Eller, J. J. Joyner, and A. Robinson. 1968. Progressive Vaccinia in Immunologically Deficient Individuals. In Immunologic Deficiency Diseases in Man. Birth Defects: Original Article Series, Bergsma, D., and R. A. Good (Eds.), Vol. 9, pp. 128–145, White Plains, The National Foundation.

Garovoy, M. R., T. B. Strom, M. Kaliner, and C B. Carpenter. 1975. Antibody-dependent lymphocyte mediated cytotoxicity mechanism and modulation by cyclic nucleotides. Cell. Immunol. 20:197–204.

Gatti, R. A. 1974. On the classification of patients with primary immunodeficiency disorders. Clin. Immunol. Immunopathol. 3:243–247.

Geha, R. S., F. S. Rosen, and E. Merler. 1973. Identification and characterization of subpopulations of lymphocytes in human peripheral blood after fractionation on discontinuous gradients of albumin. The cellular defect in X-linked agammaglobulinemia. J. Clin. Invest. 52:1726–1734.

Gelfand, E. W. 1977. Personal communication.

Gelfand, E. W., W. D. Biggar, and R. P. Orange. 1974. Immune deficiency: evaluation, diagnosis and therapy. Pediat. Clin. North Am. 21(4):745–776.

Gelfand, E. W., H. M. Dosch, W. D. Biggar, and I. H. Fox. 1978. Purine nucleoside phosphorylase deficiency: studies of lymphocyte function. J. Clin. Invest. 61:1071–1080.

George, D. L., and U. Francke. 1976. Gene dose effect: regional mapping of human nucleoside phosphorylase on chromsome 14. Science 194(4267):851–852.

Giblett, E. R. 1975. The Emily Cooley Lecture: Genetic markers, enzyme phenotypes, and immune deficiencies. In A Seminar on Polymorphisms in Human Blood, American Association of Blood Banks.

Giblett, E. R. , A. J. Ammann, D. W. Wara, R. Sandman, and L. K. Diamond. 1975. Nucleoside phosphorylase deficiency in a child with severely defective T-cell immunity and normal B-cell immunity. Lancet 1(7914):1010–1013.

Giblett, E. R., J. E. Anderson, S.-H. Chen, Y.-S. Teng, and F. Cohen. 1974. Uridine monophosphate kinase: A new genetic polymorphism with possible clinical implications. Am. J. Hum. Genet. 26(5):627–635.

Giblett, E. R., J. E. Anderson, F. Cohen, B. Pollara, and H. J. Meuwissen. 1972. Adenosine deaminase deficiency in two patients with severely impaired cellular immunity. Lancet 2:1067–1069.

Giblett, E. R., S. J. Klebanoff, S. H. Pincus, J. Swanson, B. H. Park, and J. McCullough. 1971. Kell phenotypes in chronic granulomatous disease: a potential transfusion hazard. Lancet 1:1235–1236.

Gray, G. R., G. Stamatoyannopoulos, S. C. Naiman, M. R. Kilman, S. J. Klebanoff, T. Austin, A. Yoshida, and C. G. F. Robinson. 1973. Neutrophil dysfunction, chronic granulomatous disease, and non-spherocytic haemolytic anaemia caused by complete deficiency of glucose-6-phosphate dehydrogenase. Lancet 2:530–534.

Green, H., and T.-S. Chan. 1973. Pyrimidine starvation induced by adenosine in fibroblasts and lymphoid cells: role of adenosine deaminase. Science 182:836–837.

Harris, H., and D. A. Hopkinson. 1976. Handbook of Enzyme Electrophoresis in Human Genetics. North-Holland, Elsevier.

Harris, H., D. A. Hopkinson, and E. B. Robson. 1974. The incidence of rare alleles determining electrophoretic variants: data on 43 enzyme loci in man. Ann. Hum. Genet. 37:237–253.

Henney, C. S., and L. M. Lichtenstein. 1971. The role of cyclic AMP in the cytolytic activity of lymphocytes. J. Immunol. 107:610–612.

Hershfield, M. S., and N. M. Kredich. 1978. Inhibition of methylation by S-adenosylhomocysteine (SAH): a basis for adenosine toxicity and immune dysfunction in adenosine deaminase deficiency. (Abstr.) Clin. Res. 26:20A.

Hirschhorn, R. 1975a. Conversion of human erythrocyte-adenosine deaminase activity to different tissue-specific isozymes: Evidence for a common catalytic unit. J. Clin. Invest. 55(3):661–667.

Hirschhorn, R. 1975b. Personal communication.

Hirschhorn, R. 1977a. Defects of purine metabolism in immunodeficiency diseases. Prog. Clin. Immunol. 3:67–83.

Hirschhorn, R. 1977b. Adenosine deaminase deficiency and immunodeficiencies. Fed. Proc. 36:2166–2170.

Hirschhorn, R., N. Beratis, and F. S. Rosen. 1976. Characterization of residual enzyme activity in fibroblasts from patients with adenosine deaminase deficiency and combined immunodeficiency: evidence for a mutant enzyme. Proc. Nat. Acad. Sci. U.S.A. 73(1)213–217.

Hirschhorn, R., N. Beratis, F. S. Rosen, R. Parkman, R. Stern, and S. Polmar. 1975. Adenosine deaminase deficiency in a child diagnosed prenatally. Lancet 1:73–75.

Hirschhorn, R., J. Grossman, and G. Weissmann. 1970. Effect of cyclic 3',5'-adenosine monophosphate and theophylline on lymphocyte transformation. Proc. Soc. Exp. Biol. Med. 133:1361–1365.

Hirschhorn, R., and V. Levytska. 1974. Alteration in isozymes of adenosine deaminase during stimulation of human peripheral blood lymphocytes. Cell. Immunol. 13:387–395.

Hirschhorn, R., V. Levytska, B. Pollara, and H. J. Meuwissen. 1973. Evidence for control of several different tissue-specific isozymes of adenosine deaminase by a single genetic locus. Nature 246:200–201.

Hirschhorn, R., F. Martiniuk, and F. S. Rosen. 1978. Adenosine deaminase activity in normal tissues and tissues from a child with severe combined immunodeficiency and adenosine deaminase deficiency. Clin. Immunol. Immunopathol. 9:287–292.

Hitzig, W. H., R. Landolt, G. Muller, and P. Bodmer. 1971. Heterogeneity of phenotypic expression in a family with Swiss-type agammaglobulinemia: Observations on the acquisition of agammaglobulinemia. J. Pediat. 78:968–980.

Hohn, D. C., and R. I. Lehrer. 1975. NADPH oxidase deficiency in X-linked chronic granulomatous disease. J. Clin. Invest. 55:707–713.

Hong, R., and S. D. Horowitz. 1977. Personal communication.

Hong, R., M. Santosham, H. Schulte-Wisserman, S. Horowitz, S. H. Hsu, and J. Winklestein. 1976. Reconstitution of B- and T-lymphocyte function in severe combined immunodeficiency disease after transplantation with thymic epithelium. Lancet 2:1270–1272.

Hopkinson, D. A., P. J. L. Cook, and H. Harris. 1969. Further data on the adenosine deaminase polymorphism and a report of a new phenotype. Ann. Hum. Genet. 32:361–367.

Huber, J., and J. Kersey. 1975. Pathological Findings. In Combined Immunodeficiency Disease and Adenosine Deaminase Deficiency: A Molecular Defect, Meuwissen, H. J., R. J. Pickering, B. Pollara, and I. H. Porter (Eds.), pp. 279–288, New York, Academic Press, Inc.

Huennekens, F. M., E. Nurk, and B. W. Gabrio. 1956. Erythrocyte metabolism. I. Purine nucleoside phosphorylase. J. Biol. Chem. 221:971–981.

Huntley, C. C., and R. L. Stephenson. 1968. IgA deficiency: family studies. North Carolina Med. J. 29:325–331.

Ito, K., and H. Uchino. 1976. Control of pyrimidine biosynthesis in human lymphocytes. Inhibitory effect of guanine and guanosine on induction of enzymes for pyrimidine biosynthesis *de novo* in phytohemagglutinin-stimulated lymphocytes. J. Biol. Chem. 251:1427–1430.

Iverson, D., L. R. DeChatelet, J. K. Spitznagel, and P. Wang. 1977. Comparison of NADH and NADPH oxidase activities in granules isolated from human polymorphonuclear leukocytes with a fluorometric assay. J. Clin. Invest. 59:282–290.

Jenkins, T. 1973. Red-blood-cell adenosine deaminase deficiency in a "healthy" !Kung individual. Lancet 2:736.

Jenkins, T., A. R. Rabson, A. B. Lane, G. T. Nurse, and D. A. Hopkinson. 1976a. Adenosine deaminase deficiency not associated with immunodeficiency: family and population studies. (Abstr. 79) Mexico City., 5th Int. Congr. Hum. Genet.

Jenkins, T., A. R. Rabson, G. T. Nurse, A. B. Lane, and D. A. Hopkinson. 1976b. Deficiency of adenosine deaminase not associated with severe combined immunodeficiency. J. Pediat. 89:732–736.

Keightley, R. G., A. R. Lawton, M. D. Cooper, and E. J. Yunis. 1975. Successful fetal liver transplant in a child with severe combined immunodeficiency. Lancet 2(7490)850–853.

Kim, B. K., S. Cha, and R. E. Parks. 1968a. Purine nucleoside phosphorylase from human erythrocytes. I. Purification and properties. J. Biol. Chem. 243:1763–1770.

Kim, B. K., S. Cha, and R. E. Parks. 1968b. Purine nucleoside phosphorylase from human erythrocytes. II. Kinetic analysis and substrate binding studies. J. Biol. Chem. 243:1771–1776.

Kredich, N. M., and D. W. Martin. 1977. Role of S-adenosylhomocysteine in adenosine-mediated toxicity in cultured mouse T lymphoma cells. Cell 12:931–938.

Krenitsky, T. A., G. B. Elion, A. M. Henderson, and G. H. Hitchings. 1968. Inhibition of human purine nucleoside phosphorylase. Studies with intact erythrocytes and the purified enzyme. J. Biol. Chem. 243:2876–2881.

Lamm, L. U. 1971. A study of red cell adenosine deaminase (ADA) types in 116 Danish families. Hum. Hered. 21:63–68.

Lehrer, R. I., and M. J. Cline. 1969. Leukocyte myeloperoxidase deficiency and disseminated candidiases: role of myeloperoxidase in resistance to *Candida* infection. J. Clin. Invest. 48:1478–1488.

Lehrer, R. I., J. Hanifin, and M. J. Cline. 1969. Defective bactericidal activity in myeloperoxidase-deficient human neutrophils. Nature (Lond.) 223:78–79.

Letnansky, K., and F. Seelich. 1958. Untersuchungen zur Erweiterung der diagnostichen Möglichkeiten bei Krebs. Bestimmung der Actvität der Adenosindesaminase im Plasma. Krebsarzt. 13:80–83.

Lewis, V., J. Twomey, G. Goldstein, R. O'Reilly, E. Smithwick, R. Pahwa, S. Pahwa, R. A. Good, H. Schulte-Wisserman, S. Horowitz, R. Hong, J. Jones, O. Sieber, C. Kirkpatrick, S. Polmar, and P. Bealmear. 1977. Circulating thymic hormone activity in congenital immunodeficiency. Lancet 2:471–475.

Marsh, W. L., R. Oyen, and M. E. Nichols. 1976. Kx antigen, the McLeod phenotype and chronic granulomatous disease: further studies. Vox Sang. (Basel) 31:356–362.

Marsh, W. L., R. Oyen, M. E. Nichols, and F. H. Allen. 1975a. Chronic granulomatous disease and the Kell blood groups. Brit. J. Haematol. 29:247–262.

Marsh, W. L., H. F. Taswell, R. Oyen, M. E. Nichols, M. S. Vergara, and A. A. Pineda. 1975b. Kx antigen of the Kell system and its relationship to chronic granulomatous disease. Evidence that the Kx gene is X-linked. (Abstr.) Transfusion 15:527.

Matsaniotis, N., and C. Economou-Mavrou. 1968. Fatal generalized BCG infection: a result of immunologic deficiency. In Immunologic Deficiency Diseases in Man. Birth Defects: Original Article Series, Bergsma, D., and R. A. Good (Eds.), Vol. 9, pp. 124–128, White Plains, The National Foundation.

Meuwissen, H. J., R. J. Pickering, E. C. Moore, and B. Pollara. 1975a. Impairment of Adenosine Deaminase Activity in Combined Immunological Deficiency Disease. In Combined Immunodeficiency Disease and Adenosine Deaminase Deficiency: A

Molecular Defect. Meuwissen, H. J., R. J. Pickering, B. Pollara, and I. H. Porter (Eds.), pp. 73–83. New York, Academic Press, Inc.

Meuwissen, H. J., R. J. Pickering, B. Pollara, and I. H. Porter, Eds. 1975b. Combined Immunodeficiency Disease and Adenosine Deaminase Deficiency: A Molecular Defect. New York, Academic Press, Inc.

Meuwissen, H. J., B. Pollara, and R. J. Pickering. 1975c. Combined immunnodeficiency associated with adenosine deaminase deficiency. J. Pediat. 86:169–181.

Mills, G. C., F. C. Schmalstieg, K. B. Trimmer, A. S. Goldman, and R. M. Goldblum. 1976. Purine metabolism in adenosine deaminase deficiency. Proc. Nat. Acad. Sci. U.S.A. 73:2867–2871.

Moore, E. C., and R. B. Hurlbert. 1966. Regulation of mammalian deoxyribonucleotide biosynthesis by nucleotides as activators and inhibitors. J. Biol. Chem. 241:4802–4809.

Murray, A. W. 1971. The biological significance of purine salvage. Ann. Rev. Biochem. 40:811–826.

Nell, P. A., A. J. Ammann, R. Hong, and E. R. Stiehm. 1972. Familial selective IgA deficiency. Pediatrics 49:71–99.

Nezelof, C., M. L. Jammet, P. Lortholary, B. Labrune, and M. Lang. 1964. L'hypoplasie héréditaire du thymus: sa place et sa responsabilité dans une observation d'aplasie lymphocytaire normoplasmocytaire et normoglobulinemique due nourrisson. Arch. Fr. Pediat. 21:897–920.

Nishihara, H., S. Ishikawa, K. Shinkai, and H. Akedo. 1973. Multiple forms of human adenosine deaminase. II. Isolation and properties of a conversion factor from human lung. Biochem. Biophys. Acta 302:429–442.

Ochs, H. D., J. E. Yount, E. R. Giblett, S.-H. Chen, C. R. Scott, and R. J. Wedgwood. 1973. Adenosine deaminase deficiency and severe combined immunodeficiency syndrome. Lancet 1:1393–1394.

Ochs, U., W. Osborne, S.-H. Chen, and C. R. Scott. 1977. Human lymphocyte transformation following inhibition of purine nucleoside phosphorylase. (Abstr.) Pediat. Res. 11:491.

Osborne, W. R. A. 1972. The biochemistry of inherited forms of human red cell adenosine deaminase. Ph.D. Thesis, University of London.

Osborne, W. 1977. Personal communication.

Osborne, W. R. A., S.-H. Chen, E. R. Giblett, W. D. Biggar, A. J. Ammann, and C. R. Scott. 1977. Purine nucleoside phosphorylase deficiency: evidence for molecular heterogeneity in two families with enzyme deficient members. J. Clin. Invest. 60:741–746.

Osborne, W. R. A., S.-H. Chen, and C. R. Scott. 1978. Use of the integrated steady state rate equation to investigate product inhibition of human red cell adenosine deaminase and its relevance to immune dysfunction. J. Biol. Chem. 253:323–325.

Osborne, W. R. A., and N. Spencer. 1973. Partial purification and properties of the common inherited forms of adenosine deaminase from human erythrocytes. Biochem. J. 133:117–123.

Parkman, R., E. W. Gelfand, F. S. Rosen, A. Sanderson, and R. Hirschhorn. 1975. Severe combined immunodeficiency and adenosine deaminase deficiency. New Eng. J. Med. 292:714–719.

Patriarca, P., R. Cramer, S. Monocalvo, F. Rossi, and D. Romeo. 1971. Enzymatic bases of metabolic stimulation in leucocytes during phagocytosis: the role of activated NADPH. Arch. Biochem. Biophys. 145:255–262.

Pearl, E. R., L. B. Vogler, A. J. Okos, W. M. Crist, A. R. Lawton III, and M. D. Cooper. 1978. B-lymphocyte precursors in human bone marrow: an analysis of normal individuals and patients with antibody deficiency states. J. Immunol. 120:1169–1175.

Petersen, B. H., J. A. Graham, and G. F. Brooks. 1976. Human deficiency of the eighth component of complement. The requirement of C8 for serum *Neisseria gonorrhea* bactericidal activity. J. Clin. Invest. 57(2):283–290.

Piomelli, S., and L. Corash. 1976. Hereditary hemolytic anemia due to enzyme defects in glycolysis. Adv. Hum. Genet. 6:165–240.

Polmar, S. H., R. C. Stern, A. L. Schwartz, E. M. Wetzler, P. A. Chase, and R. Hirschhorn. 1976. Enzyme replacement therapy for adenosine deaminase deficiency and severe combined immunodeficiency. New Eng. J. Med. 295:1337–1343.

Polmar, S. H., E. M. Wetzler, and R. C. Stern. 1977. Immunopharmacologic studies of adenosine deaminase deficient lymphocytes. (Abstr.) Pediat. Res. 11:492.

Polmar, S. H., E. M. Wetzler, and R. C. Stern. 1978a. Adenosine Deaminase Deficiency: Enzyme Replacement Therapy and Investigations of the Biochemical Basis of Immunodeficiency. In Inborn Errors of Immunity and Phagocytosis, Wamberg, E., and F. Güttler (Eds.), Lancaster, MTP Press. In press.

Polmar, S. H., E. M. Wetzler, R. C. Stern, and R. Hirschhorn. 1975. Restoration of in vitro lymphocyte responses with exogenous adenosine deaminase in a patient with severe combined immunodeficiency. Lancet 2:743–746.

Polmar, S. H., E. M. Wetzler, R. C. Stern, and D. W. Martin, Jr. 1978b. Evidence for the role of ribonucleotide reductase inhibition in adenosine deaminase deficiency. Pediat. Res. 12:456.

Pyke, K. W., H.-M. Dosch, M. M. Ipp, and E. W. Gelfand. 1975. Demonstration of an intrathymic defect in a case of severe combined immunodeficiency disease. New Eng. J. Med. 295:424–428.

Radam, G., H. Strauch, and O. Prokop. 1974. Ein seltener Phänotyp im Adenosindesaminase-Polymorphismus: Hinweis auf die Existenz eines neuen Allels. Humangenetik 25(3):347–350.

Radam, G., H. Strauch, and B. Vavruša. 1975. Zur differenzierung der Varienten 5-1 und 6-1 im Adenosindesaminase-Polymorphismus. Nachweis des neuen Phänotyps ADA 5-2 in der CSSR. Humangenetik 26(2):151–154.

Raivio, K. O., A. L. Schwartz, R. C. Stern, and S. H. Polmar. 1976. Adenine and Adenosine Metabolism in Lymphocytes Deficient in Adenosine Deaminase. In Purine Metabolism in Man, Müller, M. M., E. Kaiser, and J. E. Seegmiller (Eds.), pp. 456–462. New York, Plenum Press.

Ressler, N. 1969. Tissue-characteristic forms of adenosine deaminase. Clin. Chim. Acta 24:247–251.

Rich, K. 1977. Personal communication.

Rosen, F. S. 1974. Primary immunodeficiency. Pediat. Clin. North Am. 21(3):533–549.

Rosen, F. S. 1975. Immunodeficiency. In Immunogenetics and Immunodeficiency, Benacerraf, B. (Ed.), pp. 230–257. Baltimore, University Park Press.

Rosen, F. S. 1976. Primary Immunodeficiency. In Clinical Evaluation of Immune Function in Man, Litwin, S. D., C. L. Christian, and G. W. Siskind (Eds.), pp. 207–232. New York, Grune & Stratton.

Rosen, F. S., C. A. Alper, J. Pensky, M. R. Klemperer, and V. H. Donaldson. 1971. Genetically determined heterogeneity of the C1 esterase inhibitor in patients with hereditary angioneurotic edema. J. Clin. Invest. 50:2143–2149.

Salmon, S. E., M. J. Cline, J. Schultz, and R. I. Lehrer. 1970. Myeloperoxidase deficiency. Immunological study of a genetic leukocyte defect. New Eng. J. Med. 282:250–253.

Sandman, R., A. J. Ammann, C. Grose, and D. W. Wara. 1977. Cellular immunodeficiency associated with nucleoside phosphorylase deficiency: immunologic and biochemical studies. Clin. Immunol. Immunopathol. 8:247–253.

Schmalstieg, F. C., J. A. Nelson, G. C. Mills, T. M. Monahan, A. S. Goldman, and R. M. Goldblum. 1977. Increased purine nucleotides in adenosine deaminase-deficient lymphocytes. J. Pediat. 91:48–51.

Schwartz, A. L., S. H. Polmar, R. C. Stern, and D. H. Cowan. 1978. Abnormal platelet aggregation in severe combined immunodeficiency disease with adenosine deaminase deficiency. Brit. J. Haematol. 39:189–194.

Schwarzmeier, J. D. 1974. Purin-de-novo-Synthese und Verhalten des zyklischen AMP in normalen und pathologischen Liekozyten. Wien. Klin. Wochenschr. 86:716–724.

Scott, C. R., S.-H. Chen, and E. R. Giblett. 1974. Detection of the carrier state in combined immunodeficiency disease associated with adenosine deaminase deficiency. J. Clin. Invest. 53:1194–1196.

Seegmiller, J. E., F. M. Rosenbloom, and W. N. Kelley. 1967. Enzyme defect associated with sex-linked human neurological disorder and excessive purine synthesis. Science 155:1682–1684.

Sheen, M. R., B. K. Kim, and R. E. Parks. 1968. Purine nucleoside phosphorylase from human erythrocytes. III. Inhibition by the inosine analog formycin B of the isolated enzyme and of nucleoside metabolism in intact erythrocytes and sarcoma 180 cells. Molec. Pharmacol. 4:293–299.

Siciliano, M. J., M. R. Bordelon, and P. O. Kohler. 1978. Expression of human adenosine deaminase (ADA) after fusion of ADA deficient cells with mouse fibroblasts. Proc. Nat. Acad. Sci. U.S.A. 75:936–940.

Siegenbeek van Heukelom, L. H., A. Boom, H. A. Bartstra, and G. E. J. Staal. 1976a. Characterization of adenosine deaminase isozymes from normal human erythrocytes. Clin. Chim. Acta 72:109–116.

Siegenbeek van Heukelom, L. H., G. E. J. Staal, J. W. Stoop, and B. J. M. Zegers. 1976b. An abnormal form of a purine nucleoside phosphorylase in a family with a child with severe defective T-cell and normal B-cell immunity. Clin. Chim. Acta 72:117–124.

Simmonds, H. A., G. S. Panayi, and V. Corrigall. 1978. A role for purine metabolism in the immune response: adenosine deaminase activity and deoxyadenosine catabolism. Lancet 1:60–63.

Skaper, S. D., R. C., Willis, and J. E. Seegmiller. 1976. Intracellular 5-phosphoribosyl-1-pyrophosphate: decreased availability during glutamine limitation. Science 193:587–588.

Snyder, F. F., J. Mendelsohn, and J. E. Seegmiller. 1976. Adenosine metabolism in phytohemagglutinin stimulated human lymphocytes. J. Clin. Invest. 58:654–666.

Spencer, N., D. A. Hopkinson, and H. Harris. 1968. Adenosine deaminase polymorphism in man. Ann. Hum. Genet. 32:9–14.

Stiehm, E. R., and H. H. Fudenberg. 1966. Clinical and immunological features of dysgammaglobulinemia, type I. Am. J. Med. 40:805–815.

Stoop, J. W., V. P. Eijsvoogel, B. J. M. Zegers, B. Blok-schut, D. W. van Bekkum, and R. E. Baillieux. 1976. Selective severe cellular immunodeficiency. Effect of thymus transplantation and transfer factor administration. Clin. Immunol. Immunopathol. 6:289–298.

Stoop, J. W., B. J. M. Zegers, G. F. M. Hendrickx, L. H. Siegenbeek van Heukelom, G. E. J. Staal, P. K. De Bree, S. K. Wadman, and R. E. Baillieux. 1977. Purine nucleoside phosphorylase deficiency associated with selective cellular immunodeficiency. New Eng. J. Med. 296:651–655.

Swallow, D. M., L. Evans, and D. A. Hopkinson. 1977. Several of the adenosine deaminase isozymes are glycoproteins. Nature 269:261–262.

Teng, Y.-S., J. E. Anderson, and E. R. Giblett. 1975. Cytidine deaminase: a new genetic polymorphism in man. Am. J. Hum. Genet. 27:492–497.

Tischfield, J. A., R. P. Creagan, E. A. Nichols, and F. H. Ruddle. 1974. Assignment of a gene for adenosine deaminase to human chromosome 20. Hum. Hered. 24:1–11.

Trotta, P. P., E. M. Smithwick, and M. E. Balis. 1976. A normal level of adenosine deaminase activity in the red cell lysates of carriers and patients with severe combined immunodeficiency disease. Proc. Nat. Acad. Sci. U.S.A. 73:104–108.

Tsuboi, K. K., and P. B. Hudson. 1957. Enzymes of the human erythrocyte. I. Nucleoside phosphorylase, isolation procedure. J. Biol. Chem. 224:879–887.

Turner, B. M., R. A. Fisher, and H. Harris. 1971. An association between kinetic and electrophoretic properties of human purine nucleoside phosphorylase isozymes. Eur. J. Biochem. 24:288–295.

Turner, B. M., R. A. Fisher, and H. Harris. 1974. The age-related loss of activity of four enzymes in the human erythrocyte. Clin. Chim. Acta 50:85–95.

Ullman, B., A. Cohen, and D. W. Martin. 1976. Characterization of a cell culture model for the study of adenosine deaminase and purine nucleoside phosphorylase-deficient immunologic disease. Cell 9:205–211.

Valentine, W. N., D. E. Paglia, A. P. Tartaglia, and F. Gilsanz. 1977. Hereditary hemolytic anemia with increased red cell adenosine deaminase (45- to 70-fold) and decreased adenosine triphosphate. Science 195:783–785.

van der Weyden, M. B., R. H. Buckley, and W. N. Kelley. 1974. Molecular form of adenosine deaminase in severe combined immunodeficiency. Biochem. Biophys. Res. Commun. 57:590–595.

Virelizier, J. L., M. Hamet, J. J. Ballet, and C. Griscelli. 1978. Impaired defense against vaccinia in a child with T lymphocyte deficiency associated with inosine phosphorylase defect. J. Pediat. 92:358–362.

Wara, D. W., and A. J. Ammann. 1975. Laboratory Data. In Combined Immunodeficiency Disease and Adenosine Deaminase Deficiency: A Molecular Defect, Meuwissen, H. J., R. J. Pickering, B. Pollara, and I. H. Porter (Eds.), pp. 247–253. New York, Academic Press Inc.

Watson, J., R. Epstein, and M. Cohn. 1973. Cyclic nucleotides as intracellular mediators of the expression of antigen-sensitive cells. Nature 246:405–409.

Wolf, J., R. Reid, J. Anderson, J. Rebuck, J. Lightbody, R. Johnson, J. Uberti, and L. Weiss. 1976. Cellular immunodeficiency (Nezelof) associated with ADA deficiency. Treatment with thymosin and ADA enzyme replacement. (Abstr.) J. Reticuloendothel. Soc. 20:48.

Wolfson, J. J., and V. F. Cross. 1975. The Radiologic Findings in 49 Patients with Combined Immunodeficiency. In Combined Immunodeficiency Disease and Adenosine Deaminase Deficiency: A Molecular Defect, Meuwissen, H. J., R. J. Pickering, B. Pollara, and I. H. Porter (Eds.), pp. 255–277. New York, Academic Press Inc.

Wüst, N. 1971. Adenosine deaminase in lymphocytes and its electrophoretic separation. Hum. Hered. 21:607–613.

Yulish, B., R. C. Stern, and S. H. Polmar. 1979. Partial resolution of bone lesions in a child with severe combined immunodeficiency and adenosine deaminase deficiency, following enzyme replacement therapy. Am. J. Dis. Child. In press.

Zegers, B. S. M., J. W. Stoop, G. F. M. Henricksx, S. K. Wadman, and G. E. J. Staal. 1978. Purine Nucleoside Phosphorylase Deficiency Associated with Cellular Immunodeficiency: Immunological Follow-up During Treatment. In Inborn Errors of Immunity and Phagocytosis, Wamberg, E., and F. Güttler (Eds.). Lancaster, MTP Press. In press.

Ziegler, J. B., C. H. Lee, M. B. van der Weyden, and J. Beveridge. 1978. Failure of therapy with exogenous adenosine deaminase (ADA) in ADA-negative severe combined immunodeficiency. Fed. Proc. 37:1669.

6

Approaches to Human Linkage*

MARCELLO SINISCALCO

Sloan-Kettering Institute, New York, New York, 10021

INTRODUCTION
THE PEDIGREE APPROACH
    Autosomal Linkage
    Sex Linkage:
        Y-linkage Detection
        X-linkage Detection
        X-linkage Estimation
    Mapping Via Chromosomal Variations
    Centromere Mapping
THE POPULATION APPROACH
    Fundamentals of Genetic Equilibrium
    Some Examples of "Presumptive" Linkage Disequilibrium and
       Their Use in Gene Mapping
THE SOMATIC CELL GENETICS APPROACH
    The Early Work
    Detection of Linkage Groups and Chromosomal Assignments
       with Cell Hybrids: The Synteny Test
    Genetic Mapping Through Complementation Analysis
    Subregional Mapping of Human Chromosomes
    Statistical Mapping of Gene Orders: The Radiation Co-transfer
       Test
    Cell Surface Antigens: A Target and Tool for Gene Mappers
    "Transgenotes" and "Microcell Hybrids"—Two New
       Paraphernalia of Somatic Cell Genetics
    Human-Human Hybrids and Heterokaryons

---

*This paper is dedicated to Prof. Giuseppe Montalenti on the occasion of his retirement from a distinguished career as a scientist and educator which the author of these pages always wanted and still strives to emulate.

INTRODUCTION

The author entered the trade of human gene mapping over 25 years ago. It was a small trade then, with general headquarters located at the University College of London in the old premises of the Galton Laboratory at Gower Street WC1. At the time, the only way to search for human linkages was to screen for distorted segregation ratios in informative pedigrees of the largest size. This search was no minor enterprise, and the statistical analysis was a kind of "do it yourself" job with no help from desk computers or tables of lod scores. Thus, it is no wonder that for a very long time the accumulation of data on human linkage has been excruciatingly slow. In a review lecture on the subject at the 1963 International Congress of Genetics, the examples of well-established human linkage could be enumerated on the fingers of one hand (Siniscalco, 1964). Moreover, there were practically no data on the chromosomal assignment of any human gene or linkage group, with the exception of X-borne loci whose typical criss-cross pattern of inheritance is, of course, the only condition for their ascertainment.

Today we know the chromosomal location of about 200 of the 2902 genetic markers listed in the last edition of the catalogue of *Mendelian Inheritance in Man* (McKusick, 1976). What is more important is that now there are at least 2 and as many as 30 gene markers assigned to each of the 22 autosomes and to the X and Y chromosomes.

The sequential order and subregional mapping of these genes are often known in detail or about to be established. At the time of this writing, the accumulation of new data is proceeding at a pace of about two new assignments per week. The search for human linkage, once regarded as an intellectual amusement of a few cranks, is now actively pursued by hundreds of scientists all over the world. The small trade has become a big corporation, and, like Wall Street–businessmen, experts in the field can now dial a code number to be updated with the latest developments in the market (Partridge, 1977).

What happened? It all started with the fortuitous observation of Weiss and Green in 1967 that mouse-human somatic cell hybrids undergo the gradual and preferential loss of human chromosomes, thus permitting screening for the association in the retention or loss of one or more human gene markers with that of a specific human chromosome. The advantage of studying human linkage with interspecific somatic cell hybrids lies mainly in the fact that owing to the evolutionary distance between the parental species, these hybrids can be considered as multiple heterozygotes for all genes that express themselves in cultured cells. Thus, one can investigate linkage relationships independent of the existence of genetic polymorphism within the human species — a prerequisite that is the sine qua non for the detection and estimation of linkage within pedigrees and populations. However, the greatest attraction for the ever-increasing number of newcomers in the field is the possibility of being able to study man's inheritance experimentally. Indeed, thanks to these new methodologies, human genetics, once an "applied science," has entered the circle of experimental sciences. However, it would be wrong to assume that the dramatic success of the cell-hybrid approach has rendered all other approaches obsolete. On the contrary, experience has shown that the best-mapped chromosomes are those for which data have been gathered with different approaches and can be collated, as has happened for autosomes 1, 2, 6, and 9 and the X chromosome. In addition, the methodology for the pedigree approach has also evolved considerably. Computer programs now make linkage analysis possible in complicated pedigrees and at the population level.

Another breakthrough for studies on human gene mapping at the level of cultured somatic cells has been the adaptation of the techniques of molecular hybridization to metaphase chromosomes. This approach has been successfully used for the localization of repeated or moderately repeated DNA sequences, such as those for ribosomal RNA, 5S RNA, tRNA, and histones. There have also been disputed claims on the applicability of these techniques for the mapping of unique DNA sequences such as those for globin chains in man and mouse. Several very promising new paths are developing in this field of molecular mapping. One of these makes use of molecular hybridization in solution between highly purified RNA probes and DNA prepared from rodent-human somatic cell hybrids that have retained only one human chromosome, or part of it. Another new path utilizes the same type of highly reduced hybrid somatic cells as a source of heterogeneous nuclear RNA (nRNA) coded by one residual human chromosome or chromosome fragment. Iodinated poly A RNA from these cells, enriched in human sequences through a multistep hybridization procedure, may be used as a probe to screen for chromosome specificity of highly reiterated DNA sequences by in situ hybridization to human metaphase chromosomes. Preliminary studies along these lines that have been performed in the author's laboratory have led to the identification of nRNA that is homologous to repeated DNA sequences of the human X chromosome.

There is no doubt that these molecular approaches to human gene mapping will now be greatly improved by the recent dramatic advances made in the fields of DNA restriction analysis and DNA cloning. In particular, these new methodologies are expected to yield critical data for the intracistronic mapping of those structural genes for which highly purified mRNA is available. This has already been shown to be the case in the analysis of DNA fragments containing the major globin genes.

Genetic linkage may be simply defined as the expected exception to the law of independent segregation stemming from the fact that genes, far from being the free floating units of inheritance hypothesized by Mendel, are assembled in a regular and constant fashion (linkage groups) along chromosomal DNA. Accordingly, the occurrence of crossing over between homologous chromosomes may be regarded as the phenomenon that restores complete or partial independence to genes that are part of the same linkage group. A direct consequence of linkage and crossing over is that mature haploid gametes end up carrying an admixture of parental genomes that is not so finely grained as it would be if genes were individual, segregating units, and yet it would be a much more thorough mixture than the one afforded by the mere random segregation of paternal and maternal chromosomes at meiosis.

It is generally agreed that, within each species, individual chromosomes have evolved to accommodate their architecture to the mode of action and interaction of the genetic material they carry. To describe the distribution of this material, transcribed as well as untranscribed, is the ultimate goal of linkage analysis. This goal has practically been achieved for several prokaryotes, and it is well under way for those eukaryotes that have lent themselves to the classic experimental approaches of mendelian genetics. It is fair to admit that the accumulation of this type of knowledge in man has hardly begun in spite of the remarkable advances mentioned in the strategies and technologies for studying human linkage.

This review is not meant to provide an updated critical summary on the mapping of the human genome. Such a task is already efficiently fulfilled by Dr. McKusick's short newsletter, which has been reproduced in this chapter and can be obtained from Dr. McKusick by calling (301) 955-6641, and by the regular publication of the workshops on human gene mapping (Bergsma, 1974, 1975, 1976, in press). Rather, the main aim of this writing is (1) to summarize the rationale of the different methodologic approaches so far employed, (2) to discuss the most promising avenues for the development of new methodologies, and (3) to evaluate the potentials of this type of knowledge in biomedical research with special reference to medical genetics and cancer biology.

THE PEDIGREE APPROACH

Autosomal Linkage

The "detection" of autosomal linkage is essentially based on the screening for exception to the independent segregation of the gene pairs that are under study in the offspring of informative matings, whereas the "estimation of linkage" is derived from the relative frequencies of the recombinant phenotypes that are computed separately for each pair of segregating loci. This statistical approach to linkage analysis, though valid for all species that reproduce sexually, is of course best exploited when the most informative matings (multiple backcross) can be set up experimentally. The main difficulty in applying this approach to the study of human linkage arises from the fact that calculations have to be based on families that are derived from natural populations, which very rarely involve data on more than two generations. Consequently, the phase (coupling or repulsion) of the presumably linked genes in the double heterozygous parent is unknown, thus making the family with a small number of children scarcely informative and the family with one child entirely useless. The appropriate correction for this biased sampling is a serious problem, since the exact manner in which the informative families come to notice is far from easy to ascertain. A point of logical importance in the detection of autosomal linkage has been stressed by Smith (1953). Since there are 22 pairs of autosomes in man, the possibility that any two autosomal loci chosen at random are on the same chromosome is 1:22. Thus, four out of every hundred pairs of genetic markers tested are expected to be linked. Alternatively, about the same number of false linkages would also be detected if the usual level of significance threshold (.05) is used. This means that for every hundred pairs of genetic markers tested the chance of detecting a "true" or a "false" linkage is practically the same unless much stricter levels of significance are used, such as 1×10^{-4} and less.

The detection of linkage is by no means the only methodologic difficulty when dealing with human data. Once a linkage has been established beyond reasonable doubt, the estimation of its degree is a much more serious problem — for biologic as well as statistical reasons. It has been known for a long time that certain chromosomal abnormalities that are capable of altering the recombination frequency are maintained in a condition of stable polymorphism in natural animal populations (White, 1973). The frequent occurrence of some of these chromosomal irregularities has now been proved to exist in man (Borgaonkar, 1974). This type of genetic heterogeneity among families that are derived from different natural populations may lead to contradictory and yet correct values of recombination frequency for the same pair of loci. This is especially true when one or both of the genes under examination have a high adaptive value in some ecologic environments but not in others. It is not unreasonable to expect in these cases that a chromosomal or genic factor capable of reducing cross-overs, thereby preserving a successful gene complex, might have been fixed only in those populations in which that factor occurred by chance and turned out to be advantageous. For this reason, it seems of utmost importance that pedigree data on human linkage should be collected and analyzed separately within homogeneous natural populations (i.e., true mendelian breeding units). Moreover, in view of the discovery that meiotic recombination in females is almost twice as high as that of males (Cook, 1965; Renwick and Schulze, 1965), it has become customary to estimate linkage separately for the two sexes. As a matter of fact, the finding of a significant difference in the recombination frequency between two alleged linked loci in the families with a double heterozygous mother as opposed to those with a double heterozygous father has itself become a very convenient criterion for establishing autosomal linkages (Smith, 1954). As is well known, such differences in crossing over do exist in several other species, notably in *Drosophila melanogaster*, in which meiotic recombination is entirely absent in the male.

However, it should be stressed that in the mouse, a sex difference in the frequency of meiotic crossing over has been found for some linkage groups but not for others (Dunn and Bennett, 1967).

Mathematic methods for the detection and estimation of linkage started to be developed in the early 1930s. One of these methods, known as the sibpair method of Penrose (1935), was based on the screening of pairs of sibs for independence of phenotypes related to two different loci. This simple method, which has the advantage of not requiring information on the parental phenotypes, stems from the well-known corollary that linkage between two autosomal genes, while not affecting the independent distribution of the corresponding phenotypes in the general population, results in positive or negative association within pedigrees, depending upon whether the parental genotypes are in coupling or repulsion phase. Howev-

er, this method is far from efficient, because it does not estimate the
recombination frequency, and it may yield positive or negative results for a variety of reasons such as a nonrandom distribution of the
different gametic combinations in the population, a differential fitness of some composite phenotypes, and so forth. Moreover, the
error of the method, as given by Penrose, is only accurate for families with two children (Smith, 1959). More efficient methods were
developed by Fisher (1935a,b), Finney (1940), and Bailey (1951).
These are all based on the so-called u-statistics, which, like chi-
square, test for deviations from the expected segregation ratios, irrespective of the phase of the parental genotypes.

Readers interested in the development of linkage methodologies can find a concise account of them in Kenneth Mather's book
The Measurement of Linkage in Heredity and a more extensive one
in N. T. J. Bailey's *Introduction to the Mathematical Theory of Genetic Linkage.* Currently, autosomal linkage is studied with the sequential method of Morton (1955), which makes use of a probability
ratio called "lod score" or "log odds," a short notation for "decimal
logarithm of the probability ratio." This parameter, called "z,"
measures the odds (P) in favor of linkage for each family (F) and for
different values of recombination frequency (θ_1 for males and θ_2 for
females), against the probability (P_0) of occurrence of the same family in the absence of linkage, i.e., when the recombination frequen-
cy is 0.5 for both sexes: $z = \log_{10} \{P [F (\theta_1, \theta_2)]/P_0 [F (\frac{1}{2}; \frac{1}{2})]\}$.

The lod scores are essentially an elaboration of the maximum
likelihood estimates of Haldane and Smith (1947). A simple guide
to the calculation of these quantities and to the evaluation of their
weight in favor of or against linkage can be found in Race and
Sanger's book *Blood Groups in Man* (Race and Sanger, 1975). One of
the major advantages of this method is the cumulative property of
the sum of lod scores obtained from each set of informative families,
independent of their being studied at the level of three generations
(phase known) or of two generations (phase unknown). According to
Morton (1955), linkage is considered proved when the overall sum of
lod scores at any value of recombination fraction exceeds +3. Conversely, it can be excluded when this sum is less than −2. Thus, this
method— unlike the u-statistics— allows concurrent "detection" and
"estimation" of linkage. A convenient way for a graphic description of
the relative probability of linkage at each value of recombination
frequency is to plot the antilog of the sum of lod scores against
increasing values of recombination fraction. The graph of $P (\theta) =$
$\text{antilog}_{10} z (\theta)$ is useful, since it offers an alternative way to estimate
the probability that linkage is present from the relation $\overline{P}/[\overline{P} + 21 P$
$(0.5)]$, where $\overline{P}$ is the average value of $P (\theta)$ between $\theta = 0$ and $\theta =$

0.5 and can be experimentally calculated by doubling the area under the graph.

Lod score values for every possible type of segregating sibship have been computed and tabulated (Maynard Smith, et al., 1961; Smith, 1968, 1969). However, since the number of genetic markers now available for linkage studies is over 50, the search for autosomal linkages by single pair comparisons has become a formidable task that can be fulfilled only with the help of computers.

The first computer program for handling linkage data from very large pedigrees as well as from small two- and three-generation families was written by Renwick and Schulze (1961). A simplified version of this comprehensive program has been elaborated by Ott (1974). This is considered to be the best computer method available at present to deal with linkage analysis of rare traits in large pedigrees. Falk and Edwards (1970) have prepared a much simpler program that can be run on a modestly sized computer such as the 1130 IBM. This is fully adequate for the analysis of the bulk of genetic data on human linkage that usually come from small rather than large families. A full listing of this program has recently been published, with all the details required for the storage of the data on punch cards and their subsequent use for testing deviation from independent segregation for each pair of genes considered separately (Falk, et al., 1975).

As is well known, estimates of meiotic recombination based on the frequencies of cross-overs (i.e., the recombinant phenotype combinations observed among the offspring of an informative mating) may be inaccurate because of the likelihood of multiple recombination events between the loci under consideration. For instance, when linked genes are separated by more than 20 to 30 recombination units, double cross-overs are far from rare and would be misclassified as noncross-overs. This problem, however, is not worth consideration in dealing with human linkage, because loose linkage cannot be satisfactorily estimated in human pedigrees with the available statistical methodology. The issue will have to be reconsidered when computer methods for linkage analysis in pedigrees segregating at the same time for three or more markers is developed.

Sex Linkage

In view of the sex chromosome dimorphism that characterizes humans as well as other mammals, the detection of genes located on the X or the Y chromosome with the pedigree approach is not a problem. Nevertheless, the estimation of recombination frequencies among different sex-linked loci or between these loci and their centromere, remains a very difficult task for X-linked genes and even more so for Y-linked genes.

Genes belonging to the former group cannot normally be transmitted from fathers to sons, and they follow the pattern of so-called criss-cross or diaginic inheritance (i.e., affected male→carrier daughter→affected grandsons), whereas genes of the latter group can normally be transmitted only through the male line of descent from father to all of his sons (holoandric inheritance).

Y-Linkage Detection

The first example of Y-linkage inheritance is traced back to 1731 with the report to the Royal Society of the so-called Lambert pedigree, in which a man and all of his six sons were allegedly affected by the so-called "porcupine-man syndrome" (ichthyosis hystrix). The pedigree was further reconstructed by Cockayne (1933) in 1933 on the basis of hearsay evidence and was found to involve a regular "father to all sons transmission" of the condition over six generations. However, a critical re-examination of the original literature and the direct search of the parish registers of birth made by Stern (1957) led to a radical re-evaluation of this famous pedigree. First of all, the originally affected ancestor did not have six sons; he had four sons and two daughters, and he had transmitted the condition to only one son and two of his six grandsons. Thus, holoandric inheritance was ruled out. Thirteen additional samples of alleged "complete Y-linkage inheritance" were listed by Gates in 1946 on the basis of the typical Y-segregation pattern observed in rare pedigrees. Like the porcupine trait, none of these stood the challenge of the critical analysis of the relevant literature made again by Stern (1957), who concluded that "the evidence" for Y-linkage in man is at best ambiguous. The "best" pedigrees, taken by themselves, have only a low probability of being interpretable as the result of chance segregation of autosomal genes, but such interpretation becomes more acceptable if one remembers that these pedigrees have been selected from thousands that show "ordinary autosomal or X-linked inheritance."

This conclusion does not mean that the Y chromosome is devoid of genetic information as is often maintained. The problem is that, unlike the X chromosome and the autosomes, the Y chromosome is regularly present only in single dose, thus making segregation analysis impossible with the pedigree approach. However, through the study of families with individuals bearing variant Y chromosomes, one or more factors that control the maturation of the undifferentiated gonads into testes have been assigned to the short arm of the Y chromosome (Tiepolo and Zuffardi, 1976). Recently, a male-specific cell surface–antigen has been detected using sera from multiparous females (Koo, personal communication). This finding was triggered by the discovery by Wachtel et al. (1974) of a Y chromosome–specific antigen in the mouse (H-Y). A strong correlation between mouse H-Y antibodies with H-Y antigens on cells from males of other species (including man) was also found, thus suggesting the conservation of a Y-antigen gene or genes throughout evolution. From the analysis that has been made so far of the distribution of the H-Y antigen in individuals with sex upsets (Wachtel, et al., 1975), it seems likely that this antigen is closely related to the determination of the male phenotype. Thus, it is to be expected that the true genetic variation of the H-Y locus may be discovered as soon as reagents for phenotypic characterization are available in a purified form and in adequate supply. The relationship between the long-known Y-linked transplantation genes of the mouse and those for the H-Y antigen has not been fully clarified as yet.

On the basis of the well-known facts that, on the average, males are taller than females, XYY individuals are taller than XY males, and XY females are taller than normal females, it has been suggested that the Y chromosome carries one or more genes involved in the determination of height and that these genes perform this function through a mechanism unrelated to the production of androgens (Tanner, et al. 1959).

Another marker of the human Y chromosome has recently been identified through studies of the molecular hybridization of human male and female DNA. Reiterated and male-specific DNA sequences have been isolated (Kunkel, et al. 1976) and have been shown to compose about 40 percent of the long arm of the human Y chromosome. Quantitative individual differences in these sequences, 50 percent of which are localized within the bright quinacrine fluorescent segment of the Y chromosome, have been reported (Kunkel, et al 1977). These studies have already clearly indicated that the quantitative variation in these sequences is not correlated in any way with male differentiation or the expression of the H-Y antigen.

X-Linkage Detection

According to Stern (1960), the first clear account of X-linked inheritance can be found in the writings of the Talmud (280 A.D.), where it deals with the rules for dispensation from circumcision in families in which incoercible bleeding (today's hemophilia) had occurred at circumcision. The exemption was apparently granted when at least two of these accidental deaths occurred in the same sibship and was extended only to the brothers of the deceased boy and to the first cousins of maternal descent but not to those of paternal descent. Such legislation obviously implies a remarkable knowledge of the mechanism of inheritance of hemophilia, including the criterion, still adopted today, of considering the recurrence of the disease in the same sibship as evidence for its "segregational" rather than "mutational" nature, as we would say in modern terminology. We know now, however, that this criterion may be fallacious, since a single somatic mutational event in an early pregonial cell can result in a cluster of mature germ cells carrying the mutant gene, hence making possible the multiple birth of carrier daughters from a normal hemizygous father as well as the birth of several hemophiliac sons from a normal homozygous mother. If the mutational event occurs at a very early stage, the individual phenotype may be indistinguishable from that of an affected hemizygous or a heterozygous carrier, as the case may be. Thus, the only safe criterion for proving the "segregational" nature of hemophilia, or of any other rare X-linked mutant phenotype, is, essentially, the occurrence of one or more affected males in two or more branches of the pedigree related through maternal descent.

The pattern of X-linked inheritance is easy to spot when dealing with rare mutants such as hemophilia or the Lesch-Nyhan syndrome. In such cases, the well-known basic criterion for suspecting X-linkage is the finding that the condition is practically limited to the male sex and is never transmitted from father to son. For common mutant genes, such as those for the Xg negative blood type, the color blindness of deutan or protan type, glucose-6-phosphate dehydrogenase (G6PD) variants, and so forth, a complete segregation analysis is required, possibly starting from old-age propositi in three-generation pedigrees, so that the X-linked inheritance of the mutant phenotypes can be followed from the maternal grandfather to his grandsons, without introducing ascertainment bias in the classification of the double heterozygous mothers.

In the absence of family data, confirmation of X-linkage may be obtained by demonstrating that somatic tissues of obligatory heterozygous carriers are mosaic for normal and abnormal cells, as expected in view of the random inactivation of one X chromosome per cell in the early XX embryo. However, this evidence is meaningful only when the mosaicism is expressed at the level of clonal cell populations grown in vitro. Thus, the application of this criterion is necessarily limited to those X-linked traits that express themselves in cultured cells. A classic example of the application of this methodology is illustrated by a recent study of human testicular feminization, otherwise called male pseudohermaphroditism, because the affected individuals have a female phenotype, despite their XY karyotype, and a normal level of plasma testosterone. The X-linkage of this condition (whose primary genetic defect has been shown to consist in the lack of cellular receptors to androgenic hormones) had been already firmly established in the mouse by appropriate mating analysis (Lyon and Hawkes, 1970), but could not be clearly confirmed in man by pedigree studies, since, under the given circumstances, these do not permit distinction between sex linkage and sex limitation. This confirmation has now been provided by the studies of Meyer et al. (1975), showing that fibroblast clones from an obligatory heterozygote are either normal or completely deficient in androgen receptors, as expected if the gene or genes controlling their synthesis are X-linked and regularly involved in X-inactivation.

As we will see in the following section, the distribution of X-linked traits at the population level offers another indirect criterion for spotting X-linkage. Since males are monosomic for the X chromosome, the frequency of each X-linked phenotype in males is equal to the frequency of the X-linked genes that are responsible for them. Thus, if the population is in equilibrium, the incidence of the corresponding homozygous phenotypes among females is expected to be much lower, since the chance of their occurrence is given by the square of the incidence of the same phenotype or phenotypes among males.

X-Linkage Estimation

The estimation of the degree of linkage between X-borne loci is greatly facilitated by the ease of establishing the phase (coupling or repulsion) of the double heterozygous mother. This can be promptly inferred from the hemizygous phenotype of the maternal grandfather or assessed through laboratory studies when it happens that both the segregating phenotypes can be identified at the level of individual somatic cells. Of course, if the first criterion is used, one has to make sure through appropriate genetic studies that the legal maternal grandfather is also the biologic one. The pedigrees reproduced in Figure 1 are examples of multiple segregation at two or three X-linked loci. Calculations of the Lod scores for these families are shown in Table 1.

SARDINIAN PEDIGREES SEGREGATING FOR G6PD DEFICIENCY, DEUTAN COLOR BLINDNESS, AND Xg BLOOD TYPES.

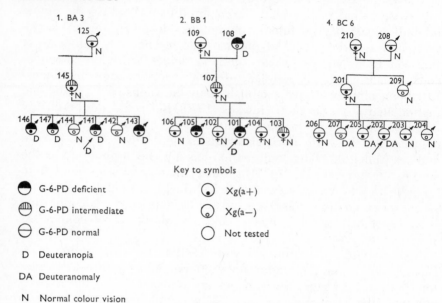

Key to symbols

⬤ G-6-PD deficient   ⊙ Xg(a+)

▥ G-6-PD intermediate   ⊘ Xg(a−)

⊖ G-6-PD normal   ◯ Not tested

D   Deuteranopia

DA   Deuteranomaly

N   Normal colour vision

Figure 1.   Sardinian pedigrees giving linkage information about the loci for G6PD and deutan (1 and 2), for G6PD and Xg (1 and 2), and for deutan and XG (1, 2 and 4). For the analysis of the degree of linkage, see Table 1. The pedigrees shown here are confined to those in which the mother was proved heterozygous for both Xg and the other character. The propositus, when presented in the part of the pedigree given here, is marked by a subscript arrow. The families were ascertained through G6PD-deficient or color-blind schoolchildren: If both abnormalities were present in a propositus, the character responsible for the ascertainment is indicated by a letter at the shaft of the arrow. (From Siniscalco, M., et al. 1966. Ann. Hum. Genet. 29:231–252.)

In families in which the phase is known, the frequency of meiotic recombination between any pair of loci is obtained from the relative frequency of the new phenotype combinations (cross-overs) directly counted among the male offspring of the double heterozygous mother. In some favorable cases, the female offspring can also be informative, but the use of this information introduces additional statistical problems for the correction of the ascertainment bias and the risk of phenotype misclassification owing to extreme X-inactivation. In general, the effort to correct for this bias is not worth the little extra information, so that most workers prefer to base their estimates of recombination frequencies only on the counts of cross-overs among males.

Table 1. Linkage Analysis by "Lod Scores" for Families Shown in Figure 1*

FAMILY NO.	SCORING SIBS	LOD SCORES AT VARIOUS LEVELS OF THE RECOMBINATION FRACTION θ:								
		0.05	0.10	0.15	0.20	0.25	0.30	0.35	0.40	0.45
G6PD and Deutan										
BA3	6 n. rec. —	1.674	1.530	1.380	1.224	1.056	.876	.684	.474	.246
BB1	3 n. rec. —	.837	.765	.690	.612	.528	.438	.342	.237	.123
Sum of lods		2.511	2.295	2.070	1.836	1.584	1.314	1.026	.711	.369
Xg and G6PD										
BA3	4 n. rec. 4 rec.	−3.442	−2.286	−1.632	−1.184	−.852	−.596	−.392	−.230	−.101
BB1	1 n. rec. 2 rec.	−1.721	−1.143	−.816	−.592	−.426	−.298	−.196	−.115	−.051
Sum of lods		−5.163	−3.429	−2.448	−1.776	−1.278	−.894	−.588	−.545	−.153
Xg and Deutan										
BA3	2 n. rec. 4 rec.	−3.442	−2.286	−1.632	−1.184	−.852	−.596	−.392	−.230	−.101
BB1	1 n. rec. 2 rec.	−1.721	−1.143	−.816	−.592	−.426	−.298	−.196	−.115	−.051
BC6	2 n. rec. 3 rec.	−2.442	−1.587	−1.104	−.786	−.551	−.374	−.237	−.133	−.096
	z2:0 e_1 1:1	.154	.131	.107	.085	.062	.041	.024	.011	.003
Sum of lods		−7.451	−4.885	−3.450	−2.477	−1.767	−1.227	−.801	−.467	−.206

*From the sum of the lod scores in this table it can be clearly seen that in the pedigrees of Figure 1 the genes for G6PD and Deutan color blindness segregate in close association, whereas those for Xg and G6PD or Xg and deutan color blindness recombine freely.

X CHROMOSOME MAPPING FROM PEDIGREE DATA WITH PARTICULAR REFERENCE TO DISTANCE OF OTHER GENES FROM THE Xg LOCUS.

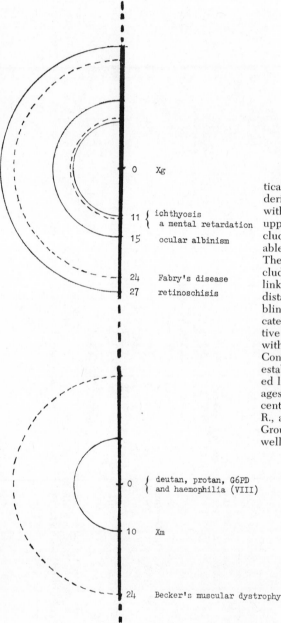

Figure 2. A partial statistical map of the X chromosome derived from linkage analysis with the pedigree approach. The upper portion of the map includes loci that are at measurable distances from the Xg locus. The lower part of the map includes loci that are closely linked to (or at a measurable distance from) the locus for color blindness. The semicircles indicate uncertainty about the relative position of the other loci with respect to the two markers. Continuous lines indicate well-established linkages, interrupted lines indicate probable linkages, and the numbers represent centimorgans. (From Race, R. R., and R. Sanger. 1968. Blood Groups in Man. Oxford, Blackwell Scientific.)

The estimation of linkage between X-linked genes is a more difficult problem when dealing with data from two-generation families. An obvious example of these difficulties is the linkage relationship between the locus for the Xg blood group antigen and a cluster of closely X-linked traits including G6PD deficiency and color blindness of deutan and protan type. This linkage was for some time considered measurable (cross-over frequency = 0.27) from data based on two-generation families (Adam, et al., 1967), but it turned out to be completely "unmeasurable" when the segregation was analyzed in pedigrees in which the phase was known (Siniscalco, et al., 1966). Figure 2 summarizes the data so far collected on X-chromosome mapping with the pedigree approach. Taken on their face value, these data identify two clusters of closely linked loci: (1) the cluster including the loci for G6PD, hemophilia, protan and deutan color blindness and, (2) the cluster including the loci for the Xg^a antigen, the precursor of the Kell antigen [X(K)], X-linked ichthyosis, ocular albinism, α-galactosidase, and possibly phosphoglycerate kinase (PGK). The pedigree data also tell that these two clusters are at a nonmeasurable distance from one another, but they offer no clues on the relative order of genes within each cluster or on their subregional mapping (Race and Sanger, 1975). We will see their importance, however, when we re-evaluate them in conjunction with other data on X-linkage collected through other methodologic approaches. A comprehensive review on the analysis of X-linkage with special reference to the bias from ascertainment and its correction has been given by J. H. Edwards (1971).

Mapping via Chromosomal Variations

The dramatic advances made in cytogenetic technology during the last ten years now make it possible to individually identify all normal human chromosomes and their numeric or structural variation. Chromosomal aberrations have been a formidable tool in experimental genetics for the cytologic mapping of *Drosophila melanogaster* and *Mus musculus*. The use of these aberrations in the study of human linkage with the pedigree approach is of course hampered by the disadvantage of having to deal with pedigrees collected from natural populations, so that individuals who happen to be heterozygous for a "chromosomal heteromorphism" are seldom also heterozygous for the genetic markers of our choice. This explains why the cytogenetic approach to human gene mapping has yielded, on its own merit, only a few positive results. These, however, are enough to illustrate some of the different ways in which chromosomal variations can be used in mapping studies. Thus, a chromosomal variation such as the "uncoiler region" of chromosome 1 has led to the assignment of the gene for the Duffy blood group (Donahue, et al., 1968) to this chromosome. A family segregating for a familial translocation yielded the assignment of the gene for the α-haptoglobin locus to chromosome 16 (Robson, et al., 1969). This assignment was later confirmed by another family segregating for chromosome 16 with a "fragile" site of a specific region on the long arm (q22), thus providing the precise subregional location of this locus (Magenis, et al., 1970). Individual heterozygotes for a deleted chromosome are the "raw material" for the so-called deletion mapping. The locus for acid phosphatase has been assigned by this method to the distal end of the short arm of chromosome 2 (Mace, et al., 1975). Also, the subregional mapping of the gene for lactate dehydrogenase-A (LDH-A) and lactate dehydrogenase-B (LDH-B) on the short arms of chromosomes 11 and 12, respectively, has been achieved in this way (Ruddle and Meera Khan, 1976). The rationale for this approach is based on the screening for a correlation between the missing chromosome segment and a qualitative or quantitative variation of the phenotype expected on the basis of the type of pedigree. Although, up to now, this approach has not yielded much positive information in terms of new assignments, it has been useful in excluding the location of several genes on a series of well-defined deleted chromosomal regions (Table 2).

Hematologic malignant clonal cell lines derived from individuals with known genotypes may occasionally offer suitable hints toward linkage detection and gene assignment. Fialkow et al. (1972) found that a patient with chronic myelocytic leukemia expressed only one allelic product at the loci for Rh and 6GPD, despite his being an obligatory heterozygote at both loci. The most economical interpretation of this finding at the time was that the two missing genes were probably both carried by the deleted portion of the so-called Philadelphia chromosome, then believed to be a deleted chromosome 21. We know now that the loci for Rh and 6PGD are syntenic but are both on the subterminal region of the short arm of chromosome 1. Moreover, it has been recognized that the Philadelphia chromosome is not the result of a deletion but is the result of a reciprocal translocation between chromosomes 22 and 9 (Rowley, 1973). Fialkow's patient is a confirmation of the suitability of tumor clonal cell lines for linkage detection, but at the same time it is a warning about the risk of deriving conclusions on gene assignment from

Table 2. Exclusion Mapping Data*

MARKER	EXCLUDED FROM:
ABO	1q25–1q32; 9q11–9q22; 11q23–11qter; 13p11–13pter; 14p11–14pter; 18q11–18q21;
MNSs	1p32–1pter; 1q25–1q32; 2p23–2pter; 22q31–2qter; 3p25–3pter; 4p16–4pter; 4q33–4qter; 5p13–5pter; 6q13–6q15; 6q25–6qter; 7pter–7q11; 7q21–7q32; 7q35–7qter; 9p24–9pter; 9q34–9qter; 10p13–10pter; 10q26–10qter; 11q21–11qter; 12p13–12pter; 13p11–13pter; 13q12–13q14; 13q31–13qter, 14p11–14pter; 15pter–15q12; 15q26–15qter; 17p12–17pter; 17q24–17qter; 18p11.3–18pter; 18q11–18q21.1; 18q22–18qter; 19q13–19qter; 20p11–20pter; 20q13–20qter; entire chr. 21; 22pter–22q11;
Rh	1q25–1q32; 3p25–3pter; 3q27–3q28; 4p16–4pter; 4q11–4q13; 4q33–4qter; 5q13–5pter; 6q27–6qter; 7p15–7p22; 7q21–7q32; 7q35–7qter; 9p21–9pter; 9q34–9qter; 10p13–10pter; 10q26–10qter; 11q23.1–11qter; 13p11–13pter; 13q32–13qter; 14p11–14pter; 15pter–15q12; 16p13–16pter; 17p12–17pter; 17q24–17qter; 18p11.3–18pter; 18q11–18q21; 19q13–19qter; 20q13–20qter; entire chr. 21; 22pter-22q11; 22q13–22qter;
Lu	13q32–13qter; 18p11–18pter;
K	4q33–4qter; 21pter–21q21; 22p11–22pter; 22q13–22qter
Le	7q35–7qter; 20q13–20qter;
Fy	1q25–1q32; 4p16–4pter; 4q33–4qter; 6q13–6q15; 6q27–6qter; 7p15–1722; 7q21–7q32; 7q35–uqter; 9p24–9pter; 9q34–9qter; 13p11–13pter; 13q12–13q14; 13q34–13qter; 14p11–14pter; 15pter–15q12; 18p11–18pter; 18q11–18q21.1; 18q22–18qter; 20p11–20pter; 20q13–20qter; 21q21–21pter; 22pter–22q11;
Jk	6q13–6q15; 7q21–7q32; 9p24–9pter; 9q34–9qter; 11q21–11qter; 18p11–18pter; 18q22–18qter; 22pter–22q11; 22q13–22qter;
α-Hp	1q25–1q32; 2p23–2pter; 4p16–4pter; 4q34–4qter; 6q25–6qter; 7q21–7q32; 9p24–9pter; 9q34–9qter; 10q26–10qter; 11p15–11pter; 11q21–11qter; 12p13–12pter; 13p11–13pter; 13q32–13qter; 14p11–14pter; 15pter–15q14; 15q26–15qter; 17p12–17pter; 17q24–17qter; 18p11–18pter; 18q11–18qter; 20q13–20qter; entire chr. 21;
Gm	1q25–1q32; 2p23–2pter; 4p16–4pter; 4q11–4q13; 4q33–4qter; 5p15–5pter; 6q27–6qter; 7q32–uqter; 11q23.1–11qter; 13q11–13pter; 13q31–13qter; 14011–14pter; 15pter–15q12; 18p11.3–18pter; 18q11–18q21.1; 13q22–18qter; 20p11–20pter; 21q21–21pter;
Gc	1q25–1q32; 4q33–4qter; 6q25p6qter; 7q32–7qter; 9p24–9pter; 9q34–9qter; 11q21–11qter; 12p13–12pter; 13p11–13pter; 13q31–13qter; 14p11–14pter; 15pter–15q14; 18p11–18pter; 18q11; 18q21; 18q22–18qter; entire chr. 21;

Table continued on following page

Table 2.   Exclusion Mapping Data* *(Continued)*

MARKER	EXCLUDED FROM:
ACP_1	1q25–1q32; 2q31–2qter; 3q27–3q28; 4p16–4pter; 4q12–4q21; 4q33–4qter; 5p15–5pter; 6q25–6qter; 7p15–7pter; 7q21–7qter; 9p24–9pter; 9q34–9qter; 10q26–10qter; 11p15–11pter; 11q21–11qter; 12p13–12pter; 13p11–13pter; 13q33–13qter; 14p11–14pter; 15pter–15q12; 16p13–16pter; 18p11–18pter; 18q11–18q21.1; 18q22–18qter; 20p11–20pter; 20q13–10qter; entire chr. 21; 22q13–22qter;
PGM_1	1q25–1q32; 2p23–2pter; 4p16–4pter; 4q33–4qter; 7q11–7pter; 7q32–7qter; 9p24–9pter; 9q34–9qter; 10q26–I0qter; 11q23.1–11qter; 13p11–13pter; 13q33–13qter; 14p11–14pter; 150ter–15q14; 15q26–15qter; 18p11–18pter; 18q11–18qter; 19q13–19qter; 20p11–20pter; entire chr. 21;
PGD	16p13–16pter;
AK_1	2p23–2pter; 3q27–3q28; 4q13–4qter; 19q13–19qter; 21pter–21q21; 22q13–22qter;
ADA	4q34–4qter; 10p13–10pter; 13p11–13pter; 13q34–13qter; 14p11–14pter; 22q13–22qter;
ESD	10p13–10pter;
GPT	4q12–4q21; 4q33–4qter; 7p15–7pter; 7q21–7q32; 9p24–9pter; 9q34–9qter; 10p13–10pter; 11q21–11qter; 18q11–18q21; 19q13–19qter; 20q13–20qter; 21pter–21q22;
HLA	1q25–1q32; 4p16–4pter; 4q11–4q13; 4q33–4qter; 5p15–5pter; 6q13–6q15; 7p15–7pter; 7q21–7q32; 9p21–9pter; 10q26–10qter; 11q21–11qter; 13q34–13qter; 15pter–15q14; 17p12–17pter; 17q24–17qter; 18p11–18pter; 18q12–18qter; 20p11–20pter; 20q13–20qter; 21pter–21q22; 22q13–22qter;
GALT	4q12–4q21;
C3	5p15–5pter; 6q13–1615; 18q11–18q21;
C4	6q13–6q15;
PGM_3	4q33–4qter; 21pter–21q21
GBG	6q13–6q15
GLO	7p15–7p22;
PEP A	18q11–18q21

*This table lists the loci excluded from specific autosomal segments by demonstration of heterozygosity for the relevant markers in patients with deletion of these chromosome regions. These data were presented at the 4th International Conference on Human Gene Mapping in 1977. (From Ferguson-Smith, 1978).

association between a given chromosomal variation and an altered phenotype found in tumor tissues.

An alternative method for autosomal gene mapping through gene dosage studies is theoretically offered by the screening of quantitative phenotypic variations in individuals with autosomal trisomies, on the assumption that the presence of an additional gene dose at a given locus should lead to a 50 percent increase in the level of the corresponding gene product. This conclusion is probably correct as witnessed by the increase of superoxide-dismutase-1 (SOD-1) in trisomy 21q (Sinet, et al., 1974) and for lactate dehydrogenase-B in trisomy 12p (Réthoré, et al., 1975), but one has to bear in mind the possibility that gene dosage–dependent variations can be completely obscured by larger variations due to the indirect phenotypic effects of the abnormal karyotype. For instance, the increase of several enzyme activities (including that of X-linked G6PD) reported in the erythrocytes of trisomy 21 patients (Mellman, et al., 1964), is most likely due to the younger erythrocyte population in these patients and to the red blood cell age dependence of most enzymes. It is possible, however, that a clear dosage effect could be shown in cultured cells (such as fibroblasts or lymphoblasts) provided that the karyotype observed in the live propositus remains unaltered. This issue could be properly explored (and, to some extent, has been already) now that the chromosomal assignment of several constitutive enzyme markers is known (Table 3). Thus, it is of primary importance that fibroblast and lymphoblast cultures are established from newborns with chromosomal aberrations and especially from spontaneous abortion or stillbirths, since these are often the result of chromosomal unbalance.

Coté and Edwards (1975) have discussed another way, besides gene dosage effect, in which autosomal trisomies can contribute to gene assignment. In view of the well-known strong correlation between maternal age and numeric chromosome aberrations, they consider the supernumerary chromosome to be regularly of maternal origin and point out that in a population sample of informative pedigrees (those having a heterozygous mother and possibly segregating for co-dominant alleles), the proportion of trisomics carrying three alleles from three of their grandparents must necessarily be greater than zero for any locus of the trisomic chromosome, independent of its distance from its centromere. This proportion can then be estimated by a likelihood method elaborated by the authors and applied to the detection of linkage or, when the linkage is already known, to investigate the origin of the trisomy. In spite of its elegant design, this approach to linkage detection is unlikely to be

Table 3.   Dosage Effect of Localized Autosomal Genes*

CHROMOSOME ASSIGNMENT	GENE PRODUCT	GENE DOSAGE
1q2 or 3–1qter	Fumarate hydratase (FH)	triplex†
2q23–2pter	Acid phosphatase-1 (ACP₁)	uniplex†
		triplex
3q21–3qter	Galactose-1-phosphate- uridyltransferase (Gal-1-PT)	triplex
8p21–8p23	Glutathione reductase (GR)	triplex
	Glutathione reductase (GR)	uniplex
9q33–9pter	Adenylate kinase-1 (AK-1)	triplex
12p12.2–12pter	Glyceraldehyde-3-phosphate dehydrogenase (GAPD)	triplex
12p12.2–12pter	Triose phosphate isomerase (TPI)	triplex
12p11–12p13	Lactate dehydrogenase-B (LDH-B)‡	uniplex and triplex
14q11–14q21	Nucleoside phosphorylase (NP)	triplex
16	Adenine phosphoribosyl- transferase (APRT)	triplex
18q23–18qter	Peptidase-A (Pep-A)	uniplex and triplex
21	Superoxide dismutase-1 (SOD-1)	triplex
21q22.1	Superoxide dismutase-1 (SOD-1)	triplex and uniplex

*Summary of the data showing dosage-dependent expression of the genes listed. The expressions "triplex" or "uniplex" indicate that the locus in question was present in triple or single dose, respectively, and that the enzyme varied accordingly in a quantitative fashion. Strictly speaking, these data do not prove that the corresponding genes are constitutively expressed, since loci with regulatory functions could also be located in the same chromosomal region. (From Krone and Wolf, 1977.)
† Terms proposed by Charles E. Ford, personal communication.
‡ Indirect evidence.

of practical value in view of the possible heterogeneity of the factors that lead to nondisjunction and the difficulty of finding a significant number of informative pedigrees within genetically homogeneous mendelian isolates, as would be especially desirable when the genotypes of the individual family members are inferred on the basis of population gene frequencies.

The structural chromosomal aberrations that are most frequently encountered in natural populations of higher organisms are inversions and balanced translocations. Man is no exception to this rule. Several instances of pericentric inversions have been reported since the era of chromosome banding began. Those inversions involving chromosome 9 seem to be particularly frequent and have been found in homozygous conditions within highly inbred populations. These inversions segregate as dominant autosomal traits and are therefore suitable tools for the chromosomal assignment of yet-unsited human polymorphic loci as well as for the subregional mapping of loci already known to be markers of the inverted chromosomes. Using pedigrees segregating for some of these inversions, de la Chapelle et al. (1974) were able to exclude the location of the loci for Gm, Inv, ABO, MNS, P, and Gc within the region p1→q13 of chromosome 9 and of those for the Dombrok, secretor, Gm, P, Duffy and transferrin within the region p11→q21 of chromosome 10. It is interesting to note that subsequent work has shown that the ABO locus is actually located on chromosome 9, but in the subterminal region of the long arm. Families segregating for pericentric inversions of chromosome 9 could help now to decide the debated question of the assignment of the Galt locus to the region 9 pter/9q 33, since it is not unlikely that some of these families may segregate individual recombinants with a tandem duplication deficiency in this region. Needless to say, some of these families may give information through the straightforward segregation analysis if the inversion heterozygotes also happen to be heterozygous at two or more loci situated within the inverted segment or near it, since the presence of the inversion may suppress crossing over and disclose a tight linkage between loci that usually segregate independently in normal individuals. In view of the finding that the great majority of inversion heterozygotes have normal phenotypes and normal offspring, it has been argued that crossing over seldom occurs in the inverted chromosomal regions so far identified.* This conclusion, however, is not fully justified in view of the well-known limitations of genetic analysis with the pedigree approach. It is obvious that most of the unbalanced genotypes of the kind discussed may be eliminated through early spontaneous abortions. At least two well-documented instances of unbalanced karyotypes born to inversion heterozygotes for chromosomes 4 or 10 have been interpreted as the consequence of crossing over within the inverted region (van der Linden, et al., 1975; Dutrillaux, et al., 1973).

Again, efforts should be made to establish cell cultures from the chromosomally unbalanced progeny of inversion heterozygotes, since they are expected to include duplication deficiencies and thus may offer opportunities for chromosome mapping via gene dosage studies in cultured cells.

Paracentric inversions are more difficult to ascertain, since no visible change in chromosome size is produced, whereas change in banding morphology can only be spotted when they alter the pat-

---

*As is well known from animal and plant cytogenetics, a crossing over within the inverted segment of a pericentric inversion may lead to duplication deficiencies, whereas a crossing over within a paracentric inversion leads to the formation of a dicentric and an acentric chromosomal fragment ("bridge and fragment").

tern of well-defined sequences of uneven bands characteristic of certain chromosomes. In *Drosophila* no serious reduction in gamete viability is encountered in the heterozygotes for this type of inversion. This is due to the absence of recombination in males and to the fact that when a single cross-over occurs during egg maturation, the dicentric chromatid is eliminated from the functional egg nucleus with the polar body (White, 1973). Small inversions — pericentric or paracentric — are known to inhibit crossing over frequencies in experimental animals in view of the lack of pairing at meiosis. These are, however, undetectable in man and of limited interest for linkage studies, since pairs of closely linked loci would be spotted anyway through pedigree analysis. Genetic polymorphism for centromeric regions has been detected by C-banding techniques (which stain centromeric heterochromatin) in all series of population cytogenetics that have been conducted so far. Pedigrees segregating for such markers are especially suited for chromosomal assignment of polymorphic genes. Although no instances of close linkage with centromeres have yet been reported, it has been determined that several loci are not located at a measurable distance from the centromeric mapping mark so far described (Ferguson-Smith, et al., 1975).

In principle, the types of structural chromosomal aberrations that are most suitable for the detection of linkage and chromosome mapping are balanced reciprocal translocations. However, their usefulness with the pedigree approach is greatly limited by the remote chance that the heterozygous carrier of the balanced translocation is also heterozygous at the relatively few loci for which man is known to be polymorphic. When this happens, genes that segregate independently in normal individuals may fail to do so in the offspring of the translocation carriers, thus leading to the identification of new syntenic groups and to their subregional mapping. This has not happened thus far, but, as we will see later, fibroblasts or lymphoid cells with inborn balanced translocations have been precious in human gene mapping with somatic cell hybrids, especially when the reciprocal balanced translocation involved the X chromosome. It is not surprising, however, that X chromosome mapping has not been helped much in the analysis of pedigrees with structurally rearranged X chromosomes. This is because the families with X-chromosomal translocations so far described happened to be uninformative with respect to the X-linked loci known at present. Moreover, there have been no reports of heterozygotes for an X chromosome inversion despite an active search for them in areas in which multiple heterozygotes for X-linked genes occur frequently. Gene dosage studies in unbalanced heterozygotes for X chromosome mutations cannot be done — neither in vivo nor in cultured cells because unbalanced X chromosomes are preferentially inactivated.

The theoretic and methodologic aspects of gene assignment and map positioning of human loci using chromosomal variations have been extensively dealt with by Renwick (1971a).

Centromere Mapping

Convincing arguments have been provided (Linder, 1969; Linder and Power, 1970) in favor of the parthenogenetic origin of the benign ovarian teratomas, thus turning these tumors into suitable tools for centromere mapping in man. Since the tumors always have a 46,XX karyotype and are usually found to be homozygous at loci for which the host is heterozygous, they are thought to originate from an individual germ cell arrested at the first meiotic division, so that homozygosity would be a necessary consequence at any locus unless random exchanges between homologous chromosomes occurred between the locus and its centromere.

The rationale for centromere mapping is based on the theory of multiple chiasmata formation of Mather (1935) and Whitehouse (1950) and is inspired by the classic studies of Bridges (1916) and Anderson (1926) on attached X chromosomes in flies and by the more recent work of Lindsley et al. (1956) and of Merriam and Frost (1964) on *Drosophila*. When "homologous" loci separate from one another during the first meiotic division, it is called "reductional" with respect to the genes involved. When "sister loci" separate, the division is called "equational." According to most theories of meiosis, the centromere of each homologue stays undivided until the second meiotic division, and therefore centromeres are always separated from one another "reductionally." This implies that in an individual who is heterozygous at a given locus, the equational separation of the two alleles can be accomplished only if the original relationship between the marker and the centromere is changed through the occurrence of crossing over in the relevant chromosomal region during the first meiotic division. Thus, in practice, given a number of teratomas from multiple heterozygous hosts, the distance of each informative locus from its centromere can be established from the frequency of heterozygous tumors. This frequency is expected to vary from zero, in the absence of recombination, to a maximum of 0.66, for — theoretically — infinite numbers of recombinations. Ott et al. (1976a, b) have elaborated a convenient "lod score equation" for estimating centromere distances with the "teratoma method" and have established that the map distance of phosphoglucomutase-3 (PGM-3) — a well-known marker of human autosome 6 — from its centromere is about .17 morgan, with 95 percent confidence intervals between .07 and .34. When the host is heterozygous at two or more loci of the same linkage group, the method can also provide information on their sequential order along the chromosome.

Another obvious opportunity for centromere mapping in man is offered by families of patients with Klinefelter's syndrome (XXY) derived from maternal nondisjunction and segregating for one or more X-linked markers. Stern (1959) pointed out that XXY color blind males born to normal parents can arise (disregarding the rare event of a coincidental extreme X-inactivation) from maternal nondisjunction at the first meiotic division with recombination or at the second meiotic division without recombination.

Thus, individual families give no information, and the estimates of distances from the centromere must necessarily be based on a large number of cases collected from populations with a homogeneous distribution of the relevant allelic frequencies for each locus to be mapped. However, when the mothers of the propositi are heterozygous with genotype phase known at two or more X-linked loci, even a few families can provide important data on centromere mapping as well as on the mechanisms of nondisjunction and recombination in general.

THE POPULATION APPROACH

Fundamentals of Genetic Equilibrium

A well-known consequence of Mendelism at the population level is that the distribution of all possible genotypes for any given autosomal polymorphic genetic system is proportioned to the term of the polynomial obtained by squaring the sum of the individual allelic frequencies. Thus, given two alleles "A" and "a" with respective frequencies "p" and "q" (where $p + q = 1$) the three possible genotypes AA, Aa, and aa will occur with respective frequencies of p^2, $2pq$, and q^2. For three alleles, a^1, a^2, and a^3, with frequencies p, q, and r ($p + q + r = 1$), the six possible genotypes a^1a^1, a^2a^2, a^3a^3, a^1a^2, a^1a^3, and a^2a^3 will be in the ratio of $p^2:q^2(p^2:q^2:r^2):2pq:2pr:2qr$.

These equilibrium distributions (usually referred to as "Hardy-Weinberg" equilibria) are attained within one generation of random mating with respect to each separate set of allelic genes and will remain unaltered in the subsequent generations provided that the populations are large enough, all genotypes have the same biologic fitness, and matings continue to occur at random.

When two pairs of alleles are considered at the same time (A, a, and B, b with respective allelic frequencies p,q, and u,v) the frequencies of the nine possible genotype combinations expected under random matings are given by the product of the equilibrium genotype frequencies for each separate system. It is convenient to describe the situation with a 3×3 matrix whose entries are the Hardy-Weinberg equilibrium frequencies for the two sets of genotypes determined by each pair of alleles:

	BB (u^2)	Bb (2uv)	bb (v^2)
AA (p^2)	AABB (p^2u^2)	AABb ($2p^2uv$)	AAbb (p^2v^2)
Aa (2pq)	AaBB ($2pqu^2$)	AaBb (4pquv)	Aabb ($2pqv^2$)
aa (q^2)	aaBB (q^2u^2)	aaBb ($2q^2uv$)	aabb (q^2v^2)

Since the results of random mating of individuals are the same as random union of gametes, one can also represent the population just described with a 2×2 matrix of the haploid gametic combinations:

	B:(u)	B:(v)
A:(p)	AB (pu)	Ab (pv)
a:(q)	aB (qu)	ab (qv)

Consequently, the equilibrium with respect to the two genetic systems can be defined as the condition in which the determinant of the latter matrix ($d = pu.qv - qu.pv$) is equal to zero. It is obvious that a population in equilibrium with respect to two or more allelic gene pairs is also in equilibrium with respect to each system taken separately, but the reverse is not necessarily true. However, it can be easily verified that the deviation "d" from zero in a matrix of gametic output is halved with each generation of random mating. Since there are values of gene frequencies for which the numeric value of (d) can never exceed $1/4$, it follows that even in the worst cases, equilibrium is attained very rapidly unless the loci for the two pairs of alleles under consideration are on the same chromosome and have a recombination frequency lower than 0.5. In the latter case the rate with which the deviation from equilibrium approaches zero is obviously dependent upon the closeness of the linkage. This is to say that equilibrium may never be reached, within a "historic" interval of time, when the recombination frequency (r) is practically zero, otherwise d will decrease by a factor of $1-r$ in each generation. For instance, for $r = 0.20$ (loose linkage) d will be reduced to 50 percent of its initial value within 3 generations, or approximately 100 years $[(1-0.2)^3 = 0.50]$, but for $r = 0.01$ (close linkage) a reduction in d of the same order of magnitude will take about 70 generations or 2000 years $[(1-0.01)^{69} = 0.50]$ and for $r = 0.001$, it will take as many as 700 generations or over 20,000 years $[(1-0.001)^{700} = \sim 0.50]$. Therefore, the well-known principle of population genetics that says linkage is responsible for positive or negative phenotype association within pedigrees (depending upon the arrangement of the two sets of genes — in coupling or repulsion — in the dihybrid parent) but never within populations (since in the long run, recombination, small as it may be, is expected to restore equilibrium) holds true as a generalization only for loosely linked genes. Close linkage can lead instead to the association of the relevant phenotypes at least within a "historic" interval of time. Conversely, the finding of phenotypic or allelic associations, especially those occurring in some natural populations but not in others, is a strong indication of genetic linkage between the correspondent genes (linkage disequilibrium). However, in evaluating data on phenotypic or allelic associations it should be reckoned that true genetic disequilibrium may also be the result of other factors besides close genetic linkage. For instance (1) common environmental influences in favor of two or more unrelated phenotypes (e.g., higher fitness of sickle cell, thalassemia, and G6PD deficiency traits in malarial environments), (2) inbreeding and — in general — selective matings resulting from social or ethnic stratification, and (3) migration (founder effect) and admixture of populations previously stabilized at different equilibrium levels, are all well-known factors of genetic disequilibrium. Nor should it be forgotten that "genetic disequilibrium" can also be the artifactual result of a series of factors such as (1) epistatic interactions between independent gene products (e.g., between Lewis and ABH secretor), (2) pleiotropic effects of the same gene, (3) sampling bias, and, last but not least (4) an incorrect genetic hypothesis.

It may sound iconoclastic, but one cannot help feeling that the current knowledge on the most popular examples of "linkage disequilibrium" will have to be critically reassessed as soon as it is possible to classify the relevant phenotypes at a level much closer to the primary gene products or, even better, when the genes at disequilibrium and the distance between them can be physically mapped at the nucleotide level, as has already happened for the β-globin gene and its neighboring region (see section on The Molecular Approach).

Nevertheless, the examples that are about to be given are still worth mentioning to illustrate how, in principle, the "population approach" may contribute data on the mapping of the human genome.

Some Examples of "Presumptive" Linkage Disequilibrium and Their Use in Gene Mapping

The most dramatic examples of association between sets of alleles of different autosomal loci are those related to the so-called complex loci Rh, Gm, and HLA. Bodmer and Bodmer (1978) have masterfully reviewed this topic with respect to the HLA system, which is the human genetic polymorphism that is best analyzed with respect to linkage disequilibrium. As is well known, the HLA system includes at least four loci (HLA-A, HLA-B, HLA-C, HLA-D and HLA-DR) clustered within an interval of about 2 percent recombination units on the short arm of autosome 6. Numerous alleles have been identified for each of these loci, and their distribution has been studied on a worldwide scale. From these studies it has emerged that certain allelic combinations (or "haplotypes") have frequencies that are significantly larger than those expected at equilibrium. That is, certain alleles of the four different loci are more frequently found on the same chromosome than is to be expected by chance. In particular, from the analysis of all pairs and combinations of alleles at the four different loci, it has been concluded that some of the alleles at the HLA-B locus are in strong linkage disequilibrium with some of the alleles of the HLA-C, HLA-DR, and HLA-A loci. These data have been interpreted as evidence in favor of the maintenance of the HLA linkage disequilibria through a differential fitness of some haplotype combinations. The lower the frequency of crossing over, the higher the chance that linked genes are in disequilibrium, and thus, the findings suggest that the locus HLA-B must necessarily be intermediate to the loci for HLA-A and HLA-DR, as well as to the loci for HLA-DR and HLA-C. Population data on linkage disequilibrium, coupled with direct estimates of genetic recombination in families segregating for the appropriate haplotypes have led to the hypothesis of the following sequence of the four loci within the HLA cluster:

```
D            B          C            A
    0.8          0.2         0.8
```

These conclusions, however, are by no means free of obscurities. For instance, HLA-C alleles do not show linkage disequilibrium with the alleles of either the HLA-A or HLA-D loci, and, more strangely, cases of families with two HLA recombinants have been reported in spite of the very close linkage between the corresponding loci (Suciu-Foca, et al., 1976).

Another example of the usefulness of the population approach to mapping of gene distances has recently been contributed by our own studies on the population genetics of four X-linked polymorphisms in Sardinia (Filippi, et al., 1977). A mutant gene ($Gd^{mediterranean}$) at the G6PD locus is in equilibrium with respect to the genes for the Xg^a antigen (Xg^a and Xg) and to the genes controlling color blindness of deutan type (D^+, D^-, DA^-), but is in clear-cut disequilibrium with the genes controlling color blindness of protan type (P^+, P^-PA^-). In view of the evidence that is available from previous studies that the $Gd^{mediterranean}$ mutant had been accumulated in Sardinia as a result of its higher fitness in malarial environments, we concluded that a sudden outbreak of selection in favor of only one of the four X-linked loci just mentioned might have created (or exaggerated), within a historic interval of time, a condition of disequilibrium to a degree inversely proportional to the frequency of meiotic recombination between the locus for G6PD and the other loci. That is, the observed disequilibrium between G6PD and protan alleles is most likely the result of an interaction between "founder effect," selection, and close linkage during the last 2500 years. In any case, taken at face value, the above data suggest that the locus for G6PD is closer to the locus for protan color blindness than it is to the loci for deutan color blindness and the Xg^a antigen.

THE SOMATIC CELL GENETICS APPROACH

The Early Work

In 1959 Pontecorvo predicted that within a decade human inheritance would be studied at the level of cultured somatic cells, using the same rationale and experimental strategies that he and his colleagues had devised and successfully applied to the genetic analysis of filamentous fungi. With respect to time, this prediction could not have been more accurate, but things actually happened somewhat differently from what Pontecorvo had visualized. One of the general expectations was that linkage groups could be identified through partial haploidization due to accidental chromosome loss in cultured cells from multiple heterozygotes. Another expectation was the statistical mapping of suitable cell markers (i.e., those belonging to the same linkage groups and amenable to positive or negative selection) in terms of mitotic recombination between homologous chromosomes on the assumption that, as in fungi, somatic pairing and crossing over would be found to occur regularly in cultured mammalian cells. With these expectations in mind, it is not surprising that the pioneers of mammalian somatic cell genetics concentrated their efforts on the implementation of technology for the maintenance of diploid cells in culture and on the definition of selective strategies for the prompt isolation of mutant cell types, their revertants, and their recombinant phenotypes. These efforts were by no means fruitless. In the early 1960s, thanks mainly to the work of Eagle (1969), Puck (1972), and their colleagues, the techniques for the growth of mammalian cells in vitro had developed to the point that clones of diploid cells could be grown at ease from primary explants of human skin. Mammalian cells were already looked upon as "microorganisms" and were therefore amenable to the applications of the experimental strategies of microbial genetics. The current most popular nonleaky mutants, which control enzymes of the purine and pyrimidine salvage pathways (thymidine kinase [TK] and hypoxanthine-guanine phosphoribosyl transferase [HGPRT]), had already been isolated in murine and human established cell lines (Kit, et al., 1963; Szybalski and Szybalska, 1962). The equally popular hypoxanthine-aminopterine-thymidine (HAT) medium (which by blocking de novo purine and pyrimidine synthesis makes cell survival dependent on the regular function of the salvage pathway) had been devised by Szybalski to select for "transformants" of the HGPRT-deficient mutant HeLa cells (Szybalski and Szybalska, 1962). Thus, the biologic tools necessary to study human genetics by cell hybridization had been at hand for quite a while but were not used for this purpose.

The discovery of intraspecific and interspecific spontaneous cell fusion, Littlefield's (1964) successful isolation of hybrids between TK-deficient and HGPRT-deficient murine lines by double selection against the parental cells, and Weiss and Green's (1967) basic finding that the murine-human hybrids are unstable at the exclusive expense of the human genome could all have occurred at least a decade earlier if the relevant cell mutants had been co-cultivated in the HAT medium. Evidently, the idea that mammalian cells, especially those from different species, could fuse and grow regularly as true hybrids was beyond expectation.

After the discovery of the experimentally induced fusion with inactivated Sendai virus, which rendered the production of heterokaryons and hybrids of all kinds easy and accessible to everybody, there was no more doubt that the time was ripe for a "parasexual approach" to the genetic analysis of man and all other eukaryotes that do not lend themselves to the traditional methodologies of experimental genetics. The formation of hybrid synkaryons was looked upon as the equivalent of the "diploidization" that takes place in heterokarytoc mycelia whereas the random loss of chromosomes from the hybrid genome was equated with the "haploidization" that completes the parasexual cycle of the filamentous fungi. Thus, the basic strategy for the identification of linkage groups was expected to be the screening for the mitotic segregation of cell markers from intraspecific hybrids derived from the fusion of parental cells that differ from one another for several genetic traits. Correspondingly, the possibility of establishing the gene order within each linkage group was thought to depend upon the occurrence of somatic crossing over between homologous chromosomes. Engel et al. (1969) were able to confirm some of these expectations by showing the occurrence of complementation with chromosomal segregation in intraspecific hybrids between TK-deficient and HGPRT-deficient murine cells. At the same time Puck (1972) had isolated an array of auxotrophic mutants in Chinese hamster ovary cells and shown that somatic hybrids between them could be isolated and maintained in minimum media with the occasional appearance of cell segregants bearing a modal chromosome number equal to that of the pseudodiploid parental cells. Some preliminary studies had indicated that the fusion of human diploid cells among themselves or with human heteroploid cells yielded hybrids with a relatively stable genome and two functionally active X chromosomes (Siniscalco, et al., 1969; Silagi, et al., 1969). In view of these findings and with the models mentioned in mind, this writer proposed to screen for mitotic pairing and mitotic recombination by means of human-human hybrids to be obtained from the fusion of male diploid cells derived from individuals with two or more X-linked mutants classifiable at the individual cell level (Siniscalco, 1970). However, these experiments were never performed because in the meantime the discovery of the unstable murine-human hybrid, with its unlimited potentialities for human gene mapping, made all other approaches appear at once extremely laborious and obsolete.

Detection of Linkage Groups and Chromosomal Assignments with Cell Hybrids: The Synteny Test

The rationale for the somatic cell hybrid approach to the mapping of human chromosomes is well known and straightforward. Since rodent-human hybrid cells (such as man-mouse, man-hamster, and man-rat) undergo the spontaneous and preferential loss of the human chromosomes, the expectation is that human markers coded by genes of the same "linkage group" are "retained" or "lost" in association, regardless of the distance of the corresponding loci along the chromosome. Thus, the first step toward "linkage detection" with cell hybrids is to screen for concordance in the pattern with which the human markers are retained or lost by the hybrid genome. Markers that show this concordance are called "syntenic" and the experimental procedure which leads to their detection is called the "synteny test." This Greek neologism (syn = together, toenia = ribbon) was introduced by Dr. J. H. Renwick (1971b) to distinguish the mere condition of markers located on the same chromosome from that of true genetic linkage measurable in terms of meiotic recombination among the offspring of informative matings. However, it must be noted that the synteny of human markers in cell hybrids may also be the result of factors totally unrelated to chromosomal linkage, such as a nonrandom chromosome loss, the possible metabolic interdependence of unrelated gene products, and the frequent occurrence of chromosomal rearrangement in cultured cells. Accordingly, in the language of cell hybridizers, the term *synteny* has lost its original precise meaning and is used more loosely for the operational classification of genetic markers that are concordantly retained or lost by the unstable interspecific hybrid cells. Given these circumstances, a still-unsettled issue is the minimum number of hybrid clones required to accept the identification of a "linkage group," and its "chromosomal assignment," as well established. The problem is hard to approach with rigorous statistics in view of the fact that each interspecific hybrid cell of the unstable type is a biologic entity of its own, because its genetic constitution varies in a totally unpredictable fashion even within the same clone. A generally accepted policy is to consider the evidence in favor of linkage collected through cell hybrids "provisional", unless it is based on two or more consistent series of primary hybrid clones produced in different laboratories with the use of different rodent and human parental cell types. Creagan and Ruddle (1975) have pointed out that an optimal panel of five hybrid clones is theoretically sufficient to spot $2^5 = 32$ "linkage groups," i.e., more than can possibly occur in man, who has only 24 types of "different" chromosomes (22 autosomes and the X and Y chromosomes). On the basis of this argument, McKusick and Ruddle (1977) go as far as suggesting that ideal panels of hybrid clones of the kind illustrated in Table 4 should be accumulated, frozen, and stored to be made available upon request to whoever is interested in the quick chromosomal assignments of newly discovered human markers. Unfor-

Table 4. Clone Panel for Gene Assignments with the "Synteny Test" *

CLONES	HUMAN CHROMOSOMES PRESENT										
	1	2	3	4	5	6	7	8	...	22	X,Y
A	+	+	+	+	−	−	−	−			
B	+	+	−	−	+	+	−	−			
C	+	−	+	−	+	−	+	−			

*This table illustrates how three properly selected hybrid clones can be sufficient to detect the synteny between a given genetic marker and one among eight different chromosomes. See text for further discussion. (From Creagan and Ruddle, 1975).

tunately, this possibility remains for the moment an unfulfilled dream, since the chance of finding such "ideal clone panels" within each set of primary hybrid clones from separate fusion experiments (as the correct methodologic approach requires for the reasons just discussed) is practically zero. Moreover, the experience accumulated so far indicates that even if such goals should eventually be fulfilled, perhaps through the combined use of selective procedures that insure the retention of specific chromosomes, it is practically impossible to avoid the chromosomal constitution of each primary clone undergoing changes, even after a few weeks of propagation in culture, let alone after revival from a long storage in liquid nitrogen. This suggests that the growth of hybrid cells with the lowest number of human chromosomes is probably the most selectively favored each time a so-called clonal population of hybrid cells (which in fact is always a mixture of hybrid cells with a variable number of human chromosomes) is exposed to an abrupt change of its microenvironment, such as the switch from one selective medium to another and thawing from the frozen state.

It is obvious that gene mapping with the "synteny test" is limited to those genetic markers that are regularly expressed in cultured cells and that can be unequivocally differentiated from the homologous murine markers through electrophoretic and/or immunologic characterization or other methods. It is for this reason that the majority of human genes mapped so far with this approach are those coding for constitutive enzymes, which are often referred to as "household functions." The mapping of genetic markers that are expressed only in highly specialized cells (such as hemoglobin, immunoglobins, hormones, and the like, which are called by contrast "luxury functions") is hard to achieve because of the difficulty of propagating these cells in culture and because their specialized function is usually no longer expressed when they are hybridized to well-growing murine undifferentiated cells. As is well known, this "extinction" of gene expression in somatic cell hybrids between different types of specialized cells has been one of the major items of investigation since the early days of somatic cell hybridization. These studies have contributed important clues to the understanding of the cellular mechanism that regulates gene expression in the eukaryotes (Ephrussi, 1972). For instance, it has been shown that the production of albumin is suppressed in somatic cell hybrids between rat hepatoma cells (albumin producing) and fibroblasts from the same or a different species (Peterson and Weiss, 1972; Darlington, 1974). However, when the ratio of the parental genomes in the individual hybrid cell is of two hepatoma to one fibroblast genome, the production of rat albumin is no longer suppressed, and even the homologous gene — which was silent in the fibroblastic parental cell type — is reactivated.

These observations have been extensively reviewed and discussed by Ephrussi (1972), Weiss, et al. (1975) and most recently Davidson (1974) with respect to their specific potentials for an experimental approach to the study of cell differentiation. In theory, the re-expression of human "luxury functions" in these types of hybrids should offer a unique opportunity to map the relevant structural genes, but in practice attempts toward this goal have been unsuccessful. This is due to the fact that during the long time required for the isolation of critical hybrid clones, many chromosomal rearrangements take place, so that it is very difficult to spot a syntenic association between the specialized function eventually recovered and the retention of an individual human chromosome (Rankin and Darlington, 1979). The only studies of this type relevant to gene mapping are those that report the assignment (yet to be confirmed) of three presumptive regulatory genes to the X chromosome of man, mouse, or cat, namely, (1) a regulator of the rat tyrosine aminotransferase in rat-human hybrids (Croce, et al., 1973), (2) a regulator for the expression of hemoglobin synthesis in mouse erythroleukemic-mouse fibroblast hybrids (Benoff and Skoultchi, 1977), and (3) a regulator for the expression of an endogenous B-tropic C-type murine virus in murine-feline hybrids (O'Brien, 1976). We shall see, however, that thanks to the striking advances of molecular biology during the last few years, it is now possible to apply the synteny test even to the mapping of genes that are not transcribed, let alone translated.

Genetic Mapping Through Complementation Analysis

Rodent cells that are deficient in a specific enzyme that renders them amenable to positive or negative selection in culture are so far the best tools for the chromosomal assignment of the complementary human gene that codes for the same enzymatic function. The experimental strategy to achieve this goal includes several steps. A fusion mixture of deficient rodent cells and normal human diploid fibroblasts or lymphocytes is grown in a selective medium that is lethal only for the rodent parental cell type. In a matter of a few weeks, this leads to the isolation of several primary clones of "complemented" hybrid cells, which, at this stage, can usually be morphologically distinguished from either type of parental cell. Each primary hybrid clone is then split into two subsets, which are grown under the conditions of "forward" or "backward" selection to secure the retention or loss of the human complementary gene and, hopefully, of the entire chromosome that carries it. As is well known, this methodology was in fact the type of experimental strategy employed for the first assignments of human genes using cell hybrids, namely, that of thymidine kinase to chromosome 17 (Weiss and Green, 1967; Miller, et al., 1971a) and of hypoxanthine-guanine phosphoribosyltransferase to the X chromosome (Nabholz, et al., 1969). Other human genes assigned in this way are those for adenine phosphoribosyltransferase (APRT) to chromosome 16 (Tischfield and Ruddle, 1974), serine hydroxymethyltransferase (SHMT) to chromosome 12 (Jones, et al., 1972), and adenosine kinase to chromosome 10 (Chan, et al., 1978). It is of interest that the syntenic association between human HGPRT and the X chromosome was actually established before the availability of the refined cytologic methods that now permit the direct identification of the human chromosomes within the murine genome. Bodmer and his colleagues (Nabholz, et al., 1969) arrived at this conclusion indirectly by simply establishing that HGPRT was regularly syntenic with human G6PD, whose X-linkage had already been well established through pedigree studies. Following the same rationale, our group confirmed the X-linkage of human phosphoglycerate kinase, PGK (Meera Khan, et al., 1971) and α-galactosidase, α-gal (Grzeschik, et al., 1972a). This shows that the complementation test can also be used for the detection of "linkage groups," provided that a rodent cell line with the appropriate mutant phenotype is available. At present, there are essentially three classes of rodent cell mutants that can be used for such types of studies: (1) the mutants of the nucleic acids pathways, (2) the auxotrophic mutants, and (3) the temperature-sensitive mutants. The selective retention of the corresponding human complementary genes, and of the chromosomes that carry them, is obtained by submitting the three different types of rodent-human hybrids to the appropriate selection procedures, which are based on (1) the forced use of a salvage pathway, (2) growth into the relevant minimum medium, or (3) exposure to the nonpermissive temperature. Several examples of the practically unlimited number of mutants that are expected within each of these classes have been identified and successfully used in hybridization experiments. The chromosomal assignment of the corresponding human complementary genes has been achieved for only a few of them, but further progress in the field is clearly only a question of time and routine work. An interesting new protocol for the isolation of heterozygotes and hybrids between parental cells of any type has been recently reported by Wright (1978). The first step of this procedure consists in the poisoning of each type of cell to be fused with a biochemical inhibitor (such as iodocetouride and diethylpyrocarbonate), which irreversibly arrests the cell's proliferative activity. When two parental cell types, each poisoned by a different inhibitor, are fused, their heterokaryotes, which are damaged in different vital functions, survive as a result of intergenomic complementation and eventually develop into actively growing hybrid cells. As the author indicates, the major drawbacks of this technique, whose general applicability has still to be evaluated, are the lack of specific inhibitors, the subtlety of the experimental protocol, and, above all, the legitimate question of whether the parental genomes are altered in some other way besides the vital functions complemented in the hybrid.

At any rate, there can be little doubt that in the not-too-distant future there will be enough rodent mutant cells and corresponding selective media for the prompt isolation of rodent-human hybrid cells that have selectively retained or lost the wanted human chromosome or chromosomes (Siniscalco, 1979). The accomplishment of such a target, as discussed in a later section of this review, is expected to be greatly expedited by the use of the so-called microcell hybrids derived from the fusion of mutant rodent cells with experimentally induced micronucleated human cells, which carry only a fraction of the human genome — often as small as one individual chromosome. Only under such circumstances can a systematic effort for the chromosomal mapping of the endless number of human markers that are still unassigned be eventually carried out with the least effort and the highest degree of success and reliability.

For the time being, the likelihood of correctly identifying the chromosomal assignment of any human gene that exerts a given "complementary function" (and of detecting the linkage group to which it belongs) is hampered by the same difficulties described in the previous section, i.e., the simultaneous retention of other human chromosomes in addition to the critical one and the frequent occurrence of de novo chromosomal rearrangements in culture that often lead to the retention of the sole complementary gene rather than of the entire chromosome that carries it. Once again, an efficient remedy to these difficulties is to rely only on conclusions based on the concordant results of the independent fusion experiments involving the use of "different" parental cell types.

Subregional Mapping of Human Chromosomes

The potentialities of the "complementation test" for human gene mapping were greatly enhanced when it was suggested and shown (Siniscalco, 1970; Grzeschik, et al., 1972b) that hybrids between HGPRT (−) murine cells and HGPRT (+) human cells carrying a balanced X-autosomal translocation could be used to construct a cytologic map of the X chromosome and of the autosome that happens to be involved in the translocation ("subregional mapping"). The rationale for this new protocol stemmed from the interesting finding of Opitz and Pallister in 1969 (reported by Opitz, et al., 1973) of a woman who was heterozygous for a balanced translocation between the long arm of the X chromosome and that of autosome 14 (46,Xt[X, 14: q13, q32]) and whose normal X chromosome was constantly late in replicating (and therefore was presumably inactive) in all of her somatic cells. Thus, the expectation was that hybrids between her somatic cells and murine HGPRT-deficient cells selected in HAT-medium should have obligatorily retained one or the other of the translocation chromosomes, depending upon the subregional location of the HGPRT locus along the X chromosome.

The first set of experiments carried out according to this rationale in our laboratory is an eloquent testimonial of the difficulties that can be met in these studies as a result of the frequent occurrence of de novo chromosomal rearrangements in cell hybrids. Namely, we found that under the condition of "conservative strategies" (i.e., when the HAT selection was kept to the minimum essential to avoid the possible chromosomal breaking action of aminopterin), the segregation of human HGPRT, G6PD, and PGK was regularly syntenic in mouse-human hybrids derived from normal human parental cells but not so in those derived from fibroblasts with the inborn X-14 translocation chromosomes just described. In particular, these data suggested that the human gene for PGK was located on the distal side of the translocation break point and that the genes for HGPRT and G6PD were located on its proximal side (Grzeschik, et al., 1972b). Subsequent studies of Ricciuti and Ruddle (1973) showed instead regular synteny of all three X-linked markers with the translocation chromosome that included the larger portion of autosome 14 and the fraction of the X chromosome long arm distal to the break point ($Xq_{13} \rightarrow Xqter$). Moreover, the screening of the same set of hybrids for the segregation of other human markers disclosed a new syntenic relationship (never before observed) between the X-linked markers and human nucleophosphorylase (NP), thus permitting the assignment of the corresponding gene to autosome 14. These conclusions were proved to be the correct ones by additional studies carried out by several other investigators (including ourselves) with the use of the same as well as of other human cell strains with X-autosomal translocations (Brown, et al., 1976; Grzeschik and Siniscalco, 1976; Seravalli, et al., 1976).

The extensive application of this experimental protocol, coupled with the harvest of numerous new types of reciprocal balanced translocations, which has followed the outbreak of the chromosome banding era, have led to the direct or indirect subregional mapping of the majority of the human loci reported in Dr. McKusick's list on pages 288–293.

Statistical Mapping of Gene Orders: The Radiation Co-transfer Test

In the early stages of human somatic cell genetics Miller et al. (1971b) showed that besides their unique potential for mapping human genes with the classic "synteny test," the murine-human hybrids could be used to screen for the "mitotic separation" of genes already known to be part of the same "linkage group" and hence to map their sequential order in a statistical fashion (Siniscalco, 1974). This approach has recently been further developed and improved by Goss and Harris (1975). They have demonstrated that if human cells are irradiated with increasing doses of gamma rays before fusion with murine cells, the probability of co-transference of linked genes into the cell hybrids is inversely proportional to the distance between them (Goss and Harris, 1975). Using this elegant method (which will be referred to from now on as the "radiation co-transfer test") Goss and Harris (1977a) have obtained estimates of genetic distances between six human X-linked markers (one of which, phosphoryribosylpyrophosphate synthetase, has actually been assigned to the X chromosome through this very type of study [Becker, et al., 1979]) and of eight markers of autosome 1 (Goss and Harris, 1977b).

The conclusions drawn from these estimates on the relative position of the loci investigated are on the whole in good agreement with the data on the subregional mapping of the same genes based on the classic "synteny test" in cell hybrids carrying human reciprocal translocations. However, this agreement may be largely illusory, since,

Table 5. Co-Transfer of Human X-Linked Markers in HAT-Selected Hybrids Between CHO-YH21 Cells and Irradiated Human Lymphoid Cells*

Dose of X-Rays (Kilorads)	Clone Identification Number	Human X-Linked Markers Retained by HAT-Selected Hybrid Clones			% of Co-Transfer of G6PD	
		G6PD	PGK	α-gal	At the clonal level	At the cell level
0	1	+ (199/310)	+	+		64
	4	+ (310/450)	+	+		69
	5	+ (330/500)	+	+	100	66 } 67
	8	+ (220/300)	+	+		73
	10	+ (189/300)	+	+		63
1	1	+ (60/300)	−	−		20
	2	+ (59/280)	+	+		21
	5	+ (87/430)	+	+		20
	6	+ (150/390)	+	+		38
	8	+ (60/275)	−	+	67	22 } 21
	11	+ (132/400)	+	+		33
	12	− (22/320)	−	−		7
	19	− (17/290)	−	−		6
	20	− (33/410)	−	−		8
2	1	− (8/517)	−	−		2
	4	− (9/290)	+	+		3
	5	− (12/300)	+	+	50	4 } 10
	8	+ (53/405)	−	−		13

4	10	+	(86/390)	—	—	} 22
	12	+	(42/270)	—	—	} 16
	15	+	(50/350)	+	+	} 14
	20	—	(6/280)	+	+	} 2
4	3	—	(0/290)	—	—	} 0
	9	—	(4/250)	—	—	} 2
	10	—	(5/300)	—	—	} 2 } 33 } 5
	11	+	(38/310)	—	—	} 12
	17	+	(33/290)	—	—	} 11
	19	—	(4/150)	—	—	} 3
5	1	+	(51/390)	—	—	} 13
	6	—	(0/240)	—	—	} 0
	17	+	(16/500)	—	—	} 13 } 20 } 5
	18	—	(0/190)	—	—	} 0
	19	—	(9/210)	—	—	} 4
	20	—	(0/360)	—	—	} 0

aThis table describes the percent of co-transfer of X-linked genes into cell hybrids after fusion of CHO-YH21 (deficient in HGPRT and G6PD) with human lymphoid cells irradiated with 0,1,2,4,5 kilorads prior to fusion. All HAT-selected clones reported were found to be HGPRT-positive and their hybrid nature was established independently by Giemsa-11 differential staining. The co-transfer of human G6PD was classified both electrophoretically on lysate of clonal cell populations or cytochemically on random cell samples from each clone. The number of cells that were found to be positive for G6PD and the total number of cells screened are reported in brackets. Needless to say, the cytochemical assay has never been found to be positive on the parental CHO-YH21 cells. From these data it is clear that the percent of co-transfer of human G6PD estimated at the clonal level is grossly overestimated. This point is further illustrated in Figure 3 and discussed in the text. On their face value the pattern of co-transfer of PGK and α-gal (classified only electrophoretically at the clonal level), at different doses of radiation, agrees in general with that reported by Goss and Harris (1975, 1977a) but one cannot help feeling that the situation could be considerably changed if these markers were also studied at the individual cell level.

unfortunately, both methodologic approaches suffer from technical drawbacks that bear negatively on the fiducial limits of the estimates of genetic distances that they provide separately.

On the one hand, a sequence established through "cytologic mapping" can be affected by (1) the difficulty in classifying the precise break site of the reciprocal translocation, (2) the occurrence of de novo rearrangements in culture, and (3) the not-too-unlikely possibility that other unrecognized additional chromosomal alterations (such as inversions) may co-exist with the visible reciprocal translocation in the parental human strain. On the other hand, the "radiation co-transfer method" not only overlooks the occurrence of de novo chromosomal breakages in culture but also fails to consider the possibility that the retention of an unselected marker may be affected by circumstances other than its proximity to the selected locus. For instance, in somatic cell hybrids between HGPRT-deficient Chinese hamster cells and normal irradiated human lymphocytes, genes that are more proximal to the centromere (such as PGK as opposed to α-gal) are more likely to be transferred on a centromeric fragment and thus may have a higher chance of being retained by the hybrid genome, even when they happen to have been separated from the selectively favored HGPRT locus. To evaluate the magnitude of these drawbacks, we have recently repeated the experiment of Goss and Harris following their protocol exactly, except for the choice of the rodent parental line, which, in our case, was a Chinese hamster line (CHO-YH21) deficient in both HGPRT and G6PD, obtained from Dr. Chasin (Chasin, 1975). The hybrids from these cells and normal human lymphoid cells offer the advantage of being classifiable for the retention of human G6PD at the level of each individual primary clone using a cytochemical staining method for spotting the presence of G6PD. The parental human cells were irradiated following the Goss and Harris (1977a, b) protocol with 0,1,2,4,5 kilorads, and a number of primary hybrid clones were isolated in the HAT medium and grown for estimating the frequency with which human G6PD, PGK, and α-gal were co-transferred with the selected marker HGPRT. Table 5 and Figure 3 show that these estimates, though based on a much lower number of clones, are essentially in agreement at each irradiation dose with those reported by Goss and Harris. However, when the G6PD phenotype of the same clones was determined at the individual cell level, it became clear that the frequencies of the HGPRT-G6PD co-transfer had been grossly overestimated, since every G6PD-positive hybrid clone (including those derived from unirradiated human parental cells) had a large number of G6PD-negative cells, and, correspondingly, several of the apparently G6PD-negative clones had some G6PD-positive cells. Under the given

CO-TRANSFER OF HUMAN HGPRT AND G6PD MEASURED AT THE CLONAL (EMPTY CIRCLES) AND THE INDIVIDUAL CELL LEVEL (FULL CIRCLES)

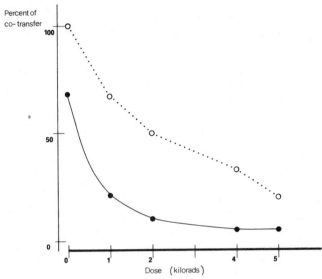

Figure 3. This figure illustrates graphically the discordance in the estimates of the per cent of HGPRT-G6PD co-transfer that is obtained at the clonal level (empty circles) and at the individual cell level (full circles). The data are the same as those reported in Table 7. (See text for further discussion.) (From Siniscalco, M. 1979. In Genetics and Human Biology: Possibilities and Realities, Porter, R. (Ed.), Ciba Foundation Symposium. New York, Elsevier-North Holland Pub. Co.)

experimental circumstances the percentage of G6PD-negative cells in the hybrid clones at zero radiation dose (±0.33) can be taken as a measure of the spontaneous rate of "mitotic separation" between the loci for HGPRT and G6PD. From the graph in Figure 3 it appears that the discordance between the two estimates of HGPRT-G6PD co-transfer (i.e., that at the cellular level versus that at the clonal level) increases with the radiation dose applied to the human parental cells prior to fusion. This suggests that the irradiated chromosomes may be more susceptible to de novo chromosomal breaks in culture and/or that the human loci in some of the hybrid clones must be transferred on separate chromosomal fragments with the subsequent obligatory retention of HGPRT and the frequent loss of G6PD. In the face of these observations the sequential order "centromere-PGK-α-gal-HGPRT-SAX-G6PD," reported by Goss and Harris (1977a) must be considered "provisional" with respect to the sequence of the latter three loci. This conclusion is not meant to question the usefulness of the "radiation co-transfer test." On the contrary, this author believes, along with Goss and Harris, that their experimental procedure will eventually become the choice tool for establishing the sequential order of genes within each linkage group (statistical mapping) and for a fast preliminary screening of the syntenic relationship between human markers amenable to positive selection in cell hybrids and other human markers as yet unassigned (linkage detection). The observations just reported simply stress the need for shortening the duration of the test to minimize the disturbing effect of de novo chromosomal breakages. This can be achieved by screening for the co-transfer of human gene products at the level of the individual cells and the early primary clones within a few weeks from the fusion event. Unpublished data from our laboratory indicate, for example, that the co-transfer of HGPRT and G6PD can be precisely assessed within one to three weeks from the fusion experiment when human irradiated lymphoid cells are fused with the already mentioned Chinese hamster cells YH21, which are deficient in both enzyme activities. Ten days of HAT selection are sufficient in this case to identify the actively growing hybrid clones, whose hybrid nature is checked by screening the Petri dishes on an inverted Leitz fluorescent microscope after having sequentially exposed the clones to a polyvalent anti-human species-specific antibody raised in rabbit and to a guinea pig antirabbit Ig antibody conjugated with rhodamine. Staining for G6PD activity at these early stages of clonal growth allows a much more precise classification of the G6PD-HGPRT co-transfer and, most important of all, permits distinction between the various circumstances that can lead to the loss of G6PD from the rodent-human hybrids of the type discussed. Namely, clones that stain homogeneously for G6PD in all their cells are those in which the target site, including the loci for HGPRT and G6PD has been co-transferred unbroken. Clones with a total absence of G6PD-positive cells or a preponderance of G6PD-negative cells (usually distributed around the periphery of the clone) indicate a radiation-induced break within the target site, followed by the co-transfer of the genes on separate chromosomal fragments with a subsequent loss of the unselected marker. Finally, the finding of large clones with single well-defined sectors of G6PD-negative cells among a majority of G6PD-positive ones suggests that the loss of the human G6PD locus has arisen in an individual progenitor cell as a consequence of de novo chromosomal breakage and was replicated as a distinct phenotypic feature only among its daughter cells (Fig. 4). This modified protocol for the mapping of human genes with the "radiation co-transfer" test is particularly suited for those human genetic markers that can be detected by immunofluorescence on the cell surface of living cells. For instance, the presence of the

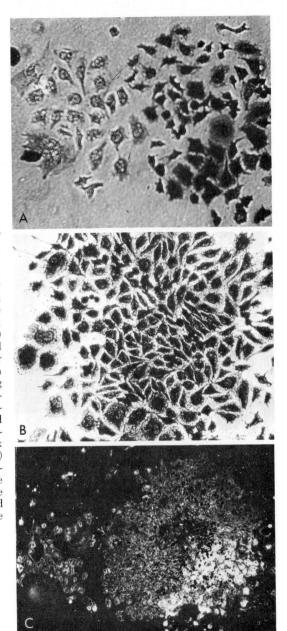

Figure 4. *A*, Two HAT-surviving hybrid clones ten days after fusion: one is G6PD(+) and one is G6PD(−). Magnification 400×. *B*, One large G6PD(+) hybrid clone three weeks after fusion. Magnification 250×. *C*, A large hybrid clone three weeks after fusion, showing a sector of G6PD(−) cells. Magnification 250×; bright field.

Co-transference of human G6PD studied cytochemically in early hybrid clones derived from fusion between Chinese hamster cells (CHO-YH 21; deficient in HGPRT and G6PD) and normal human lymphoid cells that were irradiated prior to fusion. The parental human cells were removed by washing 24 hours after plating of the fusion mixture, whereas the parental rodent cells were all killed after one week of HAT selection. G6PD(+) cells are dark stained. The sector of G6PD(−) hybrid cells seen in *C*, is probably the consequence of de novo breakage in the target site that occurred in a single hybrid cell at a very early stage of the clonal growth.

human X-linked surface antigen (SAX) can be established at the individual cell level by indirect immunofluorescence using a mouse antihuman SAX-3 serum followed by a rabbit antimouse Ig antibody conjugated with fluorescein. These types of genetic markers, as discussed in the next paragraph, are likely to become the most popular research targets as well as research tools for cell hybridizers in the years to come.

Cell Surface Antigens: A Target and Tool for Gene Mappers

Weiss and Green (1967) were fully aware of the unique potentials of their newly discovered unstable man-mouse cell hybrids for an altogether new approach to the study of human cell surface antigens. Using a polyvalent antihuman serum and a mixed agglutination reaction, they had noticed that the expression of human species-specific antigens in hybrid cells was quantitatively correlated with the number of the residual human chromosomes, but that their presence was detectable even in hybrid lines with very few human chromosomes. In view of these findings, they concluded that genes for surface antigens were probably widely distributed among different human chromosomes and could therefore be mapped by screening for correlations between the retention or loss of a given antigenic specificity and that of an individual human chromosome. Nabholz et al. (1969) supported this contention by showing that in their series of man-mouse hybrids the response of the individual clones to a polyvalent antihuman cytotoxic antiserum was correlated with the retention or loss of the human LDH isoenzymes. Soon after the loci for human LDH-A and LDH-B had been assigned to chromosomes 11 and 12 respectively, Puck and colleagues (1971) unequivocally demonstrated the existence of a syntenic relationship between the retention of human LDH-A and the susceptibility of Chinese hamster-human hybrid clones to a lethal antihuman cytotoxic antiserum. This implied that autosome 11 carries genes coding for cell surface lethal antigenic markers. Recently, Buck and Bodmer (1975) devised a new experimental protocol for the detection of chromosome-specific surface antigens. This is based on the use of highly reduced murine-human hybrids as immunogens in the appropriate live mouse strain (i.e., the one from which the parental murine cell line has been derived) to trigger the production of antibodies against surface antigens coded by genes of the residual human chromosomes. Using this procedure Buck and Bodmer were able to confirm the assignment of "genes" for surface antigens of autosome 11 (SA-11) (Buck and Bodmer, 1975) and to detect an X chromosome–

specific surface antigen (SAX), which segregates syntenically with the retention or loss of human X-linked markers (Buck and Bodmer, 1976) and has been shown by the radiation co-transfer test— as we already saw— to be part of the cluster of genes located between Xq 26 and Xqter. The existence of SAX antigens has lately been confirmed by Ruddle's group (Dorman, et al., 1977) and by ourselves (Schwab and Siniscalco, 1977) using the same experimental protocol but different types of highly reduced man-mouse hybrid lines as immunogens. Pending a direct comparison of the three anti-SAX sera so far produced we have proposed to refer to the corresponding antigens as SAX-1 (Oxford), SAX-2 (New Haven), and SAX-3 (New York). Preliminary mapping data, based on the radiation co-transfer test (Buck, et al., 1976) and on the analysis of a highly reduced mouse-man hybrid, which has retained only an undetectable (HGPRT-bearing) fragment of the human X chromosome (Seravalli et al., 1977), indicate that the gene or genes for SAX markers are located distal to Xq26 and that they are closer to HGPRT than to G6PD.

During the last few years the extensive use of highly reduced somatic cell hybrids as target cells against polyvalent antihuman sera (à la Puck) or as immunogens in compatible mice (à la Bodmer) has led to the identification of several new examples of human chromosome–specific surface antigens coded by genes of autosomes 6, 7, 10, 12, and 14 (see M. McKusick's newsletter on pp. 288–293). It is probable that at the time of this writing several new ones have already been identified, especially in consequence of the greater ease with which highly reduced rodent-human hybrids ("microcell hybrids") can now be obtained through the so-called microcell mediated transfer of individual human chromosomes into the rodent recipient cell (see next paragraph). Moreover, the recent major discovery of Kohler and Milstein (1975) that antibody-forming cells (splenocytes) from immunized mice can be immortalized through their fusion with mouse myeloma cells (hybridomas) implies that the preparation of monoclonal antibodies against each of the newly discovered human chromosome–specific surface antigens is only a matter of time (Fig. 5).

Thus, it is not unrealistic to expect that the combined use of these new techniques will soon lead to the identification of at least one and possibly more genes for surface antigens per human chromosome and to the preparation of an unlimited supply of a monoclonal antibody for each of them. These immunoreagents, coupled with the use of techniques that permit the isolation of cells on the basis of their surface antigenic moieties (cell flow sorter [Hulett et al., 1973], derivatized microbeads [Molday, et al., 1977], immunoadsorption [Schlossman and Hudson, 1973] and so on) will dramatically simplify the experimental

**EXPERIMENTAL PROTOCOLS FOR THE
IDENTIFICATION OF CHROMOSOME
SPECIFIC ANTIGENS AND PRODUCTION
OF MONOCLONAL ANTIBODIES
AGAINST THEM.**

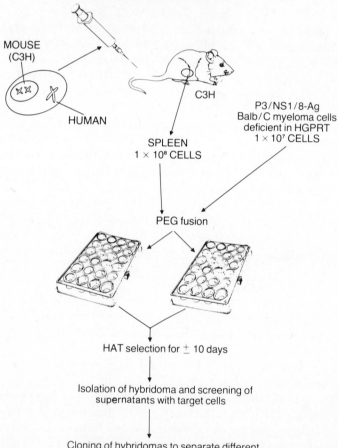

IMMUNOGENS (TARGET CELLS):
Mouse—Man hybrid cells which have retained
only one whole or a fraction of a human chromosome.

MOUSE
(C3H)

HUMAN

C3H

P3/NS1/8-Ag
Balb/C myeloma cells
deficient in HGPRT
1×10^7 CELLS

SPLEEN
1×10^8 CELLS

PEG fusion

HAT selection for $\pm$ 10 days

Isolation of hybridoma and screening of
supernatants with target cells

Cloning of hybridomas to separate different
classes of monoclonal antibodies

Figure 5. The rationale of the protocols for the identification of chromosome-specific surface antigens and the production of monoclonal antibodies against them is clearly illustrated in this figure. (For further explanation see text.)

strategies for the production of somatic cell hybrids and in particular will make possible the fast isolation of rodent-human hybrids that have retained the wanted human chromosome or chromosomes or chromosomal fragment or fragments. Apart from being a valuable contribution to the human gene map, each newly discovered chromosome–specific surface antigen and its corresponding monoclonal antibody represent additional precious tools for investigating the expression of specific gene products at the level of the individual cell surfaces. This means that in due course cell-cell interactions, which are believed to be at the root of cell differentiation, can be investigated in terms of specific genetic signals appearing on cell surfaces: Does normal differentiation directly depend upon given sequential patterns with which specific gene products are expressed on the cell's surface? What patterns are these, and what is the relative role of nature and nurture in determining them? Are "tumor-specific antigens" new aberrant products or, rather, the unbalanced immunologic phenotype resulting from overproduction and/or re-expression of one or more of the regular chromosome-specific surface antigens? Does any chromosome, besides 6 and 15, carry major genes involved in the production of the histocompatibility antigens? These are some of the questions that may become the obvious targets of experimentation for somatic cell geneticists if the harvest of mapping data on chromosome–specific cell surface antigens proceeds during the next decade in the way that the mapping of human biochemical markers has gone during the past decade.

"Transgenotes" and "Microcell Hybrids" — Two Most Useful Additions to the Paraphernalia of Somatic Cell Genetics

Two novel experimental strategies for a parasexual approach to the mapping of mammalian genes have been successfully developed during the last few years. Both are based on the transfer of a minimal amount of genetic information from a normal donor cell to a mutant recipient one, thus offering an opportunity for the detection of genetic linkage at a much finer degree of resolution than that afforded so far by the standard synteny test with unstable interspecific somatic cell hybrids. The "transgenotes" (probably so named in view of their analogy with the bacterial heterogenotes) are mutant mammalian cells that have been "corrected" only in their deficient function through a "chromosome-mediated gene transfer." The methodology for their isolation, first developed by McBride and Ozer (1973), consists in the addition of metaphase chromosomes, isolated from a normal donor cell, to the selective culture medium that is lethal to the mutant cells. The chromosomes of the donor cells are rapidly ingested by the recipient cells and degraded in their lysosomal vescicles. Approximately one in five million of the mutant cells so treated develops into an actively growing clone whose individual cells are corrected in their deficient function and have to be considered true "transformants" in that they acquire and transmit to their descendants the normal phenotypic function expressed by the donor cells. Using this experimental approach McBride and colleagues (McBride and Ozer, 1973; McBride, et al., 1978) have been able to correct the HGPRT deficiency or the TK deficiency of murine mutant cell lines with the addition of metaphase chromosomes from normal Chinese hamster or human cells. These experiments have been successfully repeated by other investigators (Willecke and Ruddle, 1975; Willecke, et al., 1976) with the following general conclusions: (1) the frequency of phenotype transformation through this chromosome-mediated gene transfer is between 10^{-5} and 10^{-7}; (2) in all experiments so far performed independent of the species of origin of the donor chromosomes, the transfer of the HGRPT gene into murine cells has never been associated with the transfer of an intact human chromosome or detectable chromosomal fragment; (3) the transgenotes are classified as "unstable" or "stable" depending upon their ability to retain the transgenome after release of the selective pressure; and (4) the transgenome has been found to be associated with different host chromosomes in stable transgenotes rescued from separate experiments, but it has not been established as yet whether or not the donor DNA fragment is linearly inserted by covalent bonding into the host DNA.

The use of "transgenotes" in linkage analysis is reminiscent of the rationale for the mapping of bacterial genes by co-transduction and co-transformation. An auxotrophic cell mutant is corrected in its deficient metabolic function through the chromosomal-mediated transfer of the complementing donor gene, and the resultant "transgenote" is screened for the co-transfer of other donor cell markers known to belong to the same linkage group. The transgenotes so far produced have been derived from the correction of mouse HGPRT-deficient (Mo-HGPRT⁻) or TK-deficient (MoTK⁻) cell lines with the addition of metaphase chromosomes from normal Chinese hamster (CH) or human (Hu) cells (CH HGPRT⁺→Mo-HGPRT⁻; Hu HGPRT⁺→Mo-HGPRT⁻; CH TK⁺→Mo TK⁻; and Hu TK⁺→Mo TK⁻). Interestingly, the co-transfer of other X-linked genes was never observed in the HGPRT-corrected transgenotes (McBride and Athwal, 1976; Willecke, 1978), whereas the transfer of TK was associated with that of galacto-kinase (GaK) in 20 percent of the TK-corrected transgenotes, independent of the source (hamster or human) of the normal chromosomes used in the experiments (Wullems, et al., 1977). These findings suggest that the human genes for TK and GaK are much closer to one another than HGPRT is to G6PD, PGK, α-gal, and SAX. Since the genes for TK and GaK have been assigned, via cytogenetic mapping with somatic cell hybrids, to a region of human autosome 17 that composes approximately .2 percent of the total haploid human genome, it follows that the maximum size of the "transgenome" may be of the same order of magnitude, which corresponds approximately to 5 × 10^6 nucleotide base pairs. The minimal size of the transgenome is unknown. The occurrence of the TK-GaK co-transfer, which also occurs when Chinese hamster chromosomes are used as the donor, indicates that this linkage must have appeared at a very early stage of mammalian evolution and illustrates the usefulness of these studies in comparative biology.

The "microcell hybrids" are the products of fusion between mutant mammalian cells and artificially induced micronucleated cells from the same or different species. The production of viable microcell hybrids was forecast by the pioneering work of Ege and Ringertz (1974) but was only recently achieved for the first time by Fournier and Ruddle (1977). The major advantage of this methodology lies in the fact that the direction of the microcell-mediated transfer of individual chromosomes can be decided by the investigator and that the wanted types of highly reduced hybrids can be isolated in a matter of a few weeks. With the use of this methodology Kozak et al. (1975) and Fournier and Ruddle (1977a,b) have introduced mouse chromosomes into mouse cells, Chinese hamster cells and human cells. For the first time, this permitted the application of the strategies of somatic cell genetics for the mapping of a number of murine biochemic markers that could never have been mapped with the classic mating analysis because they are not polymorphic within the species (Kozak and Ruddle, 1977; Fournier and Ruddle, 1977a,b,c). For some time it looked as if the microcell-mediated transfer of human chromosomes into rodent mutant cells could not be fulfilled, since the Ege and Ringertz (1974) technique was not suitable for producing human micronucleated cells. This difficulty has recently been overcome by Dr. Ruddle's group (Fournier and Ruddle, 1977a) and Dr. Johnson's group (Johnson, et al., 1975), so that this technique can now be used routinely for the production of highly reduced rodent-human hybrids (clone panels) needed for the detection of linkage with the "synteny test" and for the chromosomal assignment of human genes that complement the newly identified rodent mutants, whose list grows steadily every day. Moreover, in view of their fast production, the microcell hybrids promise to be a much better tool for investigating the chromosomal basis of complex phenomena such as the integration of viral genomes in mammalian cells, the expression of tumor antigens, and the mechanism of normal and abnormal cell regulation. Last but not least, the microcell-mediated transfer of human chromosomes will speed up, as already pointed out, the production of rodent-human hybrids that have retained only one human chromosome and thus will indirectly contribute to the discovery of additional examples of chromosome–specific antigens and to the preparation of the corresponding monoclonal antibodies.

Human-Human Hybrids and Heterokaryons

The occurrence of genetic complementation in intraspecific somatic cell hybrids can theoretically lead to fine structure mapping of genes when a given metabolic function is restored to normal in the fusion product between parental cells that carry "different" mutations of the same gene. The use of this approach has been pioneered by the work of Puck and his colleagues (Puck, 1972), who demonstrated that large series of glycine auxotrophic mutants, experimentally induced in cultured Chinese hamster ovary cells, fall into four complementation groups.

The early demonstration that human diploid cells could be fused with one another (Siniscalco, et al., 1969) and with permanent human cells (Silagi, et al., 1969) to yield heterokaryons as well as actively growing hybrids stimulated the application of somatic cell hybridization to the study of genetic heterogeneity of human inherited diseases by complementation analysis.

Nadler et al. (1970) produced hybrids between fibroblastic strains derived from 7 unrelated galactosemic patients (all deficient in the enzyme galactose-1-phosphate uridyl transferase) and observed normal enzyme activity in 3 of the 21 possible combination pairs, thus suggesting that there may exist "different" mutants for galactosemia.

Likewise, the restoration of activity for hexosaminidase A (Hex A) after fusion of fibroblasts from Tay-Sachs disease and Sandhoff's disease patients, has permitted two independent groups of workers (Rattazzi, et al., 1974; Galjard, et al., 1974) to conclude that the deficiency in Hex A, typical for both these gangliosidoses, is the consequence of "different" mutations.

Many more studies of this type have been carried out at the level of heterokaryons in view of the ease with which they can be produced. The prototype of these studies was that of De Weerd-Kastelein and colleagues (1972) who showed complementation in some — but not all — heterokaryons derived from the fusion of fibroblasts of unrelated patients affected by xeroderma pigmentosum, a well-known recessive autosomal disorder that affects the capacity of UV-irradiated cultured cells to undergo unscheduled DNA synthesis. These, and later studies by others (De Weerd-Kastelein, et al., 1974; Kraemer, et al., 1975) have led to the conclusion that the xeroderma patients so far observed fall into at least five complementation groups.

Using the same experimental approach, Lyons and colleagues (1973) proved the existence of genetic heterogeneity among unrelated patients with maple syrup urine disease, and Gravel et al. (1975) identified four different complementation groups in methylmalonic acidemia, a genetic condition whose comprehension in biochemical terms has been greatly helped by these very studies.

Migeon et al. (1974) have unequivocally confirmed the formation of intraspecific hybrids between human diploid cells by showing that the fusion between G6PD-A and G6PD-B male cell strains yields hybrids with A-B heteropolymeric G6PD molecules. These last findings and the recent progress made in the technologies of cell fusion and hybrid isolation, revive the hope (expressed by this writer at a time that was admittedly premature) that human-human hybrids may eventually become popular tools for the genetic analysis of man at the level of somatic cells (Siniscalco, 1970).

THE MOLECULAR APPROACH

General Remarks

The discovery by Ingram (1957) that hemoglobin S differs from the normal protein by a single amino acid substitution marks the birthdate of what is known as the "molecular approach to human gene mapping." Today, one can operationally define three levels to which this approach can be applied in man as well as in other eukaryotes to investigate the structural organization of chromosomal DNA and its relationship to gene function. The first level focuses on the fine biochemical analysis of the gene end products and essentially derives data on gene mapping in an indirect fashion by comparing the primary structure of normal and mutant proteins.

The second level aims at the identification of individual DNA coding sequences through molecular hybridization studies performed with the use of specific nucleic acid probes such as purified mRNAs or their reverse transcribed cDNAs.

The third level, whose application has hardly begun and which is an obvious by-product of the two most recent achievements of the molecular biology (restriction enzyme analysis and DNA cloning), deals with the direct characterization of chromosomal DNA sequences irrespective of their being transcribed. The rationale and strategies that characterize these three levels and some of the major results obtained through their use will now be briefly summarized.

Inference from the Biochemical Analysis of Gene End Products

The rationale for gene mapping by analysis of the primary structures of the gene end products is based on the assumption that the sequence of amino acids in a protein molecule is determined by the nucleotide sequence of its coding DNA. This assumption remains true in spite of the well-known complications affecting the genetic code such as its degeneracy (more than one nucleotide triplet may code for the same amino acid) and its ambiguity (a given triplet may code for more than one amino acid). Even the recent unexpected discovery of the intervening sequences and RNA splicing (to be discussed) do not alter the general conclusion that the localization of an amino acid substitution in a given polypeptide chain is correlated with that of a mutation on the corresponding DNA nucleotide chain. Thus, the intracistronic mapping of a gene can be precisely inferred from the comparison of the detailed biochemical maps of its normal and mutant end products. Studies on human hemoglobins (Hb) are still the best example of how this type of information is gathered (Weatherall and Clegg, 1976). First, the identification of at least four major Hb polypeptide chains (α, β, γ, δ) within the individual suggested the multiplicity of the loci in the genome. This was then proved correct through the study of families that happened to segregate for more than one Hb variant. Mutants of the α-chain were found to be inherited independent of those of any of the other three major hemoglobin Hb chains (β, δ, γ), whereas the latter ones behaved as if the corresponding loci were located on the same chromosome. Moreover, in view of the close resemblance of the inferred nucleotide base sequences of the four major hemoglobin genes (as well as of the genes for myoglobin), their origin has been traced back to the same ancestral gene from which they are thought to have arisen through successive gene duplications followed by independent evolution of the duplicated segments. Since the α-chain differs most conspicuously from all other Hb chains, its coding sequence is believed to have been the first one to branch out from the evolutionary Hb tree approximately 500 million years ago. The second

THE FORMATION AND STRUCTURE OF THE FUSION-CHAIN HEMOGLOBINS LEPORE AND KENYA

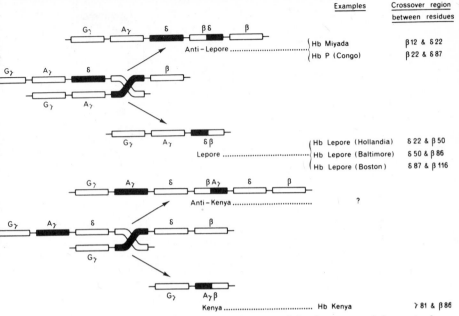

Figure 6. The figure describes the mechanism of the formation of the several fusion-chain hemoglobins so far identified. This mechanism is analogous to that hypothesized to explain the duplication and triplication of the *bar* gene in *Drosophila* and the *haptoglobin* gene in man. See text and Figure 7. (From Weatherall, D. G., and J. B. Clegg. 1976. In Annual Review of Genetics, Roman, H. L., et al. (Eds.). Palo Alto, Annual Reviews, Inc. 10:157–158.

and third split are believed to be much more recent in view of the closer resemblance between their gene end products as well as the fact that the relevant loci are still closely linked. It is of interest that the first evidence in favor of the close contiguity of the loci for β- and δ-chains of Hb was based on biochemical rather than genetic data. Molecular mapping studies performed on an unusual type of Hb variant, named Lepore after the name of its first patient carrier, had shown that the primary structure of this new chain was similar to that of the δ chain in its N-terminal end and to the β chain in its C-terminal end, thus suggesting that the Lepore gene might have been the result of an unequal cross-over during an occasional homologous pairing of the relevant DNA sequences. This interpretation has been strengthened by the finding of the so-called antiLepore gene expected under such a hypothesis, as shown in Figure 6, and by the discovery of other "Lepore-like mutants" that have arisen from the fusion of β and γ genes (e.g., hemoglobin Kenya). The fact that the β gene can recombine "unequally" with both δ and γ genes clearly indicates that the order of

GENE DUPLICATION AND TRIPLICATION IN *DROSOPHILA* AND MAN.

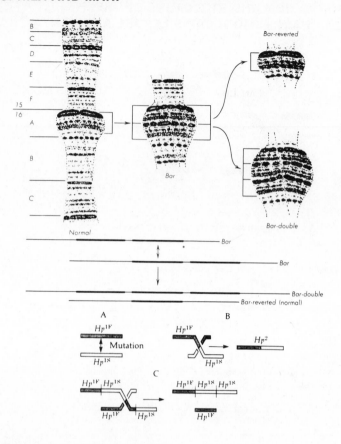

DROSOPHILA: THE BAR LOCUS
MAN: THE HAPTOGLOBIN LOCUS

Figure 7. *Top,* The bar phenotype in *Drosophila melanogaster* is due to a duplication of the 16A region, as indicated in the top part of the figure, whereas bar-double is due to a triplication of the same region of the X chromosome. The diagram in the bottom part of the figure illustrates how T. H. Morgan, C. B. Bridges and J. Schultz (1932) explained the occurrence of the above findings by unequal crossing over. It is of interest to point out that the bar females can lead to both bar-double and normal phenotypes. (From Morgan, T. H., et al. 1932. Carnegie Inst. Wash. Yrbk. 31:303–307. *Bottom,* Diagrammatic sketch of the hypothesis originally proposed by Smithies, Connell, and Dixon (1962) to explain the formation of the haptoglobin polymorphism in man through unequal crossing over. The analogy with the bar mutation is striking and well supported by biochemic data. *A,* Two haptoglobin Hp^1 alleles exist, which presumably originated by one mutating from the other; it is not clear which of the two was ancestral. *B,* Unequal crossing-over between the two alleles probably generated the Hp^2 allele. *C,* Unequal crossing-over in an Hp^2 homozygote generated another allele that probably is a triplication. (From Smithies, O., G. E. Connell, and G. H. Dixon. 1962. Nature 196: 232–236.)

276

the corresponding loci is γ-δ-β. The multiplicity of the hemoglobin gene has recently grown beyond expectation, so that we know now of at least two α and two γ hemoglobin loci. One of the most meaningful by-products of these types of studies has been the recognition of the importance of gene duplication in the evolutionary process. The existence of duplicated portions of individual chromosomal regions had been detected by early geneticists on the giant chromosome of the salivary gland of *Drosophila melanogaster*, and their occurrence, which in one case was associated with specific mendelian variation (the bar phenotype) was clearly accounted for by Sturtevant (1925) with the hypothesis of unequal crossing over. However, this type of genetic mutation was considered rare and unimportant until Smithies, Connell, and Dixson (1962) showed that the individual variation in human haptoglobins, a well-known example of biochemical polymorphism present in all human populations, had most probably arisen through this very mechanism. The interesting conclusion emerging from the biochemical mapping of the haptoglobin gene end product (the so-called α-chain) is that a duplication can, by an equal crossing over, indeed generate further duplication as well as reversion to the normal sized genes (Fig. 7) as postulated by Morgan (Morgan, et al., 1932).

Hemoglobin and haptoglobins are no longer the only examples of biochemically mapped genes in man. The extension — as well as the type — of genetic and biochemical variation detected during the last decade for immunoglobins and HLA antigens suggest that these two systems have also reached their present complexity in the evolutionary process through a combined mechanism of gene duplication and selection (Cavalli-Sforza and Bodmer, 1971). Finally, studies on the primary structure of gene end products have been the basis for sketching biologic evolution in molecular terms. These studies, which can of course be applied only to those molecules that occur throughout a large philogenetic interval (such as hemoglobins, cytochrome c, insulin, and so forth), can be considered the molecular counterpart of the comparative mapping of chromosomes (to be discussed later).

Gene Mapping Through Molecular Hybridization

The remarkable progress made during the last decade in the technique of molecular hybridization, coupled with the "heretic" discovery of the reverse transcriptases (and therefore of the in vitro synthesis of cDNA from mRNA), have expanded beyond expectation the potentials of the molecular approach to human gene mapping. The rationale for the direct identification of specific coding DNA sequences with this approach, is based on the in situ hybridization of molecular probes to metaphase chromosomes. The rationale for the in situ hybridization of specific nucleic acid probes (mRNA labeled to high specific activity with ^{125}I or their reverse transcribed ^{3}H-cDNA) to metaphase chromosomes is essentially similar to the well-known characterized hybridization reaction of excess labeled RNA to filter bound DNA. However, the rate of hybridization is decreased and the efficiency of gene detection is further hampered by the unfortunate circumstance that only about 10 to 20 per cent of the disintegrations emitted by the hybridized labeled probe contribute to the formation of silver grains on autoradiographic emulsion. In spite of these limitations, the in situ hybridization approach has been successfully applied in man and other mammals for the direct chromosomal mapping of the highly reiterated ribosomal genes (Steffensen, et al., 1974) as well as of moderately repeated DNA sequences such as those coding for 5S RNA and histones (Evans, et al., 1974; Yu, et al., 1978). On the basis of in situ mRNA hybridization, Price et al. (1972) proposed that one of the human globin genes, probably α, is located on the long arm of autosome 2, whereas other globin genes are on the long arm of a B-group chromosome. The interpretation of these data has met considerable skepticism (Bishop and Jones, 1972; Prensky and Holmquist, 1973) but, to everybody's surprise, the original observations have been confirmed by Atwood and his colleagues (1976) who also showed that with the use of the same protocol they could correctly map the murine α-globin locus, whose chromosomal location had been unequivocally established by standard genetic analysis. At any rate, the conclusions of these studies are at variance with the assignment of the human globin genes made with a different technique of molecular gene mapping (see later on), thus casting some doubt about the applicability of the techniques of in situ hybridization to the direct chromosomal identification of low multiplicity or single copy genes. However, it is encouraging to know that Nunberg et al. (1978) have had no difficulties in mapping by in situ hybridization the Chinese hamster structural gene for dihydrofolate reductase when using a cell line that happens to carry a 200-fold amplification of this gene. This means that, if the overall efficiency of detection with the in situ hybridization reaction can be improved in the years to come just as much as it has been since its discovery, there should soon be no difficulty in mapping those few copy genes for which mRNA is available in pure form. The lower limit of detection is already of the order of about 20,000 nucleotides per chromosome, which is equivalent to the size of an integrated retroviral genome.

An alternative strategy for molecular gene mapping combines the technique of nucleic acid hybridization and somatic cell genetics. The best example so far of this last type of approach is the study of Deisseroth and colleagues that led to the assignment of the human α-globin gene to autosome 16 and the γ-δ-β complex locus to autosome 11. These conclusions were based on the results of a DNA-cDNA molecular hybridization assay (Cot analysis), which directly determines the presence or absence of genes by comparing the Cot curves obtained by hybridizing a specific labeled probe (in this case $^{32-}$PcDNA from the α or β-globin mRNA) with the DNA of hybrid clones containing a different subset of human chromosomes (Deisseroth, et al., 1977; Deisseroth, et al., 1978). It is obvious that this approach is plagued by the same difficulties that in general disturb the reliability of all mapping data based on the synteny test, such as the high heterogeneity in the chromosomal composition of individual hybrid clones and the frequent occurrence of de novo chromosomal rearrangements in culture. However, it is encouraging to point out that the localization of the human α gene on autosome 16 has recently been confirmed with the use of a different experimental protocol, which demonstrates once again the versatility of the methods now available for human gene mapping. Knowing that human chromosome 16 carries the gene for APRT, Deisseroth and Hendrick (1978) produced a mutant line deficient in this enzyme from clone 1745 of the Friend mouse erythroleukemia cells. After fusion of this murine line with APRT (+) human erythroid cells, the resulting hybrids were grown in the appropriate selective media to force the obligatory retention or loss of chromosome 16, so that its synteny with the production of α-globin and its mRNA could be unequivocally established.

Another example of how the experimental strategies of somatic cell genetics and molecular hybridization can be combined for investigating the substructural organization of the human chromosomes is offered by our own studies on the partial purification and characterization of presumptive X-specific human nuclear RNA (Balazs, et al., 1977). To achieve this goal we prepared total heterogeneous nuclear RNA from a hybrid cell line (A9 HRBC2) that contains only the X chromosome as the regular residual fraction of the human genome. Poly A RNA prepared from this line was labeled in vitro with ^{125}I and submitted to a first round of hybridization with murine DNA filters. The unbound ^{125}I-RNA was then hybridized to a second set of filters containing human DNA. The bound RNA was eluted and assayed for its enrichment for human RNA by hybridization on filters and in solution with human DNA prepared from tissues of individuals with one, two, or four X chromosomes. The per cent of RNA hybridized, in both these experiments, did in fact show the expected dependence on the X chromosome content of the DNA used (Balazs, et al., 1978). Moreover, when these presumptive X chromosome RNA sequences were hybridized in situ to human metaphase chromosomes, the X chromosome had two- to threefold more grains associated with it than any autosome of comparable size (Balazs, et al., 1977). These results suggest that we had prepared an RNA fraction enriched for sequences homologous to repeated DNA sequences of the human X chromosome. In view of the unique functional properties of the X chromosome through mammals (e.g., X chromosome inactivation), the possibility that there might be "qualitative" or "quantitative" differences in the repeated DNA sequences of the human X chromosome relative to the autosomes is of compelling interest.

It is obvious that these protocols can also be used for the identification and isolation of RNA transcripts and relevant DNA sequences of any other human chromosome or fraction of chromosome, since it is theoretically possible to produce 24 types of reduced man-rodent somatic cell hybrids that have each retained a different chromosome of the human haploid complement (i.e., one of the 22 autosomes or of the two heterochromosomes X and Y). Thus, we can expect that somatic cell hybrids of the type discussed may become a choice tool for the molecular biologist to dissect the human genome in nucleic acid preparations from individual chromosomes or chromosomal fractions. In particular, somatic cell hybrids that have retained only a single genetic function of the human genome may prove to be useful for "gene isolation," as we will discuss in the next paragraph.

A molecular model for studying the structure of the human X chromosome at the level of interspersed reiterated nucleotide sequences has been proposed by Kunkel and associates (1976, 1977). These authors have successfully isolated Y chromosome–specific DNA sequences by exhaustive hybridization of male to female total cellular DNA. They have also shown that the amount of Y chromosome–specific DNA varies quantitatively between individuals and is unrelated to male differentiation. Apart from its importance as a tool for investigating the molecular structure of human chromosomes, the Y chromosome-DNA probe promises to be of unlimited value for studies of molecular evolution at large.

Mapping via Restriction DNA Analysis

That restriction endonucleases, first described as bacterial weapons against invading DNA, would become the most efficient tools for gene mapping in general, let alone for human gene mapping, was an impossible guess when their existence was first reported more than 25 years ago (Luria, et al., 1952; Meselson, et al., 1968). This was mainly due to the fact that the restriction endonucleases that were initially isolated and characterized happened to be of the kind that lack a simple specificity to their DNA cleavage properties. However, as soon as the first site-specific endonucleases were discovered (Smith and Wilcox, 1970; Kelly and Smith, 1970) it was immediately realized that they could be used to construct nucleotide maps of DNA much in the same way as peptide maps of proteins (fingerprints) have been obtained using site-specific proteolytic enzymes. Thus it is not surprising that a febrile hunt for new site-specific restriction enzymes followed the first successful application of the "DNA fingerprinting" to the mapping of a viral genome (Danna and Nathans, 1971). To date over a hundred have been discovered, and the cleavage site base sequences have been determined for a good number of them. The rationale for this "physical mapping" of chromosomes is based on the successive cleavage of their DNA with an array of restriction enzymes of different specificities that generate fragments sharing common nucleotide sequences. After their fractionation by agarose or polyacrylamide gel electrophoresis, the cleaved fragments are characterized in terms of their size and nucleotide sequences, so that their native order on the chromosome can finally be inferred from the analysis of the overlapping regions. Several viral genomes have been dissected and physically mapped in this way. Among them are SV40 adenovirus, polyoma, phage λ, and filamentous coliphages (Nathans and Smith, 1975). It is obvious that the DNA restriction enzyme analysis in eukaryotes is complicated by the complexity of their genomes. For instance, restriction sites occur at random along single copy DNA genes, thus yielding an unresolved streak of innumerable electrophoretic bands (over one million) for the average mammalian genome. Even highly repeated DNA sequences, which are cleaved into discrete and regularly spaced bands, are hard to identify let alone fractionate among the background of the unresolved restricted profiles of single copy DNA.

In spite of these difficulties, the first application of the restriction enzyme analysis to the mapping of human genes has given staggering results. Two independent groups of investigators (Mears, et al., 1978a, b; Flavell, et al., 1978) have simultaneously reported cleavage maps for the β- and δ- globin genes and for their fused recombinant products (the Lepore β-δ-globin genes) obtained by hybridizing in situ a β-globin–specific DNA probe to restricted fragments of total human cellular DNA blotted on nitrocellulose filter strips according to Southern (1975). These studies have established that (1) the β- and δ-globin genes contain an intervening sequence of about 1000 base pairs, which is located between the sequences coding for amino acids 101 to 120 (of the 146 amino acid long globin chain), and which is not represented in the corresponding mRNAs; (2) the distance between the β- and δ-globin genes amounts to approximately 7000 nucleotide pairs, a distance that is much larger than the intercistronic regions known for prokaryotes; (3) the δ-gene, as previously inferred from genetic studies, is located at the 5' side of the β-globin gene; and (4) the Lepore and antiLepore genes are confirmed as the fusion products between β- and δ-globin loci following unequal pairing and crossing over with deletions of different length, depending upon the site of the intergenic recombination events.

Knowledge of the molecular pathology of thalassemias has also greatly benefited from the application of the techniques of molecular hybridization in solution and of "blot" hybridization on restricted DNA fragments derived from homozygotes for different thalassemia mutants. Both types of hybridization techniques have been employed for the characterization of β-thalassemia as well as of other forms of thalassemias. The results indicate that homozygotes for either the β^0 or the β^+ thalassemia genes carry a normal amount of structural genes coding for the β-globin chains. All evidence points to a primary defect in β-chain mRNA transcription, but the reasons for this are unclear. However, there seems to be heterogeneity with respect to the transcription of mRNA. Kan et al. (1975) have found that there is inactive β-chain mRNA in cells of β-thalassemia patients, whereas Tolstoschev et al. (1976) were unable to demonstrate any mRNA by cDNA-mRNA hybridization studies. The final answer to these questions may perhaps have to wait for the cloning of the β-chain genes and analysis of the structure of the noncoding areas. Ottolenghi et al. (1976) carried out globin gene analysis using a cDNA probe, and their results indicate that the β-δ-thalassemias as well as the black variant of hereditary persistence of fetal hemoglobin (HPFH) involve deletions of the β-globin structural gene. Mears et al. (1978a, b) have confirmed these conclusions using "blot" hybridization of β-globin cDNA on ECO-R1-restricted DNA fragments prepared from the types of patients just mentioned and established that the deletion for HPFH is greater than that of Lepore thalassemias. Similar studies have been conducted for the so-called α-thalassemia syndromes. Independent studies of Ottolenghi et al. (1974) and of Taylor et al. (1974) established the complete absence of an α-chain mRNA in the cells of fetuses homozygous for the α-thalassemia-1 gene (hydrops fetalis syndrome). Furthermore, using solution hybridization, they showed that the DNA prepared from these fetuses lacks α-chain genes. Recently, Dr. Kan and his colleagues

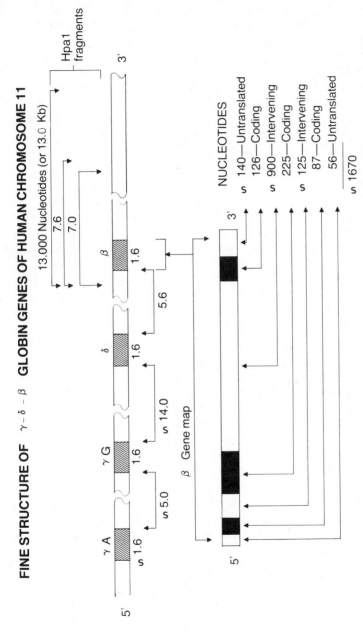

Figure 8. The upper part of the figure summarizes the results of a variety of studies (performed at all levels) that have led to the physical mapping of the γ-δ-β globin genes on human chromosome 11. This map includes the recent observation of Kan and Dozy (1978) on the DNA polymorphism, which characterizes the 3' end HpaI restriction site adjacent to the β-globin gene. The lower part of the diagram reproduces in detail the physical map of the β gene.

(1975) have shown by "blot" hybridization studies that the extent of deletion of α-globin genes is variable. Namely, the four clinical types of α-thalassemias so far mentioned (silent carriers, heterozygotes for α-thalassemia-1, hemoglobin-H disease, and hydrops fetalis) correspond to deletions of one, two, three, or all four α-globin loci, respectively. These studies have also indicated that the two "tandem duplicated" α-globin loci are separated from one another by approximately 5000 nucleotides. In conclusion, these authors suggest that both α-globin structural loci are absent in the homozygotes for the α-thalassemia-1 gene, whereas heterozygotes for the α-thalassemia-2 genes or α-thalassemia-1 genes carry a deletion of the 3' α-globin locus or of both the 5' and 3' loci in cis, respectively. Individuals affected by hemoglobin-H disease are the ones who carry both types of deletion.

A recent study by Kan and Dozy (1978a) stresses the potentials of enzyme restriction analysis as a tool for the detection of genetic polymorphism in stretches of DNA of unknown function and of its linkage relationships with other genes. These authors found that after the digestion with HpaI endonuclease (which cleaves DNA at the sequence GTTAAC), the β-globin gene, identified as such by blot hybridization with β-globin ^{3}H-cDNA, is normally included in a restricted fragment of 7600 nucleotides (7.6 kilobases or kb), whereas the β-globin gene from a patient with sickle cell anemia was included in variant fragments of 7 or 13 kb (Fig. 8). Further studies established that these variants — which are evidently the result of alterations in the normal HpaI recognition site — are inherited in a mendelian fashion and are apparently common only among African populations. In particular the 13 kb fragment is present in 87 per cent of the homozygotes for β^S mutant and only in 3 per cent of the homozygotes for the normal allele. Even though the nature of this association remains to be clarified, the expectation was that owing to the close linkage between the relevant mutational sites (the HpaI recognition site is only 5 kb away from the 3' side of the β-globin gene, i.e., closer than the latter is to the α-globin gene), individuals who happened to be double heterozygotes in cis for the β^S mutant and for the 13 kb variant should have children with either both or neither of these mutants. This is exactly what Kan and Dozy have found to be the case in a group of black American families of West African origin thus far examined. As we shall see later, this situation has recently enabled Kan and Dozy (1978b) to successfully predict the β-globin genotype of an unborn child (from two sickle cell heterozygotes) through the restriction enzyme analysis of the DNA of his amniotic fluid cells.

Foreseeable Impact of DNA Cloning on the Strategies and Methodologies of Human Gene Mapping

The techniques now available for the artificial production of recombinant DNA molecules and for their clonal replication in bacterial plasmids or viral genomes allow the isolation of mammalian genes and their amplification (Higuchi, et al., 1976; Maniatis, et al. 1976; Rabbitts, 1976). These techniques have already been successfully applied to the controlled production of gene end products in the laboratory (Villa-Komaroff, et al., 1978) and to the molecular transplant of a functioning mammalian gene between animal cells of different species (Villa-Komaroff, et al., 1978; Mulligan, et al., 1979). However, these achievements, which have been hailed by the lay press as the Promethean events of our times, are neither the newest nor the most important sides of the story. The first chemical in vitro synthesis of biologic products is over 20 years old and the transfer of genes between mammalian cells by parasexual methods has been a matter of routine for a decade as discussed extensively in the preceding pages. To a geneticist's mind, the real attraction offered by these novel methods of molecular biology is that they allow the study of biological inheritance to be approached through the direct analysis of its subject matter: the chromosomal DNA. It is to be expected that this situation will trigger a kind of Kopernikan revolution in the strategies of genetic research. Mendel had to "invent" genes to explain the "facts of life," and for over a century, geneticists kept inferring about their existence, and the differences between them, from the analysis of their more or less remote phenotypic functions. In contrast, the geneticists of tomorrow will have at hand "libraries" of isolated stretches of DNA to analyze and will spend their time figuring out the relationship between the organization of chromosomal DNA and specific biologic functions. Indeed the most striking novelty of these new approaches in gene mapping is the possibility of analyzing the structure of untranscribed as well as transcribed DNA sequences and to investigate their relative role in gene expression. Seen in this context, DNA cloning is the most appropriate tool for human gene mappers, since there can be little doubt that the key to the understanding of normal and abnormal differentiation in high organisms is hidden under the complexity of the eukaryotic "chromosome," as opposed to the simple organization of the prokaryotic "genophore." The most promising approach to achieve this goal is the random fractionation and cloning of total cell DNA ("shotgun experiment") followed by the screening of the clones of interest by molecular hybridization with specific probes, usually consisting of a cDNA plasmid prepared from the mRNAs of the genes to be mapped (Young and Hogness, 1977). This approach has been successfully applied to the construction of "libraries" of DNA fragments from small eukaryotic genomes as well as from large ones. Particularly encouraging are the studies of Maniatis et al. (1978) and of Smithies and colleagues (Blattner, et al., 1978; Smithies, et al., 1978) who have respectively isolated clones of β-globin genes from rabbit or mouse and man among over a million individual clones of 20 kb average size prepared from total cellular DNA of the corresponding species. This emphasizes the sophistication already achieved in this technology and its applicability to further physical mapping of human DNA. The advantage of the shotgun approach over the cloning of reverse transcribed complementary DNA lies in the fact that clones produced with the latter approach lack the intervening and regulatory sequences that are present in the genome but absent in the mRNA. However, the availability of the specific hybridization probes that are necessary for the selection of specific genes is for the time being limited, and this is the bottleneck that prevents the general applicability of all cloning methodologies to the study of man and other high organisms. In particular, it is clear that untranscribed sequences, which happen not to be included in "selectable" DNA fragments, could now be mapped only at a prohibitive cost and effort. In this regard it is worth emphasizing that some of the tools of somatic cell genetics could be of help. In the first instance, it is obvious that the shotgun of individual chromosomes rather than of total cellular DNA would reduce the yield of random clonal fragments by a factor equivalent to the diploid number of the species. The purification of individual human chromosomes can be achieved with the use of highly reduced murine-human hybrids of the kind discussed in the preceding pages. Some efforts along these lines are being made in different laboratories of somatic cell genetics, including ours. The rationale for the separation of human from mouse chromosomes is based upon the knowledge that the latter fluoresce relatively stronger with exposure to Hoechst 33258 (Hilwig and Gropp, 1972), and this property can be exploited for separating the two kinds of chromosomes from one another. To achieve this goal, metaphase chromosomes from mouse-human hybrid cells, which have retained only one individual human chromosome, can be sorted out in a fluorescence flow sorter at a rate of 10^5 chromosomes per minute. It has been calculated (Balazs, personal communication) that one hour of operation would thus be sufficient to yield the chromosomal equivalent of 0.01 to 0.05 μg of human DNA and that this yield could be increased at least tenfold with the use of techniques that produce partial purification of chromosomes by size (Stubblefield and Wray, 1973). A second possible use of cell hybrids in shotgun experiments refers to the partial purification of X chromosome–specific poly-A nRNA described in the previous section and reported in detail

Figure 9. The map of the human genome as reported in the last newsletter circulated by Dr. V. A. McKusick. The symbols used are the same as those in Dr. McKusick's list, which reports the full terminology of each marker in alphabetic order. The arrows indicate the recently discovered chromosome-specific membrane proteins or surface antigens.

by Balazs et al. (1977; 1978). It is conceivable that in spite of their obvious contamination with quasi homologous murine sequences, these transcripts may yield families of human cDNA that may turn out to be adequate probes for the identification of X chromosome–specific DNA clones from total cell libraries of human DNA. At any rate it is to be expected that much more efficient techniques will soon be developed for the screening of specific clones from the libraries yielded by shotgun experiments. This is likely to be a much easier task if the clones to be separated from one another carry DNA of a different species. Should this be the case it is clear that the highly reduced murine-human hybrids described in the preceding sections, and notably the microcell hybrids and heterogenotes, can be of direct relevance for the physical mapping of individual human chromosomes and genes as well as for their isolation and amplification.

THE MAP OF THE HUMAN GENOME

Dr. McKusick's Newsletter of November 1978*

This symbol indicates that the locus so marked is the site of one or more mutations that "cause" disease. Liberties have been taken with the definition of both *cause* and *disease*. For example, the polio sensitivity locus and the Ra locus are marked. In some cases it is not certain that the "disease locus" is the one that has been mapped, e.g., acid phosphatase-2 may not be the locus of the mutation in lysosomal acid phosphatase deficiency.

ABO	= ABO blood group (chr. 9)
ACO-M	= Aconitase, mitochondrial (chr. 22)
ACO-S	= Aconitase, soluble (chr. 9)
ACP-1	= Acid phosphatase-1 (chr. 2)
#ACP-2	= Acid phosphatase-2 (chr. 11)
adeB	= Formylglycinamide ribotide amidotransferase (chr. 4 or 5)
#ADA	= Adenosine deaminase (chr. 20)
#ADCP	= Adenosine deaminase complexing protein (chr. 6)
ADK	= Adenosine kinase (chr. 10)

---

*See also Figure 9.

AdV12-CMS-1p   = Adenovirus-12 chromosome modification site-1p (chr. 1)
AdV12-CMS-1q   = Adenovirus-12 chromosome modification site-1q (chr.1)
AdV12-CMS-17   = Adenovirus-12 chromosome modification site-17 (chr. 17)
#AH-3   = Adrenal hyperplasia III (21-hydroxylase deficiency) (chr. 6)
AHH   = Aryl hydrocarbon hydroxylase (chr. 2)
AK-1   = Adenylate kinase-1 (chr. 9)
AK-2   = Adenylate kinase-2 (chr. 1)
AK-3   = Adenylate kinase-3 (chr. 9)
AL   = Lethal antigen: 3 loci (a1, a2, a3) (chr. 11)
#Alb   = Albumin (chr. 4)
Acy-1   = Aminoacylase-1 (chr. 3)
Amy-1   = Amylase, salivary (chr. 1)
Amy-2   = Amylase, pancreatic (chr. 1)
#An-2   = Aniridia, type II Baltimore (chr. 1)
#ARS-A   = Arylsulfatase A (chr. 22)
#ARS-B   = Arylsulfatase B (chr. 5)
#APRT   = Adenine phosphoribosyltransferase (chr. 16)
#ASD-2   = Atrial septal defect, secundum type (chr. 6)
#ASL   = Argininosuccinate lyase (chr. 7)
#ASS   = Argininosuccinate synthetase (chr. 9)
#AT-3   = Antithrombin III (chr. 1)
AVP   = Antiviral protein (chr. 21)
AVr   = Antiviral state regulator (chr. 5)

Bevi   = Baboon M7 virus infection (chr. 6 or 19)
Bf   = Properdin factor B (chr. 6)
β2M   = β2-microglobulin (chr. 15)

#C2   = Complement component-2 (chr. 6)
C4F   = Complement component-4 fast (chr. 6)
C4S   = Complement component-4 slow (chr. 6)
C6   = Complement component-6 (chr. 6)
#C8   = Complement component-8 (chr. 6)
#Cae   = Cataract, zonular pulverulent (chr. 1)
CB   = Colorblindness (deutan and protan) (X chr.)
#CF7   = Clotting factor VII (chr. 8)
Ch   = Chido blood group (chr. 6) — same as C4S
#CML   = Chronic myeloid leukemia (chr. 22)
Co   = Colton blood group (chr. 7)
#Col-1   = Collagen I (α1 and α2) (chr. 7 and 17)
CS   = Citrate synthase, mitochondrial (chr. 12)

#Dia-1   = NADH-diaphorase (chr. 6 or 22)
#DMJ   = Juvenile diabetes mellitus (chr. 6)
Do   = Dombrock blood group (chr. 1)
DCE   = Desmosterol-to-cholesterol enzyme (chr. 20)
#DTS   = Diphtheria toxin sensitivity (chr. 5)

#EBS-1	= Epidermolysis bullosa, Ogna type (chr. 10)
#EBV	= Epstein-Barr virus integration site (chr. 14)
#E-1	= Pseudocholinesterase-1 (chr. 1)
#E-2	= Pseudocholinesterase-2 (chr. 16)
E11S	= Echo 11 sensitivity (chr. 19)
E1–1	= Elliptocytosis-1 (chr. 11)
EMP-130	= External membrane protein-130 (chr. 10)
EMP-195	= External membrane protein-195 (chr. 14)
ENO-1	= Enolase-1 (chr. 1)
ENO-2	= Enolase-2 (chr. 12)
Es-Act	= Esterase activator (chr. 4 or 5)
EsA4	= Esterase-A4 (chr. 11)
EsD	= Esterase D (chr. 13)
FH-M	= Fumarate hydratase, mitochondrial (chr. 1)
FH-S	= Fumarate hydratase, soluble (chr. 1)
#αFUC	=Alpha-L-Fucosidase (chr. 1)
FUSE	= Polykaryocytosis inducer (chr. 10)
#Fy	= Duffy blood group (chr. 1)
Gal+−Act	= Galactose + activator (chr. 2)
#αGAL A	= α-galactosidase A (Fabry disease) (X chr.)
αGAL B	= α-galactosidase B (chr. 22)
#βGAL	= β-galactosidase A (chr. 3) (see also chr. 12 and 22)
#GALK	= Galactokinase (chr. 17)
#GALT	= Galactose-1-phosphate uridyltransferase (chr. 2, 8 or 9)
#GALE	= Galactose-4-epimerase (chr. 1)
GAPD	= Glyceraldehyde-3-phosphate dehydrogenase (chr. 12)
GAPS	= Phosphoribosyl glycineamide synthetase (chr. 21)
Gc	= Group-specific component (chr. 4)
GDH	= Glucose dehydrogenase (chr. 1)
GLO-1	= Glyoxylase I (chr. 6)
Gm	= Immunoglobulin heavy chain (chr. 8)
GOT-M	= Glutamate oxaloacetate transaminase, mitochondrial (chr. 6)
GOT-S	= Glutamate oxaloacetate transaminase, soluble (chr. 10)
#GPI	= Glucosephosphate isomerase (chr. 19)
GPT-1	= Glutamate pyruvate transaminase, soluble (chr. 10)
#GPx-1	= Glutathione peroxidase-1 (chr. 3)
#G6PD	= Glucose-6-phosphate dehydrogenase (X chr.)
#GSR	= Glutathione reductase (chr. 8)
GSS	= Glutamate-gamma-semialdehyde synthetase (chr. 10)
GUK-1 & 2	= Guanylate kinase-1 & 2 (chr. 1)
#GUS	= Beta-glucuronidase (chr. 7)
H4	= Histone H4 (chr. 7)
HADH	= Hydroxyacyl-CoA dehydrogenase (chr. 7)
HaF	= Hageman factor (chr. 7)
#Hbα	= Hemoglobin alpha chain (chr. 2, 4, 5 or 16)
#Hbβ	= Hemoglobin beta chain (chr. 2, 4, 5 or 11)
hCG	= Human chorionic gonadotropin (chr. 18)

#Hch	= Hemochromatosis (chr. 6)
#HEM-A	= Classic hemophilia (X chr.)
#HexA	= Hexosaminidase A (chr. 15)
#HexB	= Hexosaminidase B (chr. 5)
#HGPRT	= Hypoxanthine-guanine phosphoribosyltransferase (X chr.)
HK-1	= Hexokinase-1 (chr. 10)
HLA(A-D)	= Human leukocyte antigens (chr. 6)
HLA-DR	= Human leukocyte antigen, D-related (chr. 6)
Hpα	= Haptoglobin, alpha (chr. 16)
#HVS	= Herpes virus sensitivity (chr. 3)
H-Y	= Y histocompatibility antigen (Y chr.)
IgAS	= Immunoglobulin heavy chains attachment site (chr. 2)
If-1	= Interferon-1 (chr. 2)
If-2	= Interferon-2 (chr. 5)
IDH-M	= Isocitrate dehydrogenase, mitochondrial (chr. 15)
IDH-S	= Isocitrate dehydrogenase, soluble (chr. 2)
#ITP	= Inosine triphosphatase (chr. 20)
Jk	= Kidd blood group (chr. 7)
Km	= Kappa immunoglobulin light chains, Inv (chr. 7)
#LCAT	= Lecithin-cholesterol acyltransferase (chr. 16)
LDH-A	= Lactate dehydrogenase A (chr. 11)
LDH-B	= Lactate dehydrogenase B (chr. 12)
LeuRS	= Leucyl-tRNA synthetase (chr. 5)
Lp	= Lipoprotein — Lp (chr. 13)
αMAN-A	= Cytoplasmic α-D-mannosidase (chr. 15)
#αMAN-B	= Lysosomal α-D-mannosidase (chr. 19)
MDH-M	= Malate dehydrogenase, mitochondrial (chr. 7)
MDH-S	= Malate dehydrogenase, soluble (chr. 2)
ME-S	= Malic enzyme, soluble (chr. 6)
MHC	= Major histocompatibility complex (chr. 6)
MLC-W	= Mixed lymphocyte culture, weak (chr. 6)
MPI	= Mannosephosphate isomerase (chr. 15)
MRBC	= Monkey red blood cell receptor (chr. 6)
NCR	= Neutrophil chemotactic response (chr. 7)
NDF	= Neutrophil differentiation factor (chr. 6)
#NP	= Nucleoside phosphorylase (chr. 14)
#NPa	= Nail-patella syndrome (chr. 9)
#OPCA-1	= Olivopontocerebellar atrophy I (chr. 6)
P	= P blood group (chr. 6)
PA	= Plasminogen activator (chr. 6)
#PDB	= Paget disease of bone (chr. 6)
PepA	= Peptidase A (chr. 8)

PepB   = Peptidase B (chr. 12)
PepC   = Peptidase C (chr. 1)
PepD   = Peptidase D (chr. 19)
PepS   = Peptidase S (chr. 4)
Pg   = Pepsinogen (chr. 6)
PGK   = Phosphoglycerate kinase (X chr.)
PGM-1   = Phosphoglucomutase-1 (chr. 1)
PGM-2   = Phosphoglucomutase-2 (chr. 4)
PGM-3   = Phosphoglucomutase-3 (chr. 6)
6PGD   = 6-phosphogluconate dehydrogenase (chr. 1)
PRPPAT   = Phosphoribosylpyrophosphate amidotransferase (chr. 4)
PK-3   = Pyruvate kinase-3 (chr. 15)
#PKU   = Phenylketonuria (chr. 1)
PP   = Inorganic pyrophosphatase (chr. 10)
#PVS   = Polio sensitivity (chr. 19)

#RB-1   = Retinoblastoma-1 (chr. 13)
rC3b   = Receptor for C3b (chr. 6)
rC3d   = Receptor for C3d (chr. 6)
Rg   = Rodgers blood group (chr. 6) — same as C4f
#Rh   = Rhesus blood group (chr. 1)
RN5S   = 5S RNA gene(s) (chr. 1)
#RP-1   = Retinitis pigmentosa-1 (chr. 1)
rRNA   = Ribosomal RNA (chr. 13, 14, 15, 21, 22)
#RwS   = Ragweed sensitivity (chr. 6)

SA6   = Surface antigen 6 (chr. 6)
SA7   = Species antigen 7 (chr. 7)
SA11   = Surface antigen 11 (chr. 11)
SA12   = Surface antigen 12 (chr. 12)
SAX   = X-linked species (or surface) antigen (X chr.)
Sc   = Scianna blood group (chr. 1)
SHMT   = Serine hydroxymethyltransferase (chr. 12)
SOD-M   = Superoxide dismutase, mitochondrial (chr. 6)
SOD-S   = Superoxide dismutase, soluble (chr. 21)
Sph-1   = Spherocytosis, Denver type (chr. 8 or 12)
SV40-7   = SV40-integration site-7 (chr. 7)
SV40-8   = SV40-integration site-8 (chr. 8)
SV40-17   = SV40-integration site-17 (chr. 17)

TDF   = Testis determining factor (Y chr.)
Tf   = Transferrin (chr. 1)
TK-M   = Thymidine kinase, mitochondrial (chr. 16)
TK-S   = Thymidine kinase, soluble (chr. 17)
#TPI-1 & 2   = Triosephosphate isomerase-1 and -2 (chr. 12)
TrpRS   = Tryptophanyl-tRNA synthetase (chr. 14)
tsAF8   = Temperature sensitive (AF8) complementing (chr. 3)

UGPP-1   = Uridyl diphosphate glucose pyrophosphorylase-1 (chr. 1)
UGPP-2   = Uridyl diphosphate glucose pyrophosphorylase-2 (chr. 2)
UMPK   = Uridine monophosphate kinase (chr. 1)
UP   = Uridine phosphorylase (chr. 7)

#WS-1   = Waardenburg syndrome-1 (chr. 9)
#W-AGR   = Wilms tumor — aniridia/ambiguous genitalia/mental re-
                   tardation (chr. 11)

#XP-E   = Xeroderma pigmentosum, Egyptian (chr. 9)

Comparative Mapping

As mapping data pile up in man and other mammals, it be-comes progressively clear that the well-known conservation of X-linked genes throughout mammalian species may, after all, not be as special as it appeared to be a few years ago (Ohno, 1973). A great number of homologies between autosomes of human and other pri-mates have been reported at the 4th Conference on Human Gene Mapping (Pearson and Roderick, 1978). These homologies, of course, are not surprising, but a recent summary by Lalley and col-leagues (1978) indicates also that several mouse and human chro-mosomes carry homologous pairs of genes. For instance, the genes for Pgm-2, Ak-2, ENO-1, and Pgd are on mouse autosome 4 and human 1p; Pgm-1, Pep-S and Alb-1 on mouse 5 and human 4; Gus and Mor-1 on mouse 5 and human 7; Gpi-1 and Pep-D on mouse 7 and human 19; Ldh-A and β-chain globin on mouse 7 and human 11; Mpi-1 and Pk-3 on mouse 9 and human 15q; Hk-1 and Pp on mouse 10 and human 10; Glk and Tk-1 on mouse 11 and human 17q; H-2 and Glo-1 on mouse 17 and human 6p, and of course Pgk, α-gal, and G6PD on mouse X and human Xq. Moreover, from the recombinational distances of some of these gene pairs in both spe-cies, the authors just mentioned point out that some homologies may be more "conserved" than others. For instance, the genes for Pgm and Pgd are 23 map units apart in mouse and 50 map units in man, whereas the gene for glyoxidase (GLO) is only 5 map units away from the histocompatibility loci in both species. Unpublished studies of Weitkamp (1979) show that the very close linkage between the genes for human Gc-protein and albumin exists also in the Equidae, thus suggesting that the relevant fraction of mammalian DNA has been conserved unaltered throughout a very wide evolu-tionary interval. These data are unquestionably of great interest from the general standpoint of biologic evolution and emphasize once again the multidisciplinary use of linkage studies. It will be of interest to see, however, how much these homologies will stand true when similar comparisons will be possible at the level of the physical maps of the relevant DNA regions. In the meantime, in view of the extent of knowledge available for the murine map, these homologies serve as a tentative guideline to search for the human counterparts of genes already identified in the mouse as being part of a given linkage group.

PRENATAL DIAGNOSIS OF HEMOPHILIA A AND CLASSIFICATION OF HETEROZYGOTES THROUGH LINKAGE STUDIES.

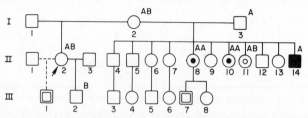

Figure 11. From the analysis of this pedigree it is clear that the individual I-2 is a double heterozygote in coupling phase (Gd^Ah^-/Gd^Bh^+). Thus, it appears from the segregation of the G6PD phenotypes that the propositus (II-2) and her first cousin II-11 must have received the normal allele to hemophilia unless recombination (which is known to be very low between these loci) has occurred. Likewise, individuals II-8 and II-10 must have received the mutant allele for hemophilia. The direct determination of factor VIII deficiency confirmed these expectations with the exception of the individual II-2 who gave borderline results. However, the G6PD phenotype of the male fetus (III-1) was in favor of the absence of hemophilia, a conclusion that was confirmed after birth. (From Edgell, C. J. S., et al. 1978. Am. J. Hum. Genet. 30:80–84.)

Human Gene Mapping and Medicine

The potential value of gene mapping data in diagnostic and preventive medicine was strongly advertised by pioneer students of human linkage (Penrose, 1951), because clinicians' help was obviously of major importance in their effort to map the human genome with the pedigree approach. The biologic basis of this claim is well known. Once a close linkage between a recessive lethal disease and a common genetic marker is established, the diagnosis of heterozygosity for the lethal mutant can be based upon the segregation of the closely linked marker in pedigrees in which both loci segregate with phase known (linkage diagnostic test). The same criterion can be used for the prenatal diagnosis of the lethal genotype itself when it happens that the gene end product of the closely linked marker is easier to identify (if not the only one identifiable) at the level of uncultured amniotic cells. The report of Edgell et al. (1978) illustrates how both goals have been achieved in families segregating at the X-linked loci for hemophilia A and G6PD in populations in which the latter gene is highly polymorphic (Fig. 11). The general applicability of the "linkage diagnostic test" has remained a matter of theoretic discussion for decades, since the instances of recognized close linkages between genes for lethal recessive diseases and normal polymorphic loci have been so far extremely rare.

However, the hopes for future application have been brightened again by the recent finding of Kan and Dozy (1978a) of a genetic polymorphism affecting the HpaI restriction sites of the DNA region that includes the gene for β-globin. As mentioned already, these authors have found that the mutant allele for sickle β-globin is associated with an Hpa 13 Kb fragment (instead of the normal 7.6 Kb) in 87 percent of black Americans of West African origin. This situation has already allowed them to prenatally diagnose the fetus' β-globin genotype in several pregnancies at risk (Kan and Dozy, 1978b) on the basis of the DNA-restricted pattern observed after hybridization of the HpaI-digested DNA of the amniotic fluid cells with labeled β-globin cDNA. A noteworthy feature of this approach to prenatal diagnosis lies in the fact that this type of test can be completed within one week and can be performed on the small amount of uncultured cells recovered from centrifugation of 10 to 15 ml. of amniotic fluid.

More recent studies by Kan and his colleagues (Kan, 1979) have established that the β^S-globin mutant is not associated with the 13 Kb fragment in East African (Kenya) and Asian populations. This suggests that the situation found among West Africans may be the result of a true linkage disequilibrium. If confirmed, this would be the first instance of a linkage disequilibrium identified through the physical mapping of DNA.

It is conceivable that genetic polymorphism in the DNA recognition sites to various restriction enzymes is a common occurrence over the entire genome. If so, it should always be possible for each known structural mutant to find a specific restricted fragment of its close neighboring DNA associated with it as a result of linkage disequilibrium. Such a situation would be of great significance to preventive medicine, since, given the appropriate molecular probes, it would allow, in general, the detection of homo- and heterozygotes for specific recessive lethal mutants and thus bring genetic counselling and prenatal screening to a much more meaningful role. This is particularly true for those mutations whose unfavorable phenotypic manifestation could be avoided or alleviated if the appropriate medical treatment were established before or soon after birth.

To a geneticist's mind, disease is the loss or the congenital lack of the adaptiveness of a given complex genotype to its environment. Seen in this context, susceptibility to common diseases can also be qualified in terms of its association with a more or less specific genetic variation. The recent finding by Comings (1979) of a common polymorphism for a human brain protein and its relationship to depressive disease and multiple sclerosis is a pertinent example. When such clear associations are found, the next step is a problem of gene mapping. As soon as a molecular probe for Dr. Comings' protein is available, for instance, it will be worth screening for polymorphism in the DNA adjacent to the protein's structural gene or genes in the hope that, like for the β^S-globin gene, a specific restricted fragment might be associated with the allelic mutant coding for the variant protein. In such case, the predisposition to the illnesses mentioned could be detected at an early stage and their manifestation avoided with the appropriate preventive measure.

Some potential applications of human gene mapping to cancer biology have been discussed at length elsewhere (Siniscalco, 1979). One refers to the possible use of the "radiation co-transfer test" of Goss and Harris to the screening for individual differences in the susceptibility to radiation-induced chromosomal damage. As has already been described in the section on Statistical Mapping of Gene Orders, when human lymphoid cells are irradiated with increasing doses of γ radiation prior to fusion with murine cells, the probability of co-transfer of human linked genes into the hybrid genome is inversely proportional to their distance. Thus, it is to be expected that lymphocytes from individuals highly susceptible to radiation-induced chromosomal damage may require a radiation dose lower than normal for the splitting of a given pair of linked genes. If this is the case, the median radiation dose needed to split a given linkage group would become a meaningful parameter to measure the individual susceptibility to DNA damage and repair at the level of the functional chromosomal DNA. Especially advantageous features of this approach are that such measurements could be performed on diploid cells freshly derived from the propositi, and, depending upon the linkage group chosen as a "target radiation site," they could provide data on the radiation sensitivity of specific human chromosomes.

A potential application of the knowledge on human gene mapping to cancer therapy has also been discussed elsewhere (Siniscalco, 1979) on the basis of the following arguments. On the one hand, it is becoming clearer than ever that malignant cells undergo numeric and/or structural chromosomal mutations that, most probably, occur at random but may become specific for given types of tumor as a result of somatic selection all the same. On the other hand, there can be little doubt that, along with the rapidly expanding knowledge on human gene mapping there will soon be available an array of chemicals and immunologic reagents, (see pp. 266–269) which can selectively kill only the cells bearing a specific type of somatic mutation associated with a gene dosage effect. Given these two sets of circumstances, it does not seem too unrealistic to start investigating the feasibility of a selective chemotherapy or immunotherapy of tumor cells based essentially on the same strategies that have been discussed at length earlier in this chapter. If selective killing of tumor cells, based on these strategies, proves to be possible in vivo as well, the cancer therapists of tomorrow will have to devise ad hoc protocols (chemical or immunologic, as the case may be) for each individual tumor based on the results of in vitro screening tests, which by analogy to the bacteriologist's antibiogram could be called "tumor-chemogram" or "immunogram" (Siniscalco, 1979).

In a more direct way, data on human gene mapping may turn out to be of critical importance with respect to the much-talked-about prospects of "gene" or "phene" therapy. We have seen that the transfer of genetic information between cultured mammalian cells is now a matter of routine for cell hybridizers. More sophisticated techniques of somatic cell genetics (microcell and chromosome-mediated transfers) or of molecular biology (cloning of mammalian genes and their insertion into a foreign eukaryotic genome by viral-mediated transformation) now permit the correction of the phenotype of mutant somatic cells in tissue culture. However, the biology of these transformation-like phenoma is at present entirely unknown, and this is why speculations about their applicability to clinical medicine still sound like science fiction at this time. It is a well-known fact that very detailed knowledge on the genetic maps of prokaryotes had to be accumulated before molecular biologists could succeed in tailoring bacterial and viral DNA to their own taste. Likewise, a great deal more work on the mapping of the eukaryotic genomes is obviously necessary before one may be able to attempt, let alone achieve, similar goals in mammalian cells.

EPILOGUE

Review papers offer their authors an opportunity to summarize in their own biased way the evolution of knowledge in their field and to speculate about its significance and practical value. This author has profited abundantly of both prerogatives to arrive at the usual, yet often forgotten, conclusion that a lot more basic work needs to be done before biologic knowledge on human gene mapping can be routinely applied to the understanding of the genetic control of normal development and disease. It will be a great reward for this lengthy writing if the latter message will get across and be of help to science policy makers and grant reviewers in their unenviable task of deciding who has to research what for the benefit of society.

ACKNOWLEDGEMENTS: The research from the author's laboratory included in this review was supported by NCI grants CA-08748, CA17085, and by the "Fund for Advanced Study of Cancer." The author wishes to thank Dr. Victor McKusick for his consent to have the latest edition of his "newsletter" reported in the review.

References

Adam, A., P. Tippett, J. Gavin, J. Noades, R. Sanger, and R. R. Race. 1967. The linkage relation of Xg to glucose-6-phosphate dehydrogenase in Israelis: the evidence of a second series of families. Ann. Hum. Genet. 30:211–218.

Adam, A., L. Ziprowski, A. Feinstein, R. Sanger, P. Tippett, G. June, and R. R. Race. 1969. Linkage relations of X-borne ichthyosis to the Xg blood groups and to other markers of the X in Israelis. Ann. Hum. Genet. 32:323–332.

Anderson, E. G. 1926. Crossing over in a case of attached X chromosomes in Drosophila melanogaster. Genetics 10:403–417.

Atwood, K. C., M. T. Yu, E. Eicher, and A. S. Henderson. 1976. Feasibility Tests for Mapping Low-Multiplicity Genes by Hybridization in Situ. In Human Gene Mapping III, Birth Defects: Original Article Series, Bergsma, D. (Ed.), Vol. 12:7, pp. 372–375. White Plains, The National Foundation.

Bailey, N. T. J. 1951. On simplifying the use of Fisher's u-statistics in the detection of linkage in man, Ann. Eugen. (Lond.) 16:26–32.

Bailey, N. T. J. (Ed.). 1961. Introduction to the Mathematical Theory of Genetic Linkage, Oxford, Clarendon Press.

Balazs, I., G. Filippi, A. Rinaldi, K. H. Grzeschik, and M. Siniscalco. Regional assignment of the locus for human steroid sulfatase (X-linked ichthyosis). In press.

Balazs, I., P. Szabo, and M. Siniscalco. 1977. Properties of Human RNA Sequences isolated from a Human-Mouse Hybrid Cell Line. In Human Gene Mapping IV, Bergsma D. (Ed.). White Plains, The National Foundation. In press.

Balazs, I., P. Szabo, and M. Siniscalco. 1978. Hybridization properties of human X-chromosomal RNA transcripts from murine-human hybrids. Somatic Cell Genet. 4:617–631.

Becker, M. A., R. C. K. Yen, P. Itkin, S. J. Goss, J. E. Seegmiller, and B. Bakay. 1979. Regional localization of the gene for human phosphoribosylpyrophosphate synthetase on the X chromosome. Science 203:1016–1019.

Benoff, S., and A. I. Skoultchi. 1977. X-linked control of hemoglobin production in somatic hybrids of mouse erythroleukemic cells and mouse lymphoma of bone marrow cells. Cell 12:263–274.

Bergsma, D. (Ed.). 1974. Human Gene Mapping, Birth Defects: Original Article Series, Vol. X:3. New York, Stratton Intercontinental Medicine Book Corp.

Bergsma, D. (Ed.). 1975. Human Gene Mapping II, Birth Defects: Original Article Series, Vol. 11:3. White Plains, The National Foundation.

Bergsma, D. (Ed.). 1976. Human Gene Mapping III, Birth Defects: Original Article Series, Vol. 12:7. White Plains, The National Foundation.

Bergsma, D. (Ed.). Human Gene Mapping IV, Birth Defects: Original Article Series, White Plains, The National Foundation. In press.

Bishop, J. O., and K. W. Jones. 1972. Chromosomal localization of human haemoglobin structural genes. Nature 240:149–150.

Blattner, F. R., A. E. Blechl, K. Denniston-Thompson, H. E. Faber, J. E. Richards, J. L. Slightom, P. W. Tucker, and O. Smithies. 1978. Cloning human fetal γ globin and mouse α-type globin DNA: preparation and screening of shotgun collections. Science 202:1279–1284.

Bodmer, W. F., and J. G. Bodmer. 1978. Evolution and function of the HLA system. Brit. Med. Bull. 34:309–316.

Borgaonkar, D. S. (Ed.). 1974. Chromosomal Variation in Man: A Catalog of Chromosomal Variants and Anomalies, 2nd ed. New York, Alan R. Liss.

Bridges, C. B. 1916. Non-disjunction as proof of the chromosome theory of heredity. Genetics 1:1 and 1:107–163.

Brown, J. A., S. Goss, H. Klinger, O. J. Miller, S. Ohno, and M. Siniscalco. 1976. Report of the Committee on the Genetic Constitution of the X and Y Chromosomes. 3rd International Conference on Human Gene Mapping, Baltimore, 1975. In Human Gene Mapping III, Birth Defects: Original Article Series, Bergsma, D. (Ed.), Vol. 12:7, pp. 55–59. White Plains, The National Foundation.

Buck, C. W., and W. F. Bodmer. 1975. The Human Species Antigen on Chromosome 11. In Human Gene Mapping II, Birth Defects: Original Article Series, Bergsma, D. (Ed.), Vol. 11:3, pp. 87–89. White Plains, The National Foundation.

Buck, C. W., and W. F. Bodmer. 1976. Serological Identification of an X-linked Human Cell Surface Antigen, SAX. In Human Gene Mapping III, Birth Defects: Original Article Series, Bergsma, D. (Ed.), Vol. 12:7, pp. 376–377. White Plains, The National Foundation.

Buck, C. W., S. J. Goss, and W. F. Bodmer. 1976. Regional Mapping of the X-Linked Gene for a Human Cell Surface Antigen, SAX. 3rd International Conference on Human Gene Mapping, Baltimore 1975. In Human Gene Mapping III, Birth Defects: Original Article Series, Bergsma, D. (Ed.), Vol. 12:7, pp. 99–100. White Plains, The National Foundation.

Cavalli-Sforza, L. L., and W. F. Bodmer. 1971. The Genetics of Human Populations, pp. 221–276. San Francisco, W. H. Freeman & Co.

Chan, T-S., R. P. Creagan, and M. P. Reardon. 1978. Adenosine kinase as a new selective marker in somatic cell genetics: Isolation of adenosine kinase–deficient mouse cell lines and human-mouse hybrid cell lines containing adenosine kinase. Somatic Cell Genet. 4:1–12.

Chasin, L. 1975. Isolation of mammalian cell mutants deficient in glucose-6-phosphate-dehydrogenease activity: Linkage to hypoxanthine phosphorybosyl transferase. Proc. Nat. Acad. Sci. U.S.A. 72:493–497.

Cockayne, E. A. 1933. Inherited Abnormalities of the Skin and Its Appendages. London, Oxford University Press.

Comings, D. E. 1979. Pc 1 Duarte, a common polymorphism of a human brain protein, and its relationship to depressive disease and multiple sclerosis. Nature 277:28–32.

Cook, P. J. L. 1965. The Lutheran-secretor recombination fraction in man: a possible sex difference, Ann. Hum. Genet., 28:393–401.

Côté, G. B., and J. H. Edwards. 1975. Centrometric linkage in autosomal trisomies. Ann. Hum. Genet. 39:51–59.

Creagan, R., and F. H. Ruddle. 1975. The Clone Panel: A Systematic Approach to Gene Mapping Using Interspecific Somatic Cell Hybrids. In Rotterdam Conference, 1974; 2nd Internation Workshop. Human Gene Mapping. Birth Defects: Original Article Series, Bergsma, D. (Ed.), pp. 109–111.

Croce, C. M., Litwack, G., and H. Koprowski. 1973. Human regulatory genes for inducible tyrosine aminotransferase in rat-human hybrids. Proc. Nat. Acad. Sci. U.S.A. 70:1268–1272.

Danna, K., and D. Nathans. 1971. Specific cleavage of simian virus 40 DNA by restriction endonuclease of Hemophilus influenzae. Proc. Nat. Acad. Sci. U.S.A. 68:2913–2917.

Darlington, G. J. 1974. Production of human albumin in mouse hepatoma–human leukocyte hybrids in somatic cell hybridization. In Davidson, R. L., and F. de la Cruz (Eds.), Somatic Cell Hybridization. New York, Raven Press, pp. 159–162.

Davidson, R. L. 1974. Gene expression in somatic cell hybrids. Ann. Rev. Genet. 8:195–218.

Deisseroth, A., and D. Hendrick. 1978. Human alpha-globin gene expression following chromosomal dependent gene transfer into mouse erythroleukemia cells. Cell 15:55–63.

Deisseroth, A., A. Nienhuis, J. Lawrence, R. Giles, P. Turner, and F. Ruddle. 1978. Chromosomal localization of human beta globin gene on human chromosome 11 in somatic cell hybrids. Proc. Nat. Acad. Sci. U.S.A. 75:1456–1460.

Deisseroth, A., A. Nienhuis, P. Turner, R. Velez, W. Anderson, F. Ruddle, J. Lawrence, R. Creagan, and R. Kucherlapati. 1977. Localization of the human α globin structural gene to chromosome 16 in somatic cell hybrids by molecular hybridization assay. Cell 12:205–218.

de la Chapelle, A., J. Schröder, K. Stenstrand, J. Fellman, R. Herva, M. Saarni, I. Anttolainen, I. Tallila, L. Tervila, L. Husa, G. Tallqvist, E. B. Robson, P. J. L. Cook, and R. Sanger. 1974. Pericentric inversions of human chromosomes 9 and 10. Am. J. Hum. Genet. 26:746–766.

DeWeerd-Kastelein, E. A., W. Keijzer, and D. Bootsma. 1972. Genetic heterogeneity of xeroderma pigmentosum demonstrated by somatic cell hybridization. Nature (New Biol.) 238:80–83.

DeWeerd-Kastelein, E A., W. Keijzer, and D. Bootsma. 1974. A third complementation group in xeroderma pigmentosum. Mutat. Res. 22:87–91.

Donahue, R. P., W. B. Bias, J. H. Renwick, and V. A. McKusick. 1968. Probable assignment of the Duffy blood group locus to chromosome 1 in man. Proc. Nat. Acad. Sci. U.S.A. 61:949–955.

Dorman, B. P., N. Shimizu, and F. H. Ruddle. 1977. A cell surface antigen linked to the human X-chromosome. In Human Gene Mapping IV, Bergsma, D. (Ed.). White Plains, The National Foundation. In press.

Dunn, L. C., and D. Bennett. 1967. Sex differences in recombination of linked genes in animals. Genet. Res. 9:211–220.

Dutrillaux, B., C. Laurent, J. M. Robert, and J. Lejeune. 1973. Inversion péricentrique, inv(10), chez la mère et aneusomie de recombinaison, inv(10), REC(10), chez son fils. Cytogenet. Cell Genet. 12:245–253.

Edgell, C. J. S., H. N. Kirkman, E. Clemons, P. D. Buchanan, and C. H. Miller. 1978. Prenatal diagnosis by linkage: hemophilia A and polymorphic glucose-6-phosphate-dehydrogenase. Am. J. Hum. Genet. 30:80–84.

Edwards, J. H. 1971. The analysis of X-linkage. Ann. Hum. Genet. 34:229–250.

Ege, R., and N. R. Ringertz. 1974. Preparation of microcells by enucleation of micronucleate cells. Exp. Cell Res. 87:378–382.

Engel, E., B. J. McGee, and H. Harris. 1969. Cytogenetic and nuclear studies on A9 and B82 cells fused together by Sendai virus. The early phase. J. Cell Sci. 5:93–120.

Ephrussi, B. 1972. Hybridization of Somatic Cells. Princeton, Princton University Press.

Evans, H. J., R. A. Buckland, and M. L. Pardue. 1974. Location of the genes coding for 18S and 28S ribosomal RNA in the human genomes. Chromosoma 48:405–426.

Falk, C. T., and J. H. Edwards. 1970. A computer approach to the analysis of family genetic data for detection of linkage (Abstr.), Genetics 64:s18.

Falk, C. T., M. E. Walker, M. D. Martin, and F. H. Allen, Jr. 1975. Autosomal linkage in humans (methodology and results of computer analysis). Series Haematologica, 8(2):153–237.

Ferguson-Smith, M. A. 1978. Gene Mapping by Exclusion. In Human Gene Mapping IV, Bergsma, D. (Ed.). The National Foundation. In press.

Ferguson-Smith, M. A., P. M. Ellis, O. Mutchinick, K. P. Glen, G. B. Côté, and J. H. Edwards. 1975. Centromeric Linkage. In Human Gene Mapping II, Birth Defects: Original Article Series, Bergsma, D. (Ed.), Vol. 11:3, pp. 130–137. White Plains, The National Foundation.

Fialkow, P. J., R. Lisker, E. R. Giblett, C. Zavala, A. Cobo, and J. C. Detter. 1972. Genetic markers in chronic myelocytic leukaemia: evidence opposing autosomal inactivation and favouring 6-PGD-Rh linkage. Ann. Hum. Genet. 35:321–326.

Filippi, G., A. Rinaldi, R. Palmarino, E. Seravalli, and M. Siniscalco. 1977. Linkage disequilibrium for two X-linked genes in Sardinia and its bearing on the statistical mapping of the human X chromosome. Genetics 86:199–212.

Finney, D. J. 1940. The detection of linkage. Ann. Eugen. (Lond.) 10:171–214.

Fisher, R. A. 1935a. The detection of linkage with "dominant" abnormalities, Ann. Eugen. (Lond.) 6:187–201.

Fisher, R. A. 1935b. The detection of linkage with recessive abnormalities, Ann. Eugen. (Lond.) 6:339–351.

Flavell, R. A., J. M. Kooter, E. De Boer, P. F. R. Little, and R. Williamson. 1978. Analysis of the β-δ-globin gene loci in normal and Hb Lepore DNA: direct determination of gene linkage and intergene distance. Cell 15:25–41.

Fournier, R. E. K., and F. H. Ruddle. 1977a. Microcell-mediated chromosome transfer. Human Cytogenetics, ICN-UCLA Symposia on Molecular Biology 7:189–199.

Fournier, R. E. K., and F. H. Ruddle. 1977b. Microcell-mediated transfer of murine chromosomes into mouse, Chinese hamster, and human somatic cells. Proc. Nat. Acad. Sci. U.S.A. 74:319–323.

Fournier, R. E. K., and F. H. Ruddle. 1977c. Stable association of the human transgenome and host murine chromosomes demonstrated with trispecific microcell hybrids. Proc. Nat. Acad. Sci. U.S.A. 74:3937–3941.

Galjaard, H., A. Hoogeveen, H. A. deWit-Verbeek, A. J. J. Reuser, W. Keijzer, A. Westerveld, and D. Bootsma. 1974. Tay-Sachs and Sandhoff's disease: intergenic complementation after somatic cell hybridization. Exp. Cell Res. 87:444–448.

Gates, R. R. 1946. Human Genetics. 2 vols. New York, The Macmillan Co.

Goss, S. J., and H. Harris. 1975. New method for mapping genes in human chromosomes. Nature 255:680–684.

Goss, S. J., and H. Harris. 1977a. Gene transfer by means of cell fusion. I. Statistical mapping of the human X-chromosome by analysis of radiation-induced gene segregation. J. Cell Sci. 25:17–37.

Goss, S. J., and H. Harris. 1977b. Gene transfer by means of cell fusion. II. The mapping of 8 loci on human chromosome 1 by statistical analysis of gene assortment in somatic cell hybrids. J. Cell Sci. 25:39–57.

Gravel, R. A., J. M. Mahoney, F. H. Ruddle, and L. E. Rosenberg. 1975. Genetic complementation in heterokaryons of human fibroblasts defective in cobalamin metabolism. Proc. Nat. Acad. Sci. U.S.A. 72:3181–3185.

Grzeschik, K. H., A. M. Grzeschik, S. Banhof, G. Romeo, M. Siniscalco, H. Van Someren, P. Meera Khan, A. Westerveld, and D. Bootsma. 1972a. X-linkage of human alpha-galactosidase. Nature (New Biol.) 240:48–50.

Grzeschik, K. H., P. W. Allderdice, A. M. Grzeschik, J. M. Opitz, O. J. Miller, and M. Siniscalco. 1972b. Cytological mapping of human X-linked genes by use of somatic cell hybrids involving an X-autosome translocation. Proc. Nat. Acad. Sci. USA 69:69–73.

Grzeschik, K. H., and M. Siniscalco. 1976. Identification of a De Novo Chromosome Rearrangement in a Man-Mouse Hybrid Clone and Its Bearing on the Cytological Map of the Human X-Chromosome. In Human Gene Mapping III, Birth Defects: Original Article Series, Bergsma, D. (Ed.), Vol. 12:7, pp. 149–156. White Plains, The National Foundation.

Haldane, J. B. S., and C. A. B. Smith. 1947. A new estimate of the linkage between the genes for haemophilia and colour-blindness in man. Ann. Eugen. (Lond.) 14:10–31.

Higuchi, R., G. V. Paddock, R. Wall, and W. Salser. 1976. A general method for cloning eukaryotic structural gene sequences. Proc. Nat. Acad. Sci. U.S.A. 73:3146–3150.

Hilwig, I., and A. Gropp. 1972. Staining of constitutive heterochromatin in mammalian chromosomes with a new fluorochrome. Exp. Cell Res. 75:122–126.

Hulett, H. R., W. A. Bonner, R. G. Sweet, and L. A. Herzenberg. 1973. Development and application of a rapid cell sorter. Clin. Chem. 19:813–816.

Ingram, V. M. 1957. Gene mutations in normal haemoglobin: The chemical difference between normal and sickle cell haemoglobin. Nature 180:326–328.

Johnson, R. T., A. M. Mullinger, and R. J. Skaer. 1975. Perturbation of mammalian cell division: human mini segregants derived from mitotic cells. Proc. R. Soc. Lond. (Biol.) 189:591–602.

Jones, C., P. Wuthier, F. T. Kao, and T. T. Puck. 1972. Evidence for linkage between human genes of LDH-B and Serine hydroxymethylase. J. Cell Physiol. 80:291–298.

Kan, Y. W. 1979. Personal Communication.

Kan, Y. W., and A. M. Dozy. 1978a. Polymorphism of DNA sequence adjacent to human β-globin structural gene: relationship to sickle mutation. Proc. Nat. Acad. Sci. U.S.A. 75:5631–5635.

Kan, Y. W., and A. M. Dozy. 1978b. Antenatal diagnosis of sickle-cell anemia by DNA analysis of amniotic fluid cells. Lancet 2:910–911.

Kan, Y. W., A. M. Dozy, H. E. Varmus, J. M. Taylor, J. P. Holland, L. E. Lie-Injo, J.

Ganesan, and D. Todd. 1975. Deletion of α-globin genes in haemoglobin H-disease demonstrates multiple α-globin structural loci. Nature 255:255–256.

Kan, Y. W., J. P. Holland, A. M. Dozy, and H. E. Varmus. 1975. Demonstration of non-functional β-globin mRNA in homozygous β⁰-thalassemia. Proc. Nat. Acad. Sci. 72:5140–5144.

Kelly, T. J., Jr., and H. O. Smith. 1970. A restriction enzyme from *Hemophilus influenzae.* II. Bas sequence of the recognition site. J. Mol. Biol. 51:393–409.

Kit, S., D. R. Dubbs, L. J. Pierkaski, and T. C. Hsu. 1963. Deletion of thymidine kinase activity from L cells resistant to bromodeoxyuridine. Exp. Cell. Res. 31:297–312.

Kohler, G., and C. Milstein. 1975. Continuous cultures of fused cells secreting antibody of predefined specificity. Nature 256:495–497.

Koo, G. Personal communication.

Kozak, C. A., E. Nichols, and F. H. Ruddle. 1975. Gene linkage analysis in the mouse by somatic cell hybridization: Assignment of adenine phosphoribosyl transferase to chromosome 8 and galactosidase to the X chromosome. Somatic Cell Genet. 1:371–382.

Kozak, C. A., and R. H. Ruddle. 1977. Assignment of the genes for thymidine kinase and galactokinase to Mus musculus chromosome 11 and the preferential segregation of this chromosome in Chinese hamster/mouse somatic cell hybrids. Somat. Cell Genet. 3:122–138.

Kraemer, K. K., H. G. Coon, R. A. Petinga, S. F. Barrett, A. E. Rahe, and J. H. Robbins. 1975. Genetic heterogeneity in xeroderma pigmentosum: complementation groups and their relationship to DNA repair rates. Proc. Nat. Acad. Sci. U.S.A. 72:59–63.

Krone, W., and U. Wolf. 1977. Chromosomal variation and gene action. Hereditas 86:31–36.

Kunkel, L. M., K. D. Smith, and S. H. Boyer. 1976. Human Y-chromosome-specific reiterated DNA. Science 191:1189–1190.

Kunkel, L. M., K. D. Smith, S. H. Boyer, D. S. Borgaonkar, S. S. Wachtel, O. J. Miller, W. R. Breg, H. W. Jones, Jr., and J. M. Rary. 1977. Analysis of human Y-chromosome-specific reiterated DNA in chromosome variants. Proc. Nat. Acad. Sci. U.S.A. 74:1245–1249.

Lalley, P., J. D. Minna, and U. Francke. 1978. Conservation of autosomal gene synteny groups in mouse and man. Nature 274:160–162.

Li, C. C. 1955. Population Genetics, p. 90. Chicago, University of Chicago Press.

Linder, D. 1969. Gene loss in human teratomas. Proc. Nat. Acad. Sci. U.S.A. 63:699–704.

Linder, D., and J. Power. 1970. Further evidence for post-meiotic origin of teratomas in the human female. Ann. Hum. Genet. 34:21–30.

Lindsley, D. L., G. Fankhauser, and R. R. Humphrey. 1956. Mapping centromeres in the Axolotl. Genetics 41:58–64.

Littlefield, J. W. 1964. Selection of hybrids from matings of fibroblasts in vitro and their presumed recombinants. Science 145:709–710.

Luria, S. E., and S. E. Human. 1952. A nonhereditary, host-induced variation of bacterial viruses. J. Bacteriol. 64:557–569.

Lyon, M. F., and S. G. Hawkes. 1970. X-linked gene for testicular feminization in the mouse. Nature 225:1217–1219.

Lyons, L. B., R. P. Cox, and J. Dancis. 1973. Complementation analysis of maple syrup urine disease in heterokaryons derived from cultured human fibroblasts. Nature 243:533–535.

Mace, M. A., J. E. Noades, E. B. Robson, M. Hulten, J. Lindsten, P. E. Polani, P. A. Jacobs, and K. E. Buckton. 1975. Segregation of ACPs and MNSs in families with structural rearrangements involving chromosome 2. Ann. Hum. Genet. 33:479–484.

Magenis, R. E., E. Hecht, and E. W. Lovrien. 1970. Heritable fragile site on chromosome 16: probable localization of haptoglobin locus in man. Science 170:85–87.

Maniatis, T., S. G. Kee, A. Efstratiadis, and F. C. Katatos. 1976. Amplification and characterization of a β-globin gene synthesized *in vitro.* Cell 8:163–182.

Maniatis, T., R. C. Hardison, E. Lacy, J. Lauer, C. O'Connell, D. Quon, G. K. Sim, and A. Efstratiadis. 1978. The isolation of structural genes from libraries of eucaryotic DNA. Cell 15:687–701.

Marsch, W. L. 1978. Linkage Relationship of the Xg and Xk Loci. In Human Gene Mapping IV, Bergsma, D. (Ed.). White Plains, The National Foundation. In press.

Mather, K. 1935. Reductional and equational separation of chromosomes in bivalents and multivalents. J. Genet. 30:53–78.

Mather, K. 1951. The Measurement of Linkage in Heredity, 2nd ed. London, Methuen & Co. Ltd.

Maynard Smith, S., L. S. Penrose, and C. A. B. Smith. 1961. Mathematical Tables for Research Workers in Human Genetics, London, Churchill Livingstone.

McBride, O. W., and R. S. Athwal. 1976. Genetic analysis by chromosome-mediated gene tranfer. In Vitro (Monogr.) 12:777–786.

McBride, O. W., J. W. Burch, and F. H. Ruddle. 1978. Cotransfer of thymidine kinase and galactokinase genes by chromosome-mediated gene transfer. Proc. Nat. Acad. Sci. U.S.A. 75:914–918.

McBride, O. W., and H. L. Ozer. 1973. Transfer of genetic information by purified metaphase chromosomes. Proc. Nat. Acad. Sci. U.S.A. 70:1258–1262.

McKusick, V. A. 1976. Mendelian Inheritance in Man, 4th ed. Baltimore, The Johns Hopkins University Press.

McKusick, V. A., and F. H. Ruddle. 1977. The status of the gene map of the human chromosomes. Science 196:390–405.

Mears, J. G., F. Ramirez, D. Leibowitz, and A. Bank. 1978. Organization of human δ- and β-globin genes in cellular DNA and the presence of intragenic inserts. Cell 15:15–23.

Mears, G. J., F. Ramirez, D. Leibowitz, F. Nakamura, A. Bloom, F. Konotey-Ahulu, and A. Bank. 1978. Changes in restricted human cellular DNA fragments containing globin gene sequences in the thalassemias and related disorders. Proc. Nat. Acad. Sci. 75:1222–1226.

Meera Khan, P., A. Westerveld, K. H. Grzeschik, B. F. Deys, O. M. Garson, and M. Siniscalco. 1971. X-linkage of human phosphoglycerate kinase confirmed in man-mouse and man-Chinese hamster somatic cell hybrids. Am. J. Hum. Genet. 23:614–623.

Mellman, W. J., F. A. Oski, T. A. Tedesco, A. Maciera-Coelho, and H. Harris. 1964. Leucocyte enzymes in Down's syndrome. Lancet 2:674–675.

Merriam, J. R., and J. N. Frost. 1964. Exchange and non-disjunction of the X-chromosomes in female Drosophila melanogaster. Genetics 49:109–122.

Meselson, M., and R. Yuan. 1968. DNA restriction enzyme from E. coli. Nature (Lond.) 217:1110–1114.

Meyer, W. J., B. R. Migeon, and C. J. Migeon. 1975. Locus on human X-chromosome for dihydrotestosterone receptor and androgen insensitivity. Proc. Nat. Acad. Sci. U.S.A. 72:1469–1472.

Migeon, B. R., R. A. Norum, and C. M. Corsaro. 1974. Isolation and analysis of somatic hybrids derived from two human diploid cells. Proc. Nat. Acad. Sci. U.S.A. 71:937–941.

Miller, O. J., P. W. Allderdice, D. A. Miller, W. R. Breg, and B. R. Migeon. 1971a. Human thymidine kinase gene locus; assignment to chromosome 17 in a hybrid of man and mouse cells. Science 173:244–245.

Miller, O. J., P. R. Cook, P. Meera Khan, S. Shin, and M. Siniscalco. 1971b. Mitotic separation of two human X-linked genes in man-mouse somatic cell hybrids. Proc. Nat. Acad. Sci. U.S.A. 68:116–120.

Molday, R. S., S. P. S. Yen, and A. Rembaum. 1977. Application of magnetic microspheres in labelling and separation of cells. Nature 268:(5619) 437–438.

Morgan, T. H., C. B. Bridges, and J. Schultz. 1932. The constitution of the germinal material in relation to heredity. Carnegie Inst. Wash. Yrbk. 31:303–307.

Morton, N. E. 1955. Sequential tests for the detection of linkage, Am. J. Hum. Genet. 7:277–318.

Mulligan, R. C., B. H. Howard, and P. Berg. 1979. Synthesis of rabbit β-globin in cultured monkey kidney cells following infection with a SV40 β-globin recombinant genome. Nature 277:108–114.

Nabholz, M., V. Miggiano, and W. Bodmer. 1969. Genetic analysis with human-mouse somatic cell hybrids. Nature 223:358–363.

Nadler, H., C. M. Chacko, and M. Rachmeler. 1970. Interallelic complementation in hybrid cells derived from human diploid strains deficient in galactose-1-phosphate uridyl transferase activity. Proc. Nat. Acad. Sci. U.S.A. 67:976–982.

Nathans, D., and H. O. Smith. 1975. Restriction endonucleases. Ann. Rev. Biochem. 44:273–293.

Nunberg, J. H., R. J. Kaufman, R. T. Schimke, G. Urlaub, and L. A. Chasin. 1978. Amplified dihydrofolate reductase genes are localized to a homogeneously staining region of a single chromosome in a methotrexate-resistant Chinese hamster ovary cell line. Proc. Nat. Acad. Sci. U.S.A. 75:5553–5556.

O'Brien, S. J. 1976. Bvr-1, a restriction locus of a type C RNA virus in the feline cellular genome: Identification, location, and phenotypic characterization in cat X mouse somatic cell hybrids. Proc. Nat. Acad. Sci. U.S.A. 73:4619–4622.

Ohno, S. 1973. Ancient linkage groups and frozen accidents. Nature 244:259–262.

Opitz, J., P. D. Pallister, and F. D. Ruddle. 1973. An (X:14) translocation, balanced, 46 chromosomes. Repository identification No. GM-74. Cytogenet. Cell Genet. 12:291–292.

Ott, J. 1974. Estimation of the recombination fraction in human pedigrees: efficient computation of the likelihood for human linkage studies. Am. J. Hum. Genet. 26:588–597.

Ott, J., F. Hecht, D. Linder, E. W. Lovrien, and B. K. McCaw. 1976a. Human centromere mapping using teratoma data. In Human Gene Mapping III, Birth Defects: Original Article Series, Bergsma, D. (Ed.), 12:7, pp. 396–398. White Plains, The National Foundation.

Ott, J., D. Linder, B. K. McCaw, E. W. Lovrien, and F. Hecht. 1976b. Estimating distances from the centromere by means of benign ovarian teratomas in man. Ann. Hum. Genet. 40:191–196.

Ottolenghi, S. et al. 1974. Gene deletion as a cause of a α thalassemia. Nature 251:389–391.

Ottolenghi, S. et al. 1976. δβ-thalassemia is due to a gene deletion. Cell 9:71–80.

Partridge, C. 1977. Personal communication. For instructions on how to dial Telenet number call (203) 436–4810.

Pearson, P. L., and T. H. Roderick. 1978. Report of the Committee on comparative mapping. Cytogenet. Cell Genet. 22:150–162.

Penrose, L. S. 1935. The detection of autosomal linkage in data which consist of pairs of brothers and sisters of unspecified parentage. Ann. Eugen. (Lond.) 6:133–138.

Penrose, L. S. 1951. Data for the study of linkage in man: phenylketeruria and the ABO and MN loci. Ann. Eugen. (Lond.) 16:241–248.

Peterson, J. A., and M. C. Weiss. 1972. Expression of differentiated functions in hepatoma cell hybrids. Induction of mouse albumin production in rat hepatoma-mouse fibroblast hybrids. Proc. Nat. Acad. Sci. U.S.A. 69:571–575.

Pontecorvo, G. 1959. Biochemistry of Human Genetics, Wolstenholme, G. E. W., and C. M. O'Connor (Eds.), p. 285. London, Churchill Livingstone.

Prensky, W., and G. Holmquist. 1973. Chromosomal localization of human haemoglobin structural genes: Techniques queried. Nature 241:44–45.

Price, P. M., J. H. Conover, and K. Hirschhorn. 1972. Chromosomal localization of human haemoglobin structural genes. Nature 237:340–342.

Puck, T. T. 1972. The Mammalian Cell as a Microorganism. Genetics and Biochemical Studies In Vitro. San Francisco, Holden-Day, Inc.

Puck, T. T., P. Wuthier, C. Jones, and F. T. Kao. 1971. Genetics of somatic mammalian cells: Lethal antigens as genetic markers for study of human linkage groups. Proc. Nat. Acad. Sci. U.S.A. 68:3102–3106.

Rabbitts, T. H. 1976. Bacterial cloning of plasmids carrying copies of rabbit globin messenger RNA. Nature 260:221–225.

Race, R., and R. Sanger. 1975. Blood Groups in Man, 6th ed. Oxford, Blackwell Scientific.

Rankin, J. K., and G. J. Darlington. 1979. Expression of human hepatic genes in mouse-hepatoma-human aminocyte hybrids. Som. Cell Genet. 5:1–10.

Rattazzi, M. D., J. A. Brown, R. G. Davidson, and T. B. Shows. 1974. Tay-Sachs and Sandhoff-Jatzkewitz diseases: Complementation of β-Hexosaminidase A deficiency by Somatic Cell Hybridization. In Human Gene Mapping II, Birth Defects: Original Article Series. Bergsma, D. (Ed.), 11:3, pp. 232–235. White Plains, The National Foundation.

Renwick, J. H. 1971a. Assignment and map-positioning of human loci using chromosomal variation. Ann. Hum. Genet. 35:79–97.

Renwick, J. H. 1971b. The mapping of human chromosomes. Ann. Rev. Genet. 5:81–120.

Renwick, J. H., and J. Schulze. 1961. A computer program for the processing of linkage data for large pedigrees (Abstr.). Excerpta Medical Int. Congr. Ser. 32, E 145.

Renwick, J. H., and J. Schulze. 1965. Male and female recombination fractions for the nail-patella:ABO linkage in man. Ann. Hum. Genet. 28:379–392.

Réthoré, M. O., J. C. Kaplan, C. Junien, J. Cruveillier, D. Dutrillaux, S. Carpenter, J. Lafourcade, J. Lejeune, and A. Aurias. 1975. Augmentation de l'activité LDH-B chez un garcon trisomique 120 par malségrégation d'une translocation maternelle t(12:14) (q12:p11). Ann. Genet. 18:81–87.

Ricciuti, F. C., and F. H. Ruddle. 1973. Assignment of three gene loci (PGK, HGPRT, G6PD) to the long arm of the human X-chromosome by somatic cell genetics. Genetics 74:661–678.

Robson, E. B., P. E. Polani, S. J. Dart, P. A. Jacobs, and J. H. Renwick. 1969. Probable assignment of the alpha locus of haptoglobin to chromosome 16 in man. Nature 223:1163.

Rowley, J. D. 1973. A new consistent chromosomal abnormality in chronic myelogenous leukaemia identified by quinacrine fluorescence and Giemsa staining. Nature 243:290–293.

Ruddle, F. H., and P. Meera Khan. 1976. Report of the Committee on the Genetic Constitution of Autosomes Other Than Chromosomes 1, 2, and 6. In Human Gene Mapping III, Birth Defects: Original Article Series, Bergsma, D. (Ed.), 12:7. White Plains, The National Foundation.

Schlossman, S. F., and L. Hudson. 1973. Specific purification of lymphocyte populations on a digestible immunoabsorbent. J. Immunol. 110:313–315.

Schwab, R., and M. Siniscalco. 1977. Confirmative Evidence for a Human X-Linked Surface Antigen and its Tentative Subregional Mapping. In Human Gene Mapping IV, Bergsma, D. (Ed.), White Plains, The National Foundation. In press.

Seravalli, E., P. DeBona, M. Velivasakis, I. Pagan-Charry, A. Hershberg, and M. Siniscalco. 1976. Further Data on the Cytological Mapping of the Human X-Chromosome with Man-Mouse Cell Hybrids. In Human Gene Mapping III, Birth Defects: Original Article Series, Bergsma, D. (Ed.), 12:7, pp. 219–222. White Plains, The National Foundation.

Seravalli, E., R. Schwab, M. Siniscalco, and B. Pernis. 1977. Characterization of a Mouse-Myeloma Lymphoblast Hybrid Line with Respect to Ig Production and Species-Specific Surface Antigens. In Human Gene Mapping IV, Bergsma, D. (ed.), White Plains, The National Foundation. In press.

Shapiro, L. G., R. Weiss, D. Webster, and J. T. France. 1978. X-linked ichthyosis due to steroid sulfatase deficiency. Lancet 1:70–72.

Silagi, S., G. Darlington, and S. A. Bruce. 1969. Hybridization of two biochemically marked human cell lines. Proc. Nat. Acad. Sci. U.S.A. 62:1085–1092.

Sinet, P. M., D. Allard, J. Lejeune, and H. Jerome. 1974. Augmentation d'activité de la superoxyde dismutase erythrocytaire dans la trisomie pour le chromosome 21. C. R. Acad. Sci. (Paris) 278:3267–3270.

Siniscalco, M. 1964. Localization of Genes on Human Chromosomes, Proc. XI Int. Congress of Genetics, pp. 851–870. Elmsford, Pergamon Press, Inc.

Siniscalco, M. 1970. Somatic cell hybrids as tools for genetic studies in man. Symp. Int. Sci. Cell Biol. 9:205–231.

Siniscalco, M. 1974. Strategies for X-Chromosome Mapping with Somatic Cell Hybrids. In Somatic Cell Hybridization, Davidson, R. L., and F. La Cruz (Eds.), pp. 35–48, New York, Raven Press.

Siniscalco, M. 1979. Human Gene Mapping and Cancer Biology. In Genetics and Human Biology: Possibilities and Realities, Porter, R. (Ed.), Ciba Foundation Symposium, London. New York, Elsevier-North Holland Pub. Co. In press.

Siniscalco, M., G. Filippi, B. Latte, S. Piomelli, M. Rattazzi, J. Gavin, R. Sanger, and R. R. Race. 1966. Failure to detect linkage between Xg and other X-borne loci in Sardinians. Ann. Hum. Genet. 29:231–252.

Siniscalco, M., H. Klinger, H. Eagle, H. Koprowski, W. Fujimoto, and E. Seegmiller. 1969. Evidence of intergenic complementaion in hybrid cells derived from two human diploid strains each carrying an X-linked mutation. Proc. Nat. Acad. Sci. U.S.A. 62:793–799.

Smith, C. A. B. 1953. The detection of linkage in human genetics. J. R. Statist. Soc., B. 15:153–192.

Smith, C. A. B. 1954. The separation of the sexes of parents in the detection of linkage in man. Ann. Eugen. (Lond.) 18:278–301.

Smith, C. A. B. 1959. Some comment on the statistical methods used in linkage investigations. Am. J. Hum. Genet. 11:289–304.

Smith, C. A. B. 1968. Linkage scores and correction in simple two- and three-generation families. Ann. Hum. Genet. 32:127–150.

Smith, C. A. B. 1969. Further linkage scores and corrections in two- and three-generation families. Ann. Hum. Genet. 33:207–223.

Smith, H. O., and K. W. Wilcox. 1970. A restriction enzyme from Hemophilus influenzae. I. Purification and general properties. J. Mol. Biol. 51:379–391.

Smithies, O., A. E. Blechl, K. Denniston-Thompson. N. Newell, J. E. Richards, J. L. Slightom, P. W. Tucker, and F. R. Blattner. 1978. Clonic human fetal γ globin and mouse α-type globin DNA: characterization and partial sequencing. Science 202:1284–1289.

Smithies, O., G. E. Connell, and G. H. Dixon. 1962. Chromosomal rearrangements and evolution of haptoglobin genes. Nature 196:232–236.

Southern, E. M. 1975. Detection of specific sequences among DNA fragments separated by gel electrophoresis. J. Mol. Biol. 18:503–517.

Steffensen, D. M., P. Duffey, and W. Prensky. 1974. Localization of 5S ribosomal RNA genes on human chromosome 1. Nature 252:741–743.

Stern, C. 1957. The problem of complete Y-linkage in man. Am. J. Genet. 9:147–166.

Stern, C. 1959. Colour blindness in Klinefelter's syndrome. Nature 183:1452–1453.

Stern, C. 1960. Principles of Human Genetics, 2nd ed. San Francisco, W. H. Freeman & Co.

Stubblefield, E., and W. Wray. 1973. Biochemical and morphological studies of partially purified Chinese hamster chromosomes. Symposia on Quantitative Biology, Cold Spring Harbor 38:835–843.

Sturtevant, A. H. 1925. The effects of unequal crossing over at the bar locus in Drosophila. Genetics 10:117–147.

Suciu-Foca, N., P. Rubinstein, and J. Dausset. 1976. Intra HLA recombinations. Tissue Antigens 8:221–231.

Szybalski, W., and E. H. Szybalska. 1962. Drug sensitivity as a genetic marker for human cell lines. Univ. Mich. Med. Bull. 28:277–293.

Tanner, J. M., A. Prader, H. Habich, and M. A. Ferguson-Smith. 1959. Genes on the Y-chromosome influencing rate of naturation in man. Lancet 2:141–144.

Taylor, J. M., et al. 1974. Genetic lesion in homozygous α thalassemia (hydrops fetalis). Nature 251:392–393.

Tiepolo, L., and O. Zuffardi. 1976. Localization of factors controlling spermatogenesis in the non-fluorescent portion of the human Y-chromosome long arm. Hum. Genet. 34:119–124.

Tischfeld, J. A., and F. H. Ruddle. 1974. Assignment of the gene for adenine phosphoribosyltransferase to human chromosome 16 by mouse-human somatic cell hybridization. Proc. Nat. Acad. Sci. U.S.A. 71:45–49.

Tolstoshev, P., et al. 1976. Presence of gene for β-globin in homozygous β^0-thalassemia. Nature 259:95–98.

van der Linden, A. G. J. M., P. L. Pearson, and J. J. P. van de Kamp. 1975. Cytological assessment of meiotic exchange in a human male with a pericentric inversion of chromosome No. 4. Cytogenet. Cell Genet. 14:126–139.

Viveros, O. H., L. Arqueros, and N. Krishner. 1968. Release of catecholamines and dopamine.β-oxidase from the adrenal medulla. Life Sci. 7:609–618.

Wachtel, S. S., G. C. Koo, W. R. Breg, S. Elias, E. A. Boyse, and O. J. Miller. 1975. Expression of H-Y antigen in human males with two Y chromosomes. New Eng. J. Med. 293:1070–1072.

Wachtel, S. S., G. C. Koo, F. E. Zuckerman, U. Hammerling, M. O. Scheid, and E. A. Boyse. 1974. Serological cross reactivity between H-Y (male) and antigen of mouse and man. Proc. Nat. Acad. Sci. U.S.A. 71:1215–1218.

Weatherall, D. J., and J. B. Clegg. 1976. Molecular genetics in human hemoglobin. In Annual Review of Genetics, Roman, H. L., A. Campbell, and L. Sandler (Eds.). Palo Alto, Calif., Annual Reviews Inc. 10:157–178.

Weiss, M. C., and H. Green. 1967. Human-mouse hybrid cell lines containing partial complements of human chromosomes and functioning human genes. Proc. Nat. Acad. Sci. U.S.A. 58:1104–1111.

Weiss, M. C., R. S. Sparkes, and R. Bertolotti. 1975. Reexpression of liver specific enzymes in hepatoma cell hybrids. Somatic Cell Genet. 1:27–40.

White, M. J. D. 1973. The Chromosomes, 6th ed., pp. 160–175. London, Chapman & Hall, Ltd.

Whitehouse, H. L. K. 1950. Mapping chromosome centromeres by the analysis of unordered tetrads. Nature 165:893.

Willecke, K. 1978. Results and prospects of chromosomal analysis of gene transfer between cultured mammalian cells. Theor. Appl. Genet. 52:97–104.

Willecke, K., R. Lange, A. Krueger, and T. Reber. 1976. Cotransfer of two linked human genes into cultured mouse cells. Proc. Nat. Acad. Sci. U.S.A. 1973:1274–1278.

Willecke, K., and F. H. Ruddle. 1975. Transfer of the gene for hypoxanthine guanine phosphoribosyltransferase on isolated human metaphase chromosomes into murine L-cells. Proc. Nat. Acad. Sci. U.S.A. 72:1792–1796.

Wright, W. E. 1978. The isolation of heterokaryons and hybrids by a selective system using irreversible biochemical inhibitors. Exp. Cell Res. 112:395–407.

Wullems, G. J., J. Van der Horst, and D. Bootsma. 1977. Transfer of the human genes coding for thymidine kinase and galactokinase to Chinese hamster cells and human Chinese hamster cell hybrids. Somatic Cell Genet. 3:281–293.

Young, M., and Hogness, D. 1977. A new approach for identifying and mapping structural genes in Drosophila melanogaster. In Eucaryotic Genetic Systems, ICN-UCLA Symposia on Molecular and Cellular Biology, VIII, pp. 315–331, New York, Academic Press, Inc.

Yu, L. C., P. Szabo, J. W. Borun, and W. Prensky. 1978. The localization of the genes coding for Histone H4 in human chromosomes. Cold Spring Harbor Symposium on Quantitative Biology, Vol. XLII, pp. 1101–1105.

NAME INDEX

SUBJECT INDEX

Page numbers in *italics* indicate illustrations. Page numbers followed by t indicate tables.

A

Aberration(s), in neural crest development, multiple endocrine neoplasia, type II and, 146
of numeric chromosomes, correlation with maternal age, gene mapping and, 241
Acid, deoxyribonucleic. See *DNA*.
orotic, in nucleoside phosphorylase deficiency, 207
Acidemia, methylmalonic, complementation groups in, 273
Aciduria, orotic, treatment of, in nucleoside phosphorylase deficiency, 209
ADA, function of, 185
phenotypes of, 186, *186*
red blood cell, quantitative variation in, 189–190
ADA[8], trimodal distribution of ADA levels and, 189
ADA activity, absence of in patients with severe combined immunodeficiency disease, 187–188
increased, studies of, 190
red blood cell lysates and, 187, *187*
ADA deficiency, 185–198
abnormalities of bone in, 192–193
causal relationship with severe combined immunodeficiency disease, evidence for, 193
clinical findings in, 190–193

ADA deficiency (*Continued*)
compared with nucleoside phosphorylase deficiency, 205
degree of required for development of severe combined immunodeficiency disease, 192
effects of increasing age on immune defects of, in severe combined immunodeficiency disease, 191–192
heterogeneity in, 191
immune defects in, biochemical basis of, 193–197
in severe combined immunodeficiency disease, effects of increasing age on immunologic defects in, 191–192
inheritance of, in severe combined immunodeficiency disease, Nezelof's syndrome and, 190
metabolism in, studies on mechanisms of, 193–194
of cells sensitive to agents stimulating adenylate cyclase activity, 195
lymphocytes, inhibition by agents that stimulate increased intracellular cyclic AMP, reversal of, 196
pharmacologic approach to, 196
prenatal diagnosis of, 190
research findings in, 185
role of ATP in immunodeficiency of, 195
segregating alleles in families with, 188
studies of metabolic mechanisms of, 193–194

319

B

Murine-human cells hybrid. See also
    Rodent-human hybrid cell(s).
  discovery of, importance to linkage
    studies of, 252
  early screening of, in radiation
    co-transfer test, 264, 265
  sorting of metaphase chromosomes
    from, fluorescence flow sorter and,
    286
  syntenic relationship between
    nucleoside phosphorylase and
    X-linked markers in, 259
Murine mutant cell line(s), correction of
    HGPRT– or thymidine kinase
    (TK)–deficiency by addition of
    metaphase chromosomes from normal
    human or Chinese hamster cells,
    conclusions from, 270
Mus musculus, cytologic map of, 237
Mutant(s), rodent cell, microcell-medi-
    ated transfer of human chromo-
    somes into, 271
  selection procedures for retention of
    corresponding human
    complementary genes and,
    256–257
  types used in complementation
    analysis, linkage detection and,
    256
  somatic cell, correction of phenotype
    of, in tissue culture, 297
Mutant phenotype(s), X-linked, criteria
    for proving segregational nature of,
    232
Mutation(s), as possible cause of XX
    male syndrome, 123–124
  different, in same gene, 272
  β-globin, in West Africans, linkage
    disequilibrium of, 295
Myeloperoxidase deficiency, inheritance
    of, 180
Myopus schisticolor, absence of H-Y
    antigen in, functional deletion of
    male-determining portion of Y
    chromosome and, X-linked inheritance
    of XY female in, 128
Myotonic dystrophy, 164–165
  hypogonadism in, hypothalamic
    dysfunction in, 164
  laboratory findings in patients with,
    165

N

Neoplasia, See also *Tumor.*
  of multiple endocrine glands, 144–153

Neoplasia *(Continued)*
  of multiple endocrine glands, cancer
    family syndrome and, 152
  type I (MEN I), 144–146
    familial tumors and, 145
    location of tumors in, 144
    thyroid involvement and, mode of
      inheritance of, types of tumors
      in, 146
  type II, 146–149
    diagnosis of tumors in, 147
    neural crest development
      aberrancy and, 146
    parathyroid hyperplasia in, 148
    relationship to multiple endocrine
      neoplasia, type III, mode of
      inheritance and treatment of,
      149
    tumors composing, 147–148
  type III, 149–150
    characteristics of, relationship to
      multiple endocrine neoplasia,
      type II, 149
    mode of inheritance in, treatment
      of, 150
Neural crest development, aberrancy of,
    multiple endocrine neoplasia, type II
    and, 146
Neural tissue, relationship to endocrine
    system, 147
Nevoid basal cell carcinoma syndrome,
    description of, 55
Nezelof's syndrome, ADA deficiency
    and, 190
  symptoms and inheritance of, 191
Noonan's syndrome, 166–167
  characteristics of, 167
  similarity to Turner's syndrome 166
NP deficiency. See *Nucleoside
    phosphorylase deficiency.*
Nucleic acid cycle, purine salvage and,
    182–185
Nucleic acid hybridization, combined
    with somatic cell genetics, in
    molecular gene mapping, 278–279
Nucleic acid probe(s), in situ
    hybridization of, to metaphase
    chromosomes, examples of, 278
Nucleoside phosphorylase (NP),
    electrophoretic patterns of, 199,
    199, 200
  comparison with control, 201–202,
    202
  function of, 198
  genetics of, 199–205
  inactive alleles of, 200
  protein of, immunologic
    cross-reactivity of, with normal
    nucleoside phosphorylase, 204

Variation (*Continued*)

patterns of, in stature analyses, 95–96

phenotypic, screening of in individuals with autosomal trisomies, 241

quantitative, in red blood cell ADA, 189–190

residual, in genetic-environmental interactions, 91

total, in offspring, assortative mating and, 78

within and among species, 74–75

within dizygotic twins, estimate of proportion of, lack of sensitivity to sample age and sex differences of, 86

Verner-Morrison syndrome, multiple endocrine neoplasia and, 145

Vertebrate(s), lower, differentiation of heterogametic gonad in, H-Y antigen expression and, 127

nonmammalian, functional sex reversal in, 126–128

Virus, Friend leukemia, preferential association of with β_2-microglobulin–H-2d^b antigen dimers, 135

genomes of, integration of, in mammalian cells, microcell hybrids and, 272

use of DNA restriction analysis in mapping of, 281

parasitic, mimicking of organogenesis-directing antigens by, 135

polytropic, infection with, consequences of lack of immune response and, 155

Vitamin D, importance of metabolization of in pseudohypoparathyroidism, 162

W

Werner's syndrome, characteristics of, 167

Wiskott-Aldrich syndrome, T-cell dysfunction in, 181

Wolffian duct, genetic male with incomplete differentiation of, 48–49

Wood lemming, absence of H-Y antigen in, functional deletion of male-determining portion of Y chromosome and X-linked inheritance of XY female in, 128

XYZ

X chromosome, construction of cytologic map of, balanced X-autosomal translocation and, 258

evolution of, 119

existence of regulatory gene on, 128–129, *129*

homozygous locus of, normal oogenesis and, 15

human, molecular model for studying structure of, 280

possible exchange of genetic material with Y chromosome during meiosis, 123, *124*

unbalanced, impossibility of gene dosage studies of, 244–245

X-chromosome mapping, data on, collected with pedigree approach, *236*, 237

X^2 goodness of fit, choosing between alternative solutions and, 93

Xenopus laevis (South African clawed toad), functional sex reversal in, 127

Xeroderma pigmentosum, fibroblasts of unrelated patients having, heterokaryons derived from, complementation groups in, 273

XX cell(s), of XX/XY chimeric gonads, competitive position of antigens on plasma membranes of, 134

XX gonadal cell(s), presence of H-Y antigen receptors on, 132

XX male(s), 42–43

presence of H-Y antigen in, 115

XX male syndrome, association with abnormal inheritance of H-Y genes of, 125

cryptic mosaicism as possible cause of, 123–124

etiology and description of, presence of H-Y antigen in, 123

mosaicism as possible cause of, 123–124

reduced levels of H-Y antigen in, frequency in dogs of, 124

XX sex reversal, 122–126

XX true hermaphroditism, 122–126

association with abnormal inheritance of H-Y genes, 125

reduced levels of H-Y antigen in, 124

XX/XY chimeric gonad(s), competitive position of antigens on plasma membranes of XX and XY cells of, 134